THE PSYCHOLOGY OF SOUND

CAMBRIDGE UNIVERSITY PRESS
C. F. CLAY, Manager
London: FETTER LANE, E.C.
Edinburgh: 100 PRINCES STREET

New York: G. P. PUTNAM'S SONS
Bombay, Calcutta and Madras: MACMILLAN AND CO., Ltd.
Toronto: J. M. DENT AND SONS, Ltd.
Tokyo: THE MARUZEN-KABUSHIKI-KAISHA

THE
PSYCHOLOGY OF SOUND

BY

HENRY J. WATT, M.A., Ph.D., D.Phil.

Lecturer on Psychology in the University of Glasgow and to the
Glasgow Provincial Committee for the Training of Teachers;
Sometime Lecturer on Psychology in the University of Liverpool

Cambridge:
at the University Press
1917

3196.

PREFACE

I HAVE undertaken this work in the interests of a purely psychological theory of the senses. A purely psychological analysis and theory of sensory experience has seemed to me for some years to be not only ideally desirable and even necessary, but really also possible. I have made two previous statements of the case for hearing. The first, published in 1911 in *The British Journal of Psychology* (vol. IV.), formed an incident in a general programme and tentative sketch of this pure psychology. The second, published in the same journal in 1914 (vol. VII.), was planned to meet the numerous attempts that had appeared in the intervening years to reform the elementary psychology of hearing. These attempts made strong appeals towards other lines of construction than those I had advocated; but I had confidence enough in the inherent appropriateness or, as it might be called technically, in the phenomenological correctness, of my 'idea' to be eager to come to grips with these others both in detail and in general. These new movements have since gained in interest and weight by the fact that Stumpf, in reviewing them in 1914, has seen fit to abandon his own generally accepted position, held since 1883, and to put himself at the head of one of the movements, though rejecting the special arguments brought forward for it by its first public exponents.

From my second statement it may still not have been clear to many that the ground and basis of my analysis and theory of hearing are as purely psychological as I believe them to be. Such revolutionary teaching in psychology must needs have the most explicit statement. I hesitate to say that this doctrine is fundamentally new. In philosophy there is nothing so new under the sun. But at least in respect of the material to which the primary general principles of science have been applied, if not also in respect of the special principles that have sprung from the new rock that has been struck, there is surely much in my doctrine that is fresh growth and that will in its time give both blossom and fruit. So I have thought it needful to make a third more generally accessible statement of my analysis and theory of hearing. There can be no mistake about its general nature and purport this time.

I have tried to be as clear as possible without going to the tiresome extreme of saying everything. So I have laid bare the critical structure of my scheme in two successive summaries. I have also added an account of my theory in more or less untechnical, and, I hope, more familiar, terms for those who are unaccustomed to psychological terminology, but desire to understand my views. I have taken some account of the fact that these readers are likely to be most interested in the musical issues of hearing.

My obligations will be obvious to the expert reader. I have not attempted to mention all theorists equally, as my aim is to expound and to prove my own theory, not to review and apportion the history and merits of all others. So I have only selected a background for my work. Besides it would be a work of supererogation to repeat what has been so well done by others. For all the simple processes of hearing I have drawn freely upon the work and observations of Stumpf. No one who follows his work closely can fail to be impressed by his meticulous concern for the true facts, and by the careful logic of his inferences. These merits have made his work and that of his collaborators deservedly authoritative. In a sense my endeavour has been merely to subject their work and that of other workers on hearing to proper psychological methods and to make it really fruitful for theory. In dealing with binaural processes I have been greatly assisted by the excellent summary of O. Klemm. Besides these chief sources my authorities are set out plainly as occasion arises.

In a question of the foundations of a science a little difference goes a long way. And the little difference from which I build has never definitely been held nor advocated by anyone, as far as I am aware, although various theories have made some approach towards it, in so far as they considered tones to be quantitatively different. Many new results flow from this basal reform which considers pitches to be, not qualitatively, but ordinally, different. These new results include a theory of tone as such, which does not limit its account to a reference to the pitch series and to tentative remarks on volume, but shows the stuff and structure common to all tones; a theory of noise, which does not harbour a persistent remainder of doubt, but is convincingly adequate, although the ground of facts is from the nature of the case inexhaustible; a theory of fusion which meets both the negative and the positive aspects of all the facts; the measurement of the real psychical basis of an admittedly immeasurable mode of sensory experience—volume; a theory of interval, which discovers a second field of form and proportion with laws already familiar in the visual field; or, in general, a purely psychological basis of analysis carried well up to the boundary of musical complexity, upon which a full and sufficient theory of musical construction may in time be raised.

No doubt my theoretical constructions must be carried somewhat further before they can be held to have passed fully over into the elements consciously used by productive musicians and appreciative listeners. The gap is not a large one and is in great part filled by a psychical field that a theorist of sensory experience dare not rush into—the field of psychical habit and attitude. That field belongs chiefly to the historian and ethnologist. No doubt theory can go somewhat further still than I have gone. But it cannot go very far, for the working musician definitely takes over at a certain point the raw materials of his art from the real psychical processes of hearing, inaccessible in full to observation, and then proceeds to construct from them vast new realms without consulting anything that lies beyond the ken of observation.

But I am not concerned about what I have not yet attained. If my theoretical efforts are valid, they will grow easily; if they are unfit to survive, the canker will be found within their body. But I think they are healthy enough to overcome in active life whatever weakness may have been born with them.

H. J. W.

GLASGOW,
    January 1917.

CONTENTS

INTRODUCTION

I. The end and aim of the study of hearing is to explain it. Every-one may be supposed to know what is meant by explanation, so that it is usually considered superfluous to state what that meaning is, especially in the introduction to a scientific book. We expect explana-tion to follow of itself from a full and correct statement or description of the facts and their connexions. Indeed a thinking mind usually desires no more than this. Not that the thinking mind delights in prosaic formulations. Far from it; it supplies for itself the poetry or the atmosphere; the mere statement of the facts and their connexions arouses this atmosphere. And by atmosphere we mean the sympathetic surroundings, kindred facts and connexions from other spheres of reality. Thus explanation seems really to mean the full and correct classification of facts and their connexions, so that they may be grouped by the mind along with already established sets of facts and connexions of a similar kind.

But more than this is usually required by the scientist. He has also to show how his system of facts is connected with those that surround it in the world of reality. Or if only a part of the events he is interested in can be fully and correctly described, he is required to show to the best of knowledge and belief what set of facts and connexions, or in a word what set of processes, already observed and familiar in other regions, occupy the unobserved regions of the events he studies. Or he endeavours to clarify his thought of one set of facts etc. by his already clear thought of other sets of facts etc. This effort of scientific thought is known as theory and in its incipient stages as hypothesis.

The study of hearing therefore begins with the statements of the facts of hearing and their connexions. These are wholly and solely matters of experience; they are psychical. For hearing means experiencing. A clear statement of these facts will call up in the mind of the thinking reader similar facts and connexions from other departments of experience, especially from the fellow processes of hearing,—the other senses. And here again these facts will be wholly and solely psychical. Where the facts of hearing cannot be observed or have not yet been successfully observed, the study of hearing will feel impelled to draw upon its knowledge of the other senses and so to form a complete statement of the facts of hearing that shall at least be most probably true. Thus far the study of hearing belongs to the science of psychology.

II. At the present time even this primary part of the study is full of the keenest disputes. Several reasons may be brought to account for the prevailing difficulties and doubts. The chief of them is the peculiar complexity of even the simplest auditory experiences, which makes their observation anything but easy. It is not only hard to arrange for the occurrence of an exactly simple sound by the isolation of its physical stimulus, but only a few persons possess the power of making fine and accurate observations on sounds, whether they happen to have educated that power or not. Complexity and obscurity are naturally increased manifold if they suggest the wrong atmosphere of classification. And this seems to have happened in the study of hearing in so far as vision has been held to be the pattern according to which the experiences of hearing might best be arranged. It seems probable that in another sense than vision or in a comparative inductive study of all the senses a better guide to° the elucidation of hearing might be found. For we must expect similar parts of experience, in this case the various senses, to work in essentially the same way. Inductive methods are obviously best if the common essential functions of all the senses are to be separated from what is special to each and from what might mislead us, if we take any single sense as the standard and pattern for hearing.

It is a familiar fact that hearing depends upon the work of the ear and of the neural organs attached to it. The study of these is physiology. But the physiology of the ear finds itself very often unable to complete its statement of the facts regarding the working of the ear and its connected organs. It is forced to theorise about the remainder. And it naturally turns for information to the psychology of hearing. If our experiences of hearing are dependent upon the ear, etc., what is more likely than that the facts of hearing will make possible some good inferences regarding the functions of the ear, etc., which cannot be directly observed. But it is obvious that if we are to have good inferences, we must base them upon the best possible psychology. Inferences from one side dare not contradict facts of the other side, but facts of the one side, especially the simpler and clearer facts of experience that are direct objects of observation, form a rule or standard for the theory of the other side. Ultimately we expect to find complete harmony between the two sides, the physiology of the ear and the psychology of hearing. And, of course, the more advanced and complete study will tend to lead the way. That is at the present time undoubtedly the psychology of hearing.

Let us then see what the psychological study of the other senses may lead us to expect of hearing. The senses may be divided for this purpose into three groups.

III. The first group contains the senses that are distributed generally throughout the body, especially over the surface of the skin and the underlying tissues and in various other parts. These are called the cutaneous and visceral senses, and include the senses of pain, touch, cold and warmth. There never has been any doubt about their great psychological similarity. They can be described in almost the same terms, and if we omit unimportant variations of degree and frequency, they can be easily included under one formula. Let us consider the nature of these terms and of the resultant formula.

The difference that is immediately evident to us between pain and touch, or between either of these and cold or warmth is called a difference of quality. We do not usually look upon cold and warmth as being so different from one another as they are from pain and touch, but there can be no doubt that once we compare them with such differences in mind, we must admit that they are very different from one another and really have nothing in common. We therefore say that warmth and cold also differ in quality, though we may readily allow that they may be more akin to one another than they are to the others. We are for the moment less concerned with their possible kinship than with their obvious differences. This difference is confirmed by the fact that warmth and cold are acknowledged to be physiologically separate senses. That applies in fact to all four—touch, pain, cold and warmth. Physiological research has recently discovered that each of these senses seems to be served by more than one set of organs or receptors, as physiologists now call them, in order to avoid the ambiguity of the word 'sense,' which is now used only in reference to experiences. The question thus arises: do these different sets of receptors for one and the same sense give sensations of different quality. And the answer is: no differences can with certainty or even with any probability be established. Thus we arrive at the highly probable conclusion: each of the cutaneous and visceral senses gives only one quality of sensation.

A second way in which these sensations vary is familiar to every one; that is intensity. We know of course that various things may happen to make a pain more intense; the skin may be heated more, a thorn may be pressed more heavily on the skin, inflammation may increase, etc., but we never fail to recognise in all this that the mere 'feeling' of pain varies in intensity. We never confuse the intensity of the pain with the process going on in the skin, so as to say, for example: 'pain has no intensity; it is only the process on the skin that has intensity.' The same holds for all the other sensations of this first group.

IV. It is quite easy to recognise that quality and intensity are attributes of sensation, and these two form the nucleus of probably every list of attributes. The constant disputes that have attended the formulation of a list of attributes are concerned with the various additions to this nucleus that have from time to time been proposed. Even yet no list has been definitely accepted by the majority of psychologists, so that the science of psychology is still devoid of any precisely formulated and methodically established foundations. The cause of this lack of agreement is to be sought in no simple confusion of thought, but in a fundamental weakness of method, namely in the assumption that, since the two attributes of quality and intensity are acceptable and accepted as they come and appear to our untutored observation, all other attributes must also be taken over from among the details of our sensory experiences as they are found and appear in our search. But this assumption ignores the possibility that while quality and intensity may be very simple and are almost never complicated attributes, some or all of the others may always be wrapt up in the complications and modifications which experiences produce upon one another. And that is just what the method we are to follow teaches us to believe to be true.

One list of attributes for example would propose to add 'localisation' as a third to its list, since all sensations have some kind of localisation, although some of them seem to have a much more precise and ready localisation than others. Another list would exclude 'localisation' because the localisation of sensations varies and so seems to be due to something else, and not itself to be a primary attribute. Why not suppose it then to be a product of the bunching together of quality and intensity, exclude it from the list, and adopt the attribute of extensity instead? The objection to this fourth attribute is that it would force us to classify the extensity of pain and touch with the volume of sounds and would leave us inquiring as to the extensity of smells. Not that such a classification is wrong, as we shall see, but no good reason was given for classifying things together that seem so different.

Some lists have included feeling-tone, using this peculiar term to express in one word the two variations of feeling-tone—pleasantness and unpleasantness. But most psychologists agree that feeling-tone cannot be an attribute. For why should it have two forms? Are not these forms more different from one another than are the variations of the intensity of either of them, say pleasant feeling-tone? And if intensity is already in the list, why is it brought in here a second time with another attribute? And why does pleasantness not pass gradually into unpleasantness without passing through a stage in which there is no feeling-tone? (Some psychologists have invented an 'indifferent' feeling-tone to fill up the gap.) But if the feeling-tone can be absent altogether, can it still be an attribute? Psychologists seem to have agreed in this case that if a given sensation possesses any attribute, that attribute cannot be made to disappear without the total disappearance of the sensation itself, and that therefore feeling-tone cannot be reckoned an attribute of sensation. These reasons do indeed seem to exclude feeling-tone altogether.

Let us consider more closely the axiom just stated: a sensation disappears if its attribute disappears. Why? Because whatever thus comes and goes without detriment to the continuance of sensation cannot really be a property of sensation but must be adventitious to it or a product of the complication of sensation. Against this it is vain to urge that even the obvious quality and intensity are intrinsically detached from one another and devoid of inner connexion. For even if we do fail to grasp their inner connexion, we are none the less concerned to discover which attributes form a constant group in the sense of the axiom. Nor does it really matter that in the course of the briefest observation, lasting a fraction of a second, the attributes are not always all observed to be present. That may be due to the rapidity of observation and not to the absence of the attributes. We are searching for firm ground upon which to build psychological theory; and if a constant group of attributes occurs, that is of the highest importance for theory, whether very brief duration seems to destroy the constancy of the group or not.

The axiom thus becomes in the first place a verbal definition: the

attributes of a sensation are to be those attributes that on sufficient
observation are always found together. But certain discoveries would
turn it into much more than this—into a real definition. One of these
is the constancy of this group of attributes, not merely for one and the
same sensation, but for all kinds of sensation. The first axiom would
then take on much wider scope and become: if any one sensation has
a certain attribute, so has every other. Or: only those attributes
are to be held to be the real attributes of sensation that on sufficient
observation are found together in all sensations; and there are such.
The second discovery is the different psychical status and origin of the
inconstant features of sensation that we might feel disposed to call
attributes. Thus we should obtain with unimpeachable methods a
sure ground for a purely psychological theory of sensations and allied
experiences. We may therefore proceed, remembering that attributes
other than quality and intensity may not appear in so uniform a guise
and that if our determination of attributes is to give us a good foundation for a science of sensations, each attribute to be possible must be
discoverable in every kind of sensation.

V. A third way in which the sensations of the first group vary is
their localisation. Pain, touch, cold and warmth are always clearly,
and often very distinctly, localised. And it is easy in the case of these
sensations to show that localisation is an experience. When one has
toothache or rheumatism, for example, one can hardly ever in any
way see where the pain is. Without exploring the skin for tender spots,
one feels the pain 'somewhere'; and rheumatism often flits about in
spasms from one place to another, each twinge of pain at once marking
itself out from the others by its localisation. And pain often seems to
be in the wrong place. Cases are familiar in which pain is localised in
the fingers and toes of a lost limb. The pain somehow appears as if it
were in the lost member. Localisation is therefore a feature of experience
that can be denied as little as can pain itself no matter how 'wrong'
it is.

But localisation is not therefore an attribute of sensation. Touch,
pain or cold are merely what they are; we ask for no more enlighten-
ment about them when we have them; we take them just as they are;
we do not need to refer to touch when we name pain; and pain is not
any more truly pain after we compare it with touch or cold, than before;
reference to touch is only a way of bringing the difference of quality
logically clearly to mind. Not so with localisation: we cannot even

experience, far less think, the localisation without some reference in our experience to the painful part, toes or tooth. If we could completely isolate a sensation, it would have no localisation. But there must be something in the sensation which justifies its getting a localisation; if we cannot localise one pain in a finger and another in a toe without some conscious awareness of these parts, by thought, or mental image or the like, there must nevertheless be some difference inherent in each pain, in virtue of which it can be referred to the correct part. This difference would be an attribute, possessed by the sensation without dependence on any other experience.

How shall we name it? That depends upon whether the supposed attribute is simple and primary or complex and derived. The schools of psychologists have divided on this alternative and have even received distinctive names, the genetic school holding to derivation and the nativistic school to primacy. The former school urges that localisation may be derived by association from combinations of the qualitative and intensive differences already admitted. But it has never succeeded in showing that there is in existence a fraction of the variations of quality and intensity which would be required to account for all the variations of localisation which occur. Nor has it established any convincing theory of the means by which the association of these differences come about. Association merely begs the question. What we need to know is *how* a particular quality comes to attach itself by association to a particular intensity, when both are given. If we say: 'Well, aren't they at the same place?' we merely beg the question. For if localisation is derived, they have of themselves no place at all; they are merely a quality and an intensity. And lastly even if they did hitch on to one another somehow, why should that give rise to a localisation? Why not to a feeling, or an idea?

The genetic school is thus defeated at every point, and the field is left to the nativistic theory. It claims no miracle of unfounded association and transformation. It is true a development must be admitted: the primary attribute develops into localisation. But how it does so is a problem which may be left for later study. Looking at the development backwards in order to determine the nature of the attribute out of which localisation develops, nativism claims that the primary attribute has a psychical kinship with localisation; it is like the latter. Is it justified in doing so?

Most assuredly. For we can readily in thought strip from localisation its garment of reference, considering only the primary differences upon which it rests. We can do so in observation as well. Let the forefinger of each hand be touched. Cease to consider the spots as being in the fingers and consider only their inner differences, staring at them as it were, as one does at times with the letters or sounds of a word, when they lose their meaning and become so oddly absurd. Their differences as mere sounds stand out more clearly than usual. So with the touches: we notice a primary inherent difference between the two which seems best describable as a difference of *order*. It is the same kind of difference as that between one and two, between first and second.

Thus we may conclude; every sensation of any sense of the first group differs from every other in respect of the attribute of order, as we may see from the differences of localisation that are so obvious in these senses. The careful and correct study of this attribute is of vital importance for the psychology of hearing as of many other departments of experience.

VI. A fourth attribute is closely connected with order. But its distinction and its study will for that reason be much easier. When we put a hand into warm or cold water, we have a mass of sensation varying in extent as more or less of the hand is immersed. Now although the extent of the cold or warmth varies, each experience is alike in being *extensive*. Each extent of cold or warmth feeling is just as extensive as any other. This extensity is not so closely bound up with localisation, as with primary order; for we should hesitate to say a localisation was extensive; space is extensive, so is a finger or a toe; but a touch's reference to a point of space or to the finger or toe is not extensive; only the touch is extensive. In other words spatiality is not implied in extensity any more than it is in mere order.

The seeming independence of extensity and localisation may largely account for the fact that extensity and its temporal counterpart, durance, usually appear even in those lists of attributes that do not contain localisation or order. Given extensity, those of the genetic school thought it possible by one means or another to manufacture positions within it out of the natural groupings of differences of quality and intensity. W. James, who was a nativist as regards extensity, thought that the perception of positions within it resulted from subdividing (36, 75). But a moment's consideration shows that orders cannot originate from mere extensity. We could make tactual or visual areas of the same size all over the sensory field; but they would be identical, unless they included differences of order. Even an increase of extent is unthinkable apart from inherent differences of order. Of course differences of quality and intensity which accompany ordinal differences may draw the attention powerfully to the latter; but they cannot create them. Probably James felt this in some vague way. He said (36, 79): " he who will have thoroughly answered this problem of discrimination, will have laid the keel of psychology." Well, one beam of that keel is a nativistic attitude towards order as well as towards extensity.

Two other attributes remain that concern our awareness of time and its differences. They are very clearly akin to the attributes of order and extensity. They may be termed order and durance. To distinguish temporal order from the order upon which localisation rests, the latter may be called systemic, as it is the order that appears when a system of receptors yielding one quality is given. But, as the psychology of hearing is in no way seriously affected by the distinction and study of the temporal attributes, important as they are in themselves and for experience in general, we shall omit any further reference to them. Our attention will be confined to the first four attributes—quality, intensity, order, and extensity.

The sensations of taste may conveniently be added to those of the first group. They present no new feature of psychological interest unless it be their variation in quality. Tastes occur in four qualities, sweet, sour, bitter and salt. Although we seem to have as good reason of a physiological kind to call them the qualities of independent senses, as in the case of warmth and cold, most people would deem the qualities of taste more akin to one another than those of the cutaneous senses. Unfortunately we have as yet no other means of gauging the kinship of different qualities than our direct introspective impression of their kinship. Thus far at least the rule holds that for every physiologically independent sense only one psychological quality occurs.

VII. The senses of the first group detach themselves from the others chiefly because the study of the attributes of sensation in them presents least difficulty and so formulates the problem to be pursued through all the other senses. This clarity and simplicity are doubtless due to the comparative physiological simplicity of their receptors and to their cognitive functions in dealing with the objects immediately surrounding the body. They are known to physiologists as the simple exteroceptive senses. A second group of senses is naturally formed by the receptors of the body (known as proprioceptive and interoceptive) that obtain for cognition data regarding the states and operations of the body itself and regarding the stimuli that affect its inner surface, i.e. the alimentary tract exclusive of the parts near the month. But as these states and operations are for the most part controlled without the aid of cognition, it is not surprising to find that the sensations of this group are in various respects obscure and difficult of study and somewhat complex. But we have every reason to believe that the formula derived from the first group is perfectly adequate to the second group. This includes the articular, and the muscular (proprioceptive) senses, and the large group of the organic (interoceptive) senses (106, 317 f., 336 f.) (that are stimulated by emptiness or fullness, filling or evacuation, of various organs).

The articular sense provides data dependent on the relative positions of the jointed limbs. It is physiologically distinct from the senses of the first group, more particularly from touch. We have no reason to suppose that more than one quality occurs in this sense. Of the other attributes intensity is the most obscure. This is almost certainly due to a want of variation in the physiological conditions upon which that attribute is dependent, and not to its psychological absence. If a limb is placed very comfortably and in perfect relaxation, awareness of its relative position gradually disappears entirely; but it is at once restored by renewed innervation. A uniform intensity would be cognitively irrelevant and therefore introspectively indefinite.

But we have still to deal with the datum of position conveyed by this sense. And our thoughts naturally turn to the attribute of order. Could it be the basis of position? To this proposal, we must surely assent. For just as in the case of localisation, position includes a system of orders and yet is more than that; it is position of the limb. To get a notion of the primary underlying attribute we must omit the phrase 'of the limb' and express the sensory datum as 'order of articular quality of uniform intensity.' Our awareness of the relation of this order to a certain limb must be gained from it by our somehow collating it with other orders. The same applies to our awareness of the particular limb to which the positions apply. In both cases we need presuppose in the sensation nothing but sets of articular sensation of different orders. And the different extents of these sets, e.g. in the contrast of the sensations from a large joint with those from a small one, point us towards the attribute of extensity.

The muscular sense provides an interesting variant upon the obscurities of the articular sense. For while it also has only one quality, its variability is chiefly intensive and hardly ordinal at all. In fact we are explicitly aware of muscular sensations as such only when they are considerably intensive and begin to give some awareness of strain or resistance. Intensity may therefore at once be conceded, while we may see ordinal variation behind whatever awareness of localisation of muscular sensation we possess, and extensity in their common variations of bulk or mass, as we pass from large muscles to small muscles. These variations in bulk doubtless imply the presence of sets of ordinal differences in the mass sensation we obtain from each muscle; and it is probable that varying numbers of the fibres of one and the same muscle are innervated in response to the varying strain or volitions directed upon the muscle. A variation in the extent of muscular sensation from one and the same muscle would thus be evoked. It is not necessary to suppose, as Myers (85) suggests, that the intensity ·of muscular sensation varies with these extents; these intensities are surely more likely to be dependent upon the strain put upon the fibre in which the receptor for muscular sensation is embedded. But our *cognition* of strain may take both variations of intensity and of extent from one and the same muscle into account.

In organic sensations, amongst which hunger, thirst, repletion, nausea, and many others are included, we find a general obscurity of attributes, but no other serious obstacle to their identification. Their qualities are all rather vague and difficult to distinguish from pressure or mixtures of pressure and pain. Their localisation, although by no means precise, is certainly clear enough to warrant the assumption of underlying orders, and they always occur in considerable bulk. We therefore feel entitled to claim that the formula of the attributes derived from the first group, holds also for the second.

The special psychological interest of this group of sensations lies in the frequent obscurity and variability of their attributes. But, as we have already suggested, this may properly be ascribed to a want of variation in the physiological correlatives of these attributes, and not to any psychical incapacity of the sensations themselves. If the stimulus to one of these senses is present, it may be sufficiently effective with only one line of variation. Hunger and thirst need not wander over the body; their intensity is enough for all purposes. And their physiological validity is further secured by their mass or bulk, dependent as that is upon the distribution of their receptors over the surface or over a representative section of the organ most immediately concerned in the related function. So we apparently never get a 'spot' of articular or muscular or organic sensation, as we do with the sensations of the first group, but always an undifferentiated mass or bulk. And yet we may properly infer from the variation of extent which accompanies the gradual immersion of the hand in cold or warm water, that the mass of any sensation of the second group is due to the fusion of many minimal extents of sensation. We also know from the cutaneous senses, and still more clearly from vision, that in area there is no accentuation or discrimination of orders unless within small ranges of that area a rapid variation of intensity (or, in vision, of quality) is also given.

VIII. The remaining senses, hearing, vision and smell, form the third group. Like those of the first group these are exteroceptive senses, sometimes distinguished as 'far' senses or distance-senses (106, 324 f.) from the former, the 'near' senses. Their sensations are much more complex and elaborate than those of the other two groups, so that they are often called 'higher,' and the others 'lower' senses. Being 'far' senses they are most important for cognition. Our problem is to express their complexity and to solve their obscurities and difficulties in terms of the simplicity of the other senses and of the attributive formula established for them.

In vision special difficulties are presented by the attributes of intensity and quality. There seems to be an indefinite, though wholly surveyable variety of qualities in vision, of which the solar spectrum exemplifies a special series. The whole range of these qualitative variations is displayed in the 'colour-figure' (Fig. 1). It is very difficult to find in vision a satisfactory equivalent to the intensity of other senses. For if the range of variations from red to green or from yellow to blue is to be taken as qualitative, so must the range from white to black. And yet there is something common to these series; in passing from yellow to blue we pass through a series of changes of brightness comparable to the series of changes

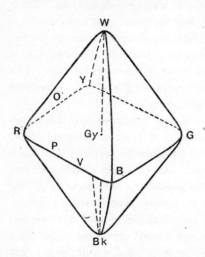

Fig. 1. R = Red, O = Orange, Y = Yellow, G = Green, B = Blue, V = Violet, P = Purple, W = White, Gy = Grey, Bk = Black.

in passing from white to black. How then shall we distinguish brightness and quality in the two series? Although it is indeed far from easy to bring vision into full harmony with the other senses, we have hardly reason to believe that such harmony is unattainable. And it is encouraging to find, as we shall, that these particular difficulties of vision do not recur in the sense of sound, if our interpretation of that sense is correct. Successful analysis of hearing would then lend added weight to the probability of vision's conforming to the proposed type.

In smell we meet with a sense that has so far baffled all the efforts of physiologists or psychologists. It possesses an amazing variety of qualities which have never even been so surveyed as to appear to be a closed or exhausted system. And they give practically no kind of limit as to how their complexity might be reduced to the mixture or interaction of a few primary qualities. Of their intensive variations there never has been any doubt. But if they are all localised about the nostrils, as seems probable, they would be devoid of all variation in order, though not of order altogether, so long as they are localised at all. Of any extensity we have only the vaguest indications. W. James thought vinegar a less extended smell than musk (36, 76). Smell is in fact a most puzzling sense. Of course it is in us in a most degenerate state. But that hardly seems a good reason why it should be difficult for us to give a psychological analysis of it.

If the qualities of vision, as all theories of colour vision suggest, promise to allow themselves to be reduced to a small number of primary qualities, of which each one or each pair forms a more or less independent sense, it would seem highly probable that the qualities of smell will some day admit of a similar reduction. In that case some general rule regarding the qualities of sensations, probably that suggested by the sensations of the first group, perhaps with slight modifications for the cases of kindred qualities, would establish itself. If the ordinal attribute of all the other senses conforms to a general rule, it is hardly likely that smell will form an utterly irreconcilable case. A similar remark applies to the intensity of vision. It is interesting to notice how the different difficulties presented by the various senses thus tend to reduce the probability of any one of them proving insuperable.

It is my intention in this work to attempt an analysis of the sense of hearing on the lines suggested by this analysis of the first two groups of senses. The analysis promises to be completely successful and thus to add its evidence to the probability of the universal applicability of the suggested formula. At the same time we shall find as we pursue the analysis beyond the simplest forms of auditory sensations, that the effort to reduce the least *complex* forms of auditory experience to types also applicable to the same forms of complexity as they appear in the other senses, adds still more to the probable truth of my formula for the attributes. So far I have of course only been concerned to establish a starting ground for analysis towards the attributive formula.

Practically every previous attempt to bring hearing into conformity with the other senses and so to procure extraneous evidence of the successful analysis and arrangement of its facts and their connexions, has followed other lines than those adopted in this work. And (without regard to the present theory) there can be no doubt in the mind of any modern psychologist that every analysis of hearing yet offered leaves so many difficulties unsolved that we must either consider it to be inadequate to the facts, or our knowledge of the facts to be inadequate to it. Where, as in hearing, the main body of the raw facts of an elementary kind hardly offers serious grounds of dispute, the latter alternative may be deemed improbable. The writer is convinced that his analysis is so much more adequate to the facts as to be preferable to any previous analysis, and as to convince us that the failure of every previous analysis to carry conviction is hardly due to any deficiency in our knowledge of the raw elementary facts of hearing. The writer's analysis thus seems fitted to bring into the elementary psychology of hearing insight and stability such as it has never hitherto shown. This result must be of the highest importance to every discipline which is associated with, draws upon, or builds upon, the elementary psychology of hearing, e.g. physical acoustics, phonetics, physiology of hearing, musical practice and aesthetics.

CHAPTER I

AUDITORY SENSATIONS AND THEIR ATTRIBUTES

IX. The whole gamut of the world's sounds falls into two halves which are perfectly obvious in their extremes although there is no clear division between them. Everyone makes a distinction between tones and noises. Tones are smooth, even, and regular in appearance, while noises are rough, uneven, and irregular.

A. *Tones.* A good preliminary survey of tones is given in the series of sounds produced by any musical instrument. When we run over the keyboard of a piano note by note from left to right; the sounds produced differ from one another in a way we usually name collectively as a difference of pitch. The pitch is said to rise as we progress, being low at first and then becoming gradually higher. Even on the piano we notice that the difference between its tones is much less noticeable in the extreme octaves than in those intervening, so that the piano seems to give us the greater part of the whole range of tones, or at least the only part that is of any use for music.

But any part, if not the whole of this range of tones, can be produced on many other musical instruments and we can readily recognise the instrument used from the sound of its tone alone. Thus we get a large number of similar series of tones, and if we are to obtain any common survey of the range of tones, we must first settle whether any of these series is the real series of tones and if not what is the primary series.

Very few, if any, musical sounds can be produced without the accompaniment of a certain amount of noise. But apart from that—and we readily learn to neglect it—we usually hear in good musical tones only a unitary sound in which no parts seem to be distinguishable. The tone has of course been made as pure as technique and tuning will allow. But everyone knows that the sounds of the rougher musical instruments often break up into parts which are distinguishable by their pitch. The elimination of these 'irregularities' of pitch is just what makes the playing of many musical instruments so difficult.

The trained ear watches for them and learns to manipulate the instrument so as to exclude them and to make the tone as pure as possible. But have they even then all been excluded? Perhaps we should find more of them if we made it our special business to analyse the pitch of tones or if we used special instruments to help our hearing.

Helmholtz has proved in a variety of ways that the pitch of the tones of musical instruments is nearly always much more complex than it appears to be. In many cases the presence of more than one pitch in a musically simple tone can be heard with the unaided ear, if a careful search is made. And if each probable component of the tone is sounded gently and repeatedly beforehand so as to prepare the attention, the range of such observations can be greatly increased. We seem to hear the prepared tone sounding on into the tone to be analysed. These results are not imaginary, as if we really did carry over what we expect into what we actually hear; for it is often to be noticed that with the latter method the equal temperament of the piano suggests as a probable component a tone that does not quite coincide in pitch with the component actually heard, but is a little sharper or flatter than it. Moreover these components can be much strengthened with the aid of suitable resonators. And as Helmholtz says, the ear recognises without resonators every component that can be strengthened by them and perceives no component unaffected by the resonator.

The results of the psychical analysis of musical sounds are confirmed by physical analysis in various other ways. And the sounds of musical instruments can be roughly imitated on the organ by the combined use of a number of stops which bring together for each tone of the scale a set of sounds whose predominant pitches coincide with the chief component pitches of the imitated sound. The primary cause of the differences between the sounds of different musical instruments is therefore physical. Hardly any musical instrument vibrates so as to evoke a tone of a perfectly simple pitch; it vibrates so as to evoke a sound in which one pitch predominates over others.

The component pitches of musical tones are usually members of a definite series. Let us call the lowest component pitch of the analysed tone c. The lowest is usually also the loudest or predominant pitch of the tone, from which it receives its name—its 'nominal' pitch. The next higher component pitch will often be an octave higher, c'; the third component will often be a fifth higher than that, g'; the fourth c^2; the fifth e^2; the sixth g^2; the eighth c^3; the ninth d^3; the tenth e^3; the twelfth g^3; and so on. The seventh and eleventh components cannot be expressed exactly with the names used in our musical scales. If we played this series of tones on a musical instrument, the physical rates of vibrations which would theoretically correspond to the predominant pitches of each would be respectively, n being the rate of vibration of c:

$$n,\ 2n,\ 3n,\ 4n,\ 5n,\ 6n,\ 7n,\ 8n,\ 9n,\ 10n,\ 11n,\ 12n,\ \text{etc.}$$

That is to say, they are all simple multiples of n. This can readily be shown with the monochord upon which the presence of components in an apparently simple tone is often demonstrated. The tones of the above series can be obtained by plucking the string when it has been stopped with a fine brush at a half, a third, a quarter, etc., of its length. Or the stopping brush may be applied to these points of the string after it has been plucked, thus isolating the physical component, if it is present. It is a familiar fact that the rate of vibration of a string is inversely proportional to its length. We thus obtain a simple rule for the components of the pitch of tones: they are one or any of a series related to the physical rate of vibration or to the pitch of the lowest predominant component in the following manner. Rate of vibration: $n,\ 2n,\ 3n,\ 4n,\ 5n,\ 6n,\ 7n,\ 8n,\ 9n,\ 10n,\ 11n,\ 12n$. Corresponding relative pitch: $c,\ c',\ g',\ c^2,\ e^2,\ g^2,\ < b^\flat,\ c^3,\ d^3,\ e^3,\ > f^3,\ g^3 \ldots$. Thus the pitch of any suspected component may easily be calculated. Component pitches may be known as partial pitches, the lowest and predominant partial being the fundamental partial, and the others the upper partials. As confusion is liable to arise if the upper partials be numbered without inclusion of the fundamental, it is usual to include the latter in the numbering as the first partial. Partials are then numbered according to their numeral in the n series above. The even partials are c' $(2n)$, c^2 $(4n)$, g^2 $(6n)$, etc.: the uneven are n (c), $3n$ (g'), $5n$ (e^2), etc.

Helmholtz, whose work on this subject is authoritative, summarised the results of his researches in a few general rules showing the usual components of the pitches of various instruments and the relation between these sets of components and the musical character of the sounds. These rules are as follows:

1. Tones of simple pitch, like those of tuning forks with resonance chambers and those of wide stopped organ pipes, sound very soft and pleasant, free from all roughness, but wanting in power, and dull at low pitches.

2. Tones containing the lower partial pitches up to about the sixth in moderate prominence are produced by the pianoforte, open organ pipes, and by the human voice and the French horn in medium strength.

The tones of the latter instruments form the transition to tones with high upper partials. The tones of flutes and of the flute stops of the organ with a low pressure of wind approach to tones of simple pitch. These tones of some six partials are fuller, richer, and more splendid than simple tones, but they are also perfectly sweet and soft so long as the higher upper partials are absent.

3. If only the uneven numbered partials are present, as in narrow stopped organ pipes, pianoforte strings struck in the middle, and clarinets, the tone sounds hollow, and when a large number of such upper partials are present, nasal. When the fundamental partial predominates, the tone sounds rich; but it sounds poor when the fundamental is not sufficiently superior in strength to the upper partials.

4. When partial pitches higher than the sixth or seventh are very distinct, the tone becomes cutting and rough. The degree of harshness may be very different. When their force is inconsiderable, the higher upper partials do not seriously detract from the musical value of the tones; on the contrary they are useful in giving character and expression to the music. Such tones are produced by bowed instruments, and most reed pipes, the oboe, bassoon, harmonium and the human voice. The rough braying tones of brass instruments are extremely penetrating and therefore give more the impression of great power than similar tones of a softer blend (29, 179 f., 30, 118 f.).

X. The character of musical tones by which we recognise from which instrument they have been produced is thus at least a peculiar combination or blend of pitches. This character may therefore well be called the pitch-blend of tones. And the above rules may be further condensed into a single statement: the pitch-blend of a tone depends upon the group of partial pitches by which it is constituted and their relative strengths.

Remarks must be made here on terminology. It is common practice to speak of the lower and upper 'partials' of a tone and of the fundamental partial, without the regular addition of the substantive usually implied—tone. The term 'partial' thus comes to have not an adjective, but a substantive meaning. This practice seems to me to be a happy one. For it will be shown, as we proceed, that the common notion of a 'partial *tone*' rather anticipates, if it does not also outrun, the warrants of tonal analysis, which yields us primarily only partial *pitches*. Although this change in terminology is trivial and negligible, so far as concerns the facts of observation in question, it is of the highest importance in so far as it gives a correct leading towards theoretical construction and deduction from these facts.

Nor has theory been without influence upon the name given to that character of tones of the same nominal pitch which varies with the instrument they come from. The word 'quality' (30, 10, etc.), (however familiar and safe it may be for musical practice) is obviously misleading in psychology; for there is no other case in which that word is used specially to designate a grouping of distinguishable moments, whether these are themselves qualitative or not. The same applies to the word 'colour,' or to the term 'clang-tint' adopted from the German. Besides both these words suggest dangerous analogies with the variety and psychical status of the visual colours. Something might be said for using the word 'clang' alone, which in English is commonly used to designate a special kind of pitch-blend, such as that given by cymbals. The French word 'timbre' although increasingly popular in psychological works, is really impossible in English, both in its French and in its English pronunciations. The word pitch-blend, on the other hand, has associations already only with mineralogy, which may be considered remote enough to be innocuous for psychology. There is no reason why we should not in psychology teach that the object well known in musical talk as the quality of tone shows itself to be psychologically a group or blend of pitches and will therefore be so named within psychology. It may then become a question for musical practice to decide whether it would not be well to adopt 'pitch-blend' in place of its own term because of the aid given by the former towards correct knowledge of the nature and means of producing the variant thus designated (108, 74 f.)

We have already obtained an answer to our next question: whether tones occur in which only one pitch is distinguishable. Such tones are by no means the philosophical fiction they are sometimes said to be. They do occur, however difficult it may be to arrange at any given moment and for any length of time for the occurrence of a tone of a single and certain pitch. If it be doubted whether such perfectly 'simple' tones occur naturally[1] there can at least be no doubt that the series of musical instruments can be arranged so as to present a series of sounds approximating towards simplicity of tone. And special physical devices of 'interference' are familiar which ensure the presentation to the ear of a perfectly uniform and regular aerial vibration and so the hearing of a tone of a single pitch[2]. Such pure tones can be procured at any height of pitch within a large range of variation and it thus becomes highly probable that every tone, no matter what the height of its pitch may be, can be obtained perfectly simple in pitch. Thus we arrive at the series of tones that is primary to all the parallel

---

[1] Cf. 102, 3 ff. Even tuning forks give at least the octave, if not other partials. The octave partial from a fork originates, not in the fork, but in the air as a result of certain physical processes (cf. Lindig): "Thus it is practically impossible for simple tones to be produced directly by any source of sound" (p. 4).

[2] Cf. *loc. cit.* Schaefer adds a second means—subjective abstraction: but, as we shall see, that is really unable to extract a pure tone from a pitch-blend.

series derived from the different musical instruments. No experimental means is known by which the pitch of a tone can be modified without any change in the auditory stimulus or in the other characteristics of the tone itself. Our series of tones thus seems to be a primary series. And our next problem is to see whether we can derive from this series such attributes as our introductory formula leads us to expect.

XI. The whole interest of the psychology of the auditory attributes must obviously centre on pitch. This variant, with whatever is involved in it, is the only important variant in the series of the tones of simple pitch. It is of course open to theory at the outset to identify pitch with any of the variable attributes of sensation. But of these intensity and temporal order are obviously irrelevant, only quality and systemic order can be seriously considered. Under which of these two heads does pitch fall?

Psychological theorists have been almost unanimous in their preference for the qualitative classification. Pitch is solely, or primarily, a variation of quality or it includes that within it, whatever else it may be. For a wholly or primarily ordinal classification not a single voice has been raised, so that its prospects might well seem hopeless.

The qualitative classification has sometimes been rejected in favour of a quantitative one. "Till the time of Aristotle tones were considered to be essentially not a $\pi o\iota\acute{o}\nu$, but a $\pi o\sigma\acute{o}\nu$" (111, 136), i.e. quantitative, not qualitative. The reason for this Stumpf finds in the Pythagoreans' exclusively mathematical treatment of hearing, which here, as elsewhere, obscured all qualitative differences. But this reason is only good so long as the treatment of tone as quantitative and not at all qualitative is radically wrong. If it is in any way right, the presumption is that the Pythagoreans saw clearly what later theorists have allowed their preconceptions to hide from their view. Mathematical interests might well be the means of drawing the attention to the quantitative aspect of tones.

Among modern writers two names may be mentioned. E. Gurney, writing in 1880 (28, 139), said that differences of pitch are not differences of kind or intensity, but differences of distance and direction, "clearly and indisputably felt as such." But, although this view makes a near approach to certain aspects of the theory developed in the present work, it does not probe down to the fundamental analysis of attributes that we have now under consideration. A quantitative treatment of pitch was urged by K. Dunlap in 1905 (11, 12).

"Mach was the first and only one to express the idea that tones lie next one another in a sensory space, like the colours in the field of vision, only with the difference that the place of any colour is changeable, whilst the place of any tone is unchangeable" (112, 55). In so far as we may identify spatial with ordinal arrangement, we may modify this statement to the effect that Mach was the first and only one to hold that tones include within them an ordinal aspect. But the series of tones varies qualitatively as well, in his opinion. It is therefore only partially ordinal. Although, as I showed in the introductory chapter, a system of localisations cannot be truly held to be primary in sensation, there can be no doubt that Mach intends the differences he defines to be considered primary. But his view is not devoid of obscurity, as he points out that the differences in question are only analogous to the differences of localisation found in vision, and not really the same (cf. 112, 55, 101, 125, etc.).

"A given tone sensation," wrote Mach, "can occur only at a fixed point of this unidimensional space, which must always be fixated if the corresponding sensation is to emerge clearly" (60, 123)[1]. Mach's work contains many suggestive hints of what I consider to be correct psychological analysis, and I find the use of the term 'fixate' in this representative sentence a happy one. The same applies to his idea of elements common to all tones, to the ordinal notion of the tonal series, and so on. But these good suggestions were not brought together by Mach in such a way as to convince even himself, not to speak of others. It would therefore be wrong to suppose that Mach had properly discovered these notions in their significance. As they appear in his work they are rather such glimpses of (what I at least consider to be) the truth as one will find, after any particular psychological field has been cleared up, in countless earlier works dealing with that field.

K. Dunlap (11, 290) actually considered the classification of pitch as local sign, but rejected it,—"since local signs do not in general vary between two extremes, but rather include a manifold of differences, which do not admit of easy schematization." And, he added, pitch admits of quantitative comparison, while local signs do not. And even Stumpf was impelled to admit, while discussing Mach's views, that the quantitative arrangement of tones is analogous to a spatial arrangement. That looks like the inevitable glimpse of a suppressed truth.

To me it seems clear that the poor support given to the ordinal

---

[1] In the 2nd ed. of 1900, cf. p. 180 ff.

classification is due entirely to misconceptions regarding the psychical status of space and to inadequate methods of dealing with the attributes. For if an attribute of localisation is admitted in the other senses, and if sounds are also localised (no matter whether the binaural basis of their localisation is familiar or not), how could any one propose introducing localisation into hearing a second time? The very idea would be absurd to any one starting out from localisation. Hence, the complete obstruction of progress caused by the prevailing excess of attention to space and localisation. The methods of dealing with the attributes we have already considered.

The nature of the case, on the contrary, really insists upon the ordinal classification so strongly as to put the qualitative alternative out of court, refuted as that clearly is by the sheer chaos of conflicting views to which it has given birth. If it was impossible in our introductory formulation of the probable attributes to admit localisation or any spatial reference as an attribute of sensation, it would be as absurd as it is unnecessary to drag it into the series of differences given by simple tones. The absence of any spatial difference from that series is no reason for supposing its absence to be due to illusion or to want of psychical variation. For the reason surely presupposed by the absence of psychical variation, namely the absence of the physiological conditions of that variation, has been denied since Helmholtz's day. There is no want of psychical variation at all, but only a want of spatial variation. And this very want confirms our view that spatial indices are not in any sense attributes of sensation. For the ordinal classification the presence of a system of orders is enough. The question then is: is the series of simple tones, the series of tones in each of which only a single pitch can be distinguished, a system of orders?

In 1883 Stumpf wrote with regard to the classification of pitch as quality: "from the psychological point of view it is so obviously correct as to need no defence" (111, 136). I feel inclined to write the same about the ordinal classification. For both statements seem able to claim justification directly from the phenomena before the mind in the tonal series. Taking this phenomenal presence to be the chief concern one might feel inclined to say: "the mere name is a matter of moonshine; what's the difference so long as you and I are pleased with our views? We shall never agree." This would indeed be the case if the proposed terms were nothing but names for the special phenomena of tone, as is primarily true of the name 'pitch.' But they are not so. They involve more complex operations of thought than do the simplest types of classification. Here we have to take many phenomenal objects together to consider their likenesses, differences, connexions and changes, and then to express our ideas about them on the basis of this large survey. The fact that the object of study is primarily phenomenal is now irrelevant. It is being treated largely as if it were real, as if its nature were largely beyond, or independent of, its presence before, or direct contact with, our thought. But it is always possible for thought to return from the realistic attitude armed with a reformed and classified conceptual vision or disposition, and taking the phenomenal attitude, referring itself most directly to the phenomenal object, to say: now, are not these tonal differences ordinal, and not qualitative? and to receive a positive answer with complete assurance. After all, that is what Stumpf meant when he said that "from the psychological point of view" his classification is "so obviously correct as to need no defence." He is wrong only in implying that there is but one psychological point of view in this case, and that any psychological point of view can dispense in such a case with a defence on the systematic lines I have just indicated.

XII. With this in mind we may now review the arguments in favour of the ordinal classification:

1. *Phenomenal evidence*. (*a*) *Direct*. My first and last argument is then: the series of pitches is ordinal; it is unidimensional; and in it every tone occupies one and only one place, which can be determined to a very high degree of accuracy. If we take the tonal series in a number of discrete pitches, e.g. the tones of the chromatic scale, and apart from differences of volume to be considered later, the series can better be described conceptually in terms of order, as 'this one,' 'that one,' 'the next one,' and so on, than in qualitative terms 'this sort of one,' 'that sort of one,' 'the other sort of one.' This is confirmed by the use of already established ordinal series,—e.g. place upon a set of real or imaginary lines, or the series, *a, b, c, d*, etc.,—for the naming of pitches. If pitches were really qualitative, we might have expected to find them named after the objects that utter the different pitches, e.g. the names of birds and animals, as colours and smells are named after flowers, etc. If reply be made that the spectral colours are now named with numbers, it should be noticed that these numbers apply only indirectly through the lines of the spectrum to the colours themselves and that this conceptual system has not yet been applied to the colours of the colour body, and probably never will be, in spite of the obvious

advantages which would accrue therefrom. In short, the series is ordinal. If we take the series in a continuous form, as given in Stern's piston bottles, or the like, it forms an ordinal continuity.

(b) *Indirect.* Those who adopt the qualitative classification admit the presence in what we ordinarily call pitch of features whose common designations ultimately imply ordinal differences. Stumpf, who has already been quoted in this connexion, says the power of spatial symbolism among tones is extraordinary. The conception of the tonal series as a 'rising' series "seems to the present day musical mind to be so directly given in the nature of tones, and so obvious, that the expression 'tone-quality' in place of 'pitch' is liable to convey no meaning" (111, 190).

Whatever may account for the 'rising' aspect of the series, it seems clear that a rising series implies an ordinal basis, just as much as does localisation. Of course it obscures the solution of the problem to look for really spatial relations within the 'rising' aspect.

2. *Evidence from discrimination.* The threshold of discrimination for simultaneous pitches lies, in the middle of the musical scale (from G to e^3, or from 90 to 1200 vibrations per second), between ten and twenty vibrations per second of difference (103, 94f.). Above these low limits of difference it is always possible to distinguish and to separate the component pitches of a sound. This is true even in the case of pitch-blends, where our ordinary knowledge of the nature of the stimulus does not lead us to expect to find component pitches. It will therefore hold à *fortiori* in the case of chords, where we do expect to find components. This independence and self-maintenance of original components is not found in vision, and vision is the only sense that gives us an easily changeable and unmistakable system of qualitative differences. Analogy between the mixture of pitches in a blend and the mixture of visual qualities can therefore hardly be held to support the qualitative classification of pitch. But if the ordinal classification of pitch is adopted, the ease of pitch analysis receives a ready explanation.

This evidence of discrimination is seconded by the evidence of memory known as absolute hearing or absolute ear. This exceeds by far the finest memory for shades of colour.

3. *Systematic evidence.* (a) *Noises and vowels.* The other classes of sounds yet to be studied—noises and vowels—admit of explanation with the help of the ordinal attribute in a simple way that is not open upon the qualitative line. The latter is compelled to assume the presence

of a new set of qualities in noises or in vowels or in both, or to attempt
to establish relations of primacy and derivation amongst these sets of
qualities. But any such relations must remain entirely hypothetical,
because there is no analogy to them in any other sense, not even in
vision. They therefore fail to carry conviction even within the qualitative camp.

(b) *The systemic attributes.* Under the name pitch we commonly
include not merely an ordinal series, but a series of changing volumes
(which we shall study later). In the other senses we have reviewed,
volumes and extents or masses imply the conjunction of extensity
with ordinal differences. We should therefore expect the volumes of
the pitch series to involve ordinal, not qualitative, differences, which
in no other case combine with extensity to give volume.

(c) *The formula of attributes.* The classification of pitch as order
seems indicated by the mere application of our introductory formula
of attributes to the series of simple tones. The presumption regarding
qualities is that hearing will contain only one or a few discrete miscible
qualities. As the latter have hardly been claimed to be present till
within recent years, they are at least not strikingly obvious. One
quality is patent, viz. the quality of hearing as such, that distinguishes
itself from taste or vision. For a parallel to order, our formula does
not lead us to look for any form of localisation, as we have already
tentatively declared that to be more than the content of any single
sensation. Why not then try to fit pitch upon order? Then the volume
of tones would yield us extensity, and all would be well. Pitch as
order would thus fully confirm the formula of attributes for all but the
crazy sense of smell, which after all could be accommodated in spite
of its obscurity. Hearing, as generally analysed to-day, is the only sense
that offers any serious difficulty in respect of the ordinal attribute.
If it were accommodated, the sense of smell might pass unchallenged.

(d) *The integrations of sensory experience.* The ordinal classification
receives great and decisive support from a systematic study of the
integrations of the several attributes in the various senses. If distance,
direction, motion, etc., result in many senses from the integration of
the attribute presumed to be inherent in differences of localisation,—
an attribute which very many of those who adopt the qualitative
classification of pitch consider to be at least non-qualitative,—and if
in sound we discover processes closely akin to distance, direction, motion,
etc., viz. distance and interval, direction, and melody, etc., which are
admittedly dependent upon variations in pitch; then it follows that

the attribute inherent in differences of pitch is at least non-qualitative, and is presumably identical with that inherent in differences of localisation,—in our case order. By a parallel study of the senses we should thus be called upon to regard pitch as essentially ordinal; and conversely the classification of pitch under order offers a key to the proper arrangement and interpretation of the complex phenomena of hearing.

4. *Psychophysical evidence.* (*a*) *Anatomical.* These psychological pleas are supported by two psychophysical ones. The first is anatomical. The afferent nerves attached to the receptor of hearing are spread over it in a thin line of varying curvature. No matter how this line of receptors functions, whether transversely or longitudinally, or in both ways, we should expect it to have some parallel representation in our elementary experiences of hearing; and the series of simple pitches is the only parallel to be found. Thus for our ordinal series in hearing we should have an ordinal series in the body.

(*b*) *Genetic.* If that plea is granted, we can then readily understand how the series of tonal experiences has been developed, without transgressing the bounds of well accepted biological principles. We can see the finger of nature shaping the marvellous organ of hearing towards perfection, and need not vainly inquire how that organ came to be allied with a series of qualities with which it has no inner kinship and which it could not have produced of itself.

In short the series of simple pitches itself and the whole theory of hearing asserts and demands the ordinal classification of pitch. I have here anticipated much evidence that can only be adequately dealt with separately as we proceed. But it is well to pull the whole mass together around the crucial point of the analysis. We have thus completely disposed of the qualitative classification in so far as that may be applied in any simple manner to the whole series of tones of simple pitch. Other forms of the qualitative classification which have been offered in recent years, will be dealt with as the sets of facts on which they are founded, come within our view.

XIII. But the ordinal nature of pitch is only part of its whole content. It is a 'rising' series besides. And if we have identified the attributes of intensity and order, we have not yet definitely settled how we are to accommodate the attributes of extensity and quality. Of these quality already has a place, as we have indicated under 3 (*c*) above; it is mere hearing as such; there must be at least one quality in all hearing. The only question which now arises is: are there several

or many forms of quality in hearing? Can any changing feature of the
tonal series other than its order be properly classified as qualitative?
I shall now discuss this question in relation to the 'rising' variation
of the tonal series, leaving other aspects of the tonal series till later.
My formula of the attributes calls for the attribute of extensity in
conjunction with order. Thus we obtain the problem: is the 'rising'
variation better classified as qualitative or as extensive? Of course
extensity alone, being a non-variable attribute as far as our attributive
formula has revealed it, could not explain a variable series; but it
could do so in the complex variable form in which we have discovered
it, especially in the second group of senses, viz. in extents, volumes,
or masses.

The following considerations favour the extensive attribute:

1. *Phenomenal evidence—direct.* My first and last argument is
as before: the series of tones of simple pitch contains a variation of
volume or mass. Low tones are great and massive and all-pervasive;
high tones are sharp, thin and circumscribed; as tones rise in pitch,
their volume shrinks gradually, pulling itself together as it were, till
it is finally almost too small and thin to be noticed. This is true whether
the series is presented continuously or in discrete pitches. And it is
confirmed by the conceptual terms commonly used to indicate these
variations of tones without regard to their specific pitches. In English
we speak of high and low tones, of sharp and flat tones, where neither
specific pitch-place or pitch-blend is referred to. Stumpf, who collated
the terms in use in a number of languages, said: "not all tongues
use spatial expressions for differences of pitch, and those that do so,
not in a thoroughly uniform manner. But yet expressions analogous
to the modern ones are the most general, and are to be found alongside
even where others predominate in technical usage" (111, 192).

Nevertheless at the time of writing the first volume of his work
on hearing, Stumpf was of the opinion that deep tones only *seem* to be
more extensive; they are not phenomenally so, they are not 'given' so
(111, 210). So he was forced to trace the spatial associations and the
spatial apprehension of tone to such differences as commonly accompany
differences of pitch, especially to differences in their duration, in their
spread throughout the organism during hearing, in their feeling-
character, and in their strength. The association is thus essential,
not accidental (111, 223). We may well agree that Stumpf has thus
shown how the association between tones and *spatial* relations, especially
those of height and depth, has arisen. Tones are not spatially higher

or lower; that is obvious to everyone in spite of the use of these terms; the terms are clearly used in a figurative sense. Nor are they spatially massive, or thin, or flat. We transfer all these terms to them because, being terms of practical life, they are more familiar and demonstrable to everyone, and so afford a ready means of describing tonal differences. The basis for a transference of terms by association is thus given.

But we surely do not mean by these terms that high tones are either more continuous than low ones (we cannot use the term 'smoother' as Stumpf did (111, 203 ff.) because that is really meaningless, unless tones have a volume which can be smooth); or are more intensive for the same power of stimulus; or come from smaller instruments; or penetrate less throughout the body; or take longer to hear and recognise and to fade out. None of all these differences corresponds directly to what is implied in the spatial references that have to be explained. Surely we mean that tones do differ phenomenally in their extent or volume. And although Stumpf did not explicitly reject the reasons given for his earlier view, yet in his second volume he definitely accepted the primacy of a variable 'extension' in tones of different pitch[1].

A word of caution must be repeated here even at the risk of boredom to those who understand. By order and extent or volume I do not mean spatial order and spatial mass or volume. If the analysis I offer is correct, I am sure the failure of previous psychologists to reach it is due, apart from lack of method in the study of the attributes common to all the senses, first and foremost to the fixed idea that there can be no order and continuity unless they be spatial[2].

---

[1] 112, 56. A. Lehmann (50, 119) also adopts this view and argues from the relation between extent of sensation and extent of stimulated surface in other senses, e.g. touch, to a variable extent of stimulated nerve fibres for tones of different volume. K. Dunlap (11, 291) may also be mentioned: "Differences in pitch are directly comparable to differences in planar or linear extent, and the physiological condition of differences in pitch accordingly is probably difference in number of nerve-endings stimulated."

[2] The obstruction of the spatial preconception is specially evident with Stumpf, who indeed comes within an ace of seeing it as such (112, 54 ff.). From his nativistic principles he ascribes a special difference (pq) to the experiences of either ear, but although these differences become associated with the spatial localisation of the ears as parts of the body and are involved in the functions of binaural localisation, they need not, Stumpf says, themselves be localisational in the ordinary sense, but only distinctive of the experiences of either ear. Having thus properly for the moment got beneath the localisational process as it were, and having suspected the presence of a 'we know not what,' he proceeds to ask "whether amongst the tones of one and the same ear differences of the kind pq are to be found," and replies: "not a trace." But in this answer he has already

The order of numbers is not spatial nor is the order of times, although the most modern of philosophers Bergson is so obsessed with the idea of space, that he would have us believe the intellect itself to be similarly afflicted and to have crushed the pulsing soul into its cast-iron moulds. No, there are many kinds of order, and space is only one of them. Why should there not also be many kinds of continuity—of however many dimensions—and tonal volume or any sensory extent be only one species thereof? Then we need only inquire why tonal volume comes to be named with terms borrowed from spatial volume and why the pitches of these volumes are said to rise. The answer, as Stumpf has shown, is clear enough.

2. *Evidence from discrimination.* As we shall see in more detail later on, we can discriminate tones in respect of their volume as well as in respect of pitch. But our judgment is much finer in the latter case. Wherever only small differences are given, we rely wholly on the change in pitch (123, 320 f.). Where the pitches offered lie so far apart as to fail to exhibit the musical relations usually borne by tones of the same octave, their difference of volume becomes more obvious. It is not possible to establish the difference of discriminability of pitches and volumes by direct experimentation with the tones of the musical range, because no independent variation of pitches and volumes is possible. But in the extremes of the tonal series, in very high and very low tones, at the limits of the musical range and beyond them, pitches become much less discriminable; they seem then to be less discriminable than the accompanying volumes (112, 57 and 123, 317 ff.).

3. *Systematic evidence.* (*a*) The presence of volumes is not quite so distinctly traceable in the case of noises and vowels; because the series formed by these sounds are not so perfect. But there can be no doubt that noises and vowels differ amongst themselves in respect of volume. In fact differences of volume are more characteristic of noises than are differences of pitch. (*b*) The implication of the attribute of extensity by the attribute of order and (*c*) by the attributive formula need only be mentioned.

(*d*) The special systematic plea for the admission of variations of volume, and so for the attribute of extensity, is given in sound by

risen from his momentary plunge back to the surface of the localisation barrier. Apart from the obvious results of mere association given in the expressions 'higher' and 'lower,' he says, "we notice no spatial togetherness of tones and none such has been maintained even to most recent times." And thereupon he admits the primacy of 'extension' amongst the tones of one ear, denied in his first volume!

the phenomena of fusion that are so characteristic of this sense.   These seem to be explicable only by reference to coincidences of volumes.

4.   Of the psychophysical arguments the anatomical (*a*) is not so evident and demands the careful examination and discussion of the rather uncertain observations that have been made.   But it seems clear on various grounds that the occurrence of even a tone of simple pitch requires the excitation of a short length of the series of neural terminations in the cochlea.   The exact amount of this length is not quite evident either on mathematical physical grounds or on the basis of experimental injury of the cochlea.   The genetic argument (*b*) is here the same as before, in so far as with the assumption of volumes the mystery of the qualitative view is removed.

XIV.   The series of tones of simple pitch then fully satisfies the requirements of our introductory attributive formula and the sense of hearing thus far conforms to the probable sensational type, making this type therefore still more probable.   It thus becomes probable that the same scheme of allocation of the attributes will apply to the other groups of sounds that do not fall within the series of tones of simple pitch.   The next problem now is whether these tones are both actually, and really or theoretically, the simplest auditory sensations.

XV.   It must be at once clear that as tones form a series of decreasing volumes, they may well be the simplest auditory experiences we ever actually obtain, but they cannot be the theoretically elementary sensation.   They may be the molecule of sensation as it were, but not the atom.   That must be true of every tone except possibly the tone of smallest volume, viz. the tone of the highest pitch at the upper limit of the range of hearing.   The rate of physical vibration required to produce this last tone varies for different persons and decreases somewhat in advanced years.   It may be set approximately at some 20,000 vibrations[1].   But it is not certain whether the sounds produced by higher rates of vibration are merely the noises which accompany the production of these rates of vibration or are themselves sounds (noises) directly produced by these rates of vibration in place of the previous tones. An answer to this question is not very important.

In dealing with the senses of the first group we have seen how the

[1] *v.* e.g. 123, 327. On the limits of the pitch range compare K. L. Schaefer (102. 7 ff.). The lowest limit may be put at an average of 16-20 vibrations.   Below that the occurrence of tone is uncertain.

variation of the extent or area of sensation is dependent upon the area of skin affected by the stimulus and thus upon the number of minimal spots of sensation of different order evoked at once. The variation of mass or volume seen in the senses of the second group thereby received a ready explanation. It seems inevitable that we should extend this explanation to the volume of hearing[1]. Each tonal volume would then be a mass of—shall we say—undifferentiated tonal orders. But surely there is a differentiation of tonal orders within the mass. Is not the pitch of a tone obviously the intensively predominating order of the volume of that tone? Of course great difficulties arise as soon as we attempt to discover in each case whether more than one order is involved in the predominance we find, and if so how many. Such questions are almost as hard to settle as it is to say whether the spot of cutaneous sensation is the absolute minimum or not. But certain indications are of great service. Stumpf says: "I will not conceal that simple mild tones sometimes seem to possess a peculiar elasticity in the matter of pitch. When the pitch of the tone of a tuning-fork is to be reproduced upon the violin, it can happen that the player oscillates within a quarter tone. When a bottle is blown whose tone lies in the small octave, and the corresponding tone is sought on the piano, the former can sound now like f, now like $f\sharp$; it seems like that one of the two tones which is just being played" (112, 114). The predominating part of the tone is here obviously far from punctate. Probably the predominance of tone becomes sharper and clearer as the pitch of tone rises, being broad and gradual like the rise of a grassy knoll in the low tones, and becoming sharp and pointed like a pyramid in the higher regions. The addition of upper partials to a tone helps to reduce its smooth predominance. How this comes about we shall consider later. For the present I shall neglect details which are subordinate to the general solution of the problem and speak of the pitch of a tone as the predominant order in that tone.

We can go still further in our intellectual apprehension of tones. Tones of simple pitch, e.g. those of a well-played tuning-fork seem to everyone wonderfully smooth and regular, beautifully rounded off systems (of elementary tonal sensations). Leaving out the aesthetic reaction we may say: tones are regular systems of ordinally different, elementary sounds, in which 'one' element predominates. And there is no sign of any want of balance and no asymmetry in any of these systems, and no difference between the different tones in respect of

---

[1] This extension is made as such by A. Lehmann (50, 120, 131); cf. below, p. 145.

the system they consist of. There could therefore be no reason for denying the supposition that the predominating pitch of each tone is central to the whole system.

In discussing the question whether there are perfectly simple tones Stumpf (112, 272) referred (without indication of the source) to a theory by Hostinsky which has some affinity with the theory just stated. But its foundation seems to be rather physiological than psychological; an apparently simple tone is held to consist of as many tones as there are neighbouring resonant fibres. And in so far as its foundation is psychological, it rests upon indirect evidence, not upon direct: because so-called simple tones form a series which would be impossible were they really simple sensations. Stumpf said of this theory and of Mach's: "In neither case is an attempt made to establish the presence of these elements, it is a case of mere hypothesis. These must justify themselves by their purpose, by the theoretical need they serve." My theory does that as well as being a direct expression of the phenomenal nature of sounds.

In discussing the same problem of simple tones at another point (112, 111 ff.) Stumpf brought forward as evidence against the view above referred to (Hostinsky) that in a simple tone none of the hypothetical neighbouring 'tones' are actually to be heard by the analytic attention. This expectation appears from my point of view as a misunderstanding of the problem. We cannot expect any but the predominating order to appear as such in the tone. But Stumpf came very near to my view in the passage quoted in the text about the pitch of simple mild tones. Only he rejected this clear indication by saying that even "if the tone really in the sensation changed its pitch within a semitone according to the momentary direction of attention, this would anyhow be quite different from hearing, apart from a middle tone, simultaneously others differing by a quarter tone upwards or downwards. Elasticity is not extension."

The theory of Hostinsky may be compared with that of Lehmann (50) referred to above (p. 28, note 1), and sketched below (pp. 145, 159 f.). Lehmann's theory is a little better than Hostinsky's in so far as the former recognises the psychical reality of volume and gives the extensive parallel in touch. C. S. Myers and others have made less confident suggestions regarding the volume of tones. But none of them has really developed the matter beyond a first suggestion.

XVI. But all these predominating pitches form a continuous series of orders. And this series has two ends, all the pitches higher than the lowest lying on one side of the pitch of the lowest tone. The ends of the series are therefore not only distinguished by their difference of order, but also by the different size of the volumes in which they regularly occur. Thus we get a perfectly adequate basis for the associations which are incorporated in the terms by which we name tones, viz. high—low, sharp—flat, rising—falling. And all the psychological characteristics of the tonal series thus far encountered have been explained.

We may finally return to the pitch-blends which, as attentive analysis shows, constitute the differences in the musical sounds of the same nominal pitch as they are produced from different instruments. Apart from special efforts of analysis these sounds seem to be quite simple. Neither their predominant pitch nor their volume seems to vary with the instrument from which they come. They vary only in the pitches which can be distinguished within these volumes. In all of them only one pitch predominates—the fundamental pitch of the tone. But whereas in tones of simple pitch no other pitches are distinguishable, the whole tone being a regular system of sounds; in pitch-blends several other auditory orders of varying dominance appear, all being much weaker than the fundamental, but varying irregularly in dominance amongst each other. None of them leaves the unity of the whole unchangeable volume so as to fall outside of it and away from it, and so to constitute a really separate tone. It is for this reason that the pitch-blends of good musical tones are ordinarily noticeable only as a variant upon the corresponding tone of simple pitch (i.e. the pitch of the fundamental). That is after all the predominant pitch. The other pitches which dominate relatively within the whole only serve to give a slightly different character to the system of sounds that constitutes the musical tone. This system has not the simple regularity of the tone of simple pitch. Its system has a slightly different character; it becomes asymmetrical, receiving a greater basis of dominance at one or other part of its volume. If the proportion given by the dominance of the fundamental is removed by its weakening, the chief character of the tone disappears, and the tone is 'poor.' The more the fundamental and the partials near it dominate, the richer will the tone be. When the higher partials become more prominent, the tone must take on a high or bright character, because its higher parts become more noticeable. Of course, as Helmholtz indicated in his summary rules, other factors than just the spread of the component pitches over the whole volume help to determine the character of a pitch-blend, e.g. fusions, harmonies, etc.

The nature of pitch-blend may be otherwise expressed in relation to the tone of simple pitch. This pure tone we may for the moment consider as the ideal of music—a fictitious philosophical ideal. All good musical pitch-blends are approximations towards this ideal. In them all the upper partials are so subordinated to the fundamental that they cannot be distinguished with the unaided ear, unless a systematic, analytic, search is made for them, or unless the hearer has acquired an unusual disposition for attending to them. An effort is obviously made by the musician to make the tones of his instrument as balanced and regular as possible, like those of pure tones. But he does not go beyond a certain point in striving towards this ideal. Once the easy analysis of partials is obviated, he is within a sphere where the advantage of keeping away from the ideal greatly exceeds the advantage of approaching it further. For a great variety of approximations to the ideal is thereby attained. These together make up a practical ideal which is close to, but not identical with the theoretical ideal with which each one separately is related.

Other evidence in favour of this interpretation of the relation of pitch-blend to the psychological constitution of the tone of simple pitch will be brought forward (below, p. 71 ff.) when we are free to consider the phenomena attendant on the simultaneous presentation of the stimuli which separately would give tones of simple pitch. Having completed our preliminary study of tones we may now pass on to the other familiar group of sounds—noises—with the presumption that the results we have obtained from the study of tones will suffice to explain the peculiar phenomena of noises, if that explanation is not also derivable directly from these phenomena themselves.

XVII. B. *Noises.* "The nature of the difference between musical tones and noises," said Helmholtz in the opening lines of his work (29, 14; 30, 9), "can generally be determined by attentive observation without artificial assistance. We perceive that generally a noise is accompanied by a rapid alternation of different kinds of sensations of sound. Think for example of the rattling of a carriage upon paving stones, the splashing or breaking of a waterfall or the waves of the sea, the rustling of leaves in a wood. In all these cases we have rapid, irregular, but distinctly perceptible alternations of various kinds of sounds, which shoot forth spasmodically. In the howling of the wind the alternation is slow, the sound slowly and gradually rises in pitch and then falls again. It is also more or less possible to separate restlessly alternating sounds in the greater number of other noises....On the other hand a musical tone strikes the ear as a perfectly undisturbed uniform sound which remains unaltered as long as it exists, and it presents no alternation of various kinds of constituents. To this then corresponds a simple regular kind of sensation, whereas in a noise many various sensations of musical tone are irregularly mixed up and as it were tumbled about in confusion." Later on, by inference from his physical and physiological theories, he showed how steady transition "between noises without any determinate pitch, and compound tones with a determinate pitch may be produced." "This actually takes place," he said, "and herein lies the proof on which Herr S. Exner has properly laid weight, that such noises must be perceived by those parts of the ear which act in distinguishing pitch[1]."

Now we are not at present concerned with the identity of the organs of hearing. In fact we must ask by what right any such proof is thus established. Does not the proof lie in the psychical identity of being that is shown to link tones and noises in spite of their great differences? Noises are essentially the same things as tones; only tones are regular and of determinate pitch, while noises are irregular and of more or less indeterminate pitch. Not that they have no pitch at all. It merely changes rapidly, or there are many pitches at once, so that none predominates so as to determine which pitch the mass of sound shall be held to have. Obviously then, one and the same organ, especially such a complex series of organs as those of the basilar membrane, may produce both tones and noises. It has only to act regularly in the one case and irregularly in the other. Variants that are essentially the same in nature, even although this nature be psychical, can be produced by the same organ. The argument then is primarily psychical.

The critical point of Helmholtz's exposition is therefore the postulation of indeterminateness of pitch and the assumption of its existence in noise. No exception can be taken to the methods by which Helmholtz established the existence of indeterminate pitches. But one might well ask whether Helmholtz's psychological system will accommodate such a thing and how. It certainly does not exclude it; for he took over the chief terms[2] describing tones in a rather free untechnical sense and without comment from ordinary speech. And so he was free to extend the notions conveyed by them whenever he saw reason to do so. This is of course a merit in his method. And impatient of psychological subtleties, one might feel inclined to say: Helmholtz did well not to bother over purely subjective matters, which in any case cannot be decided, being a mere matter of personal fancy. But such a view would ignore the primacy of the psychical problem, which has just been

---

[1] 30, 151 from H.'s fourth edition. Earlier he did not agree with Exner.

[2] In the first pages of his work Helmholtz spoke of the force, pitch and *Klangfarbe* (which Ellis translates as 'quality') of musical tones. Later on (29, 232) he spoke of the different quality of a tone sensation according to its pitch, thus using quality in the technical attributive sense.

indicated, and will be set out more fully as we proceed, and would try to improve on neutrality by adopting an unfriendly attitude. If Helmholtz's progress was not obstructed by any wrong preliminary classification of pitch, it was not aided by a right preliminary view. And it never got the help of this right view, although in certain respects the physical and physiological ground which Helmholtz prepared for the reception of psychological analysis would have suited it admirably. Popular psychology, like popular dietary, has good reason to be highly successful. But it is just as likely to be incapable of improvement.

And Helmholtz was forced to justify whatever psychological assumptions he made or adopted, as soon as they seemed questionable. Thus in his study of pitch-blends he began by assuming in an apparently very harmless way, that "the ear...does not hear merely *that* one musical tone...but it hears besides a whole series of higher tones, which we call the...upper partial tones" (29, 37; 30, 22). Had Helmholtz kept strictly to the facts, he should have written here partial *pitches* instead of partial *tones,* just as I have done. But he seems again to have taken over the common usage without questioning its psychological validity and without even carefully scrutinising its exactness as a description. Had he limited himself to partial pitches his judgment upon the discussion raised by Ohm and Seebeck[1] and his psychological reflections upon the analysis of tones (29, 102 ff.; 30, 62 ff.) would undoubtedly have been very different. He would not have thought the difference between the analysis of mixed colours and pitch-blends was due to greater instrumental practice in the latter case. The use of the innocent looking word 'tone' instead of 'pitch' led him to expect of tonal analysis by mere attention what it can never do. It can never make tones more separate than they originally are when given to it.

An immense amount of obstruction has been created by this little word *tone* so innocently and so plausibly inserted instead of the certain fact of pitch. Stumpf's discussion of the psychological nature of noises, for example, was profoundly affected by it. At many points he used the word tone where obviously only pitch was meant. Thus when a

---

[1] 29, 100 ff.; 30, 58 ff.: "The dispute turns upon whether in all cases upper partials can be perceived analytically in their individual existence; that is, whether the ear when unaided by resonators or other physical auxiliaries, which themselves alter the mass of musical sound heard by the observer, can by mere direction and intensity of attention distinguish whether, and if so in what force, the octave, the twelfth, etc. of the fundamental exists in the given musical sound."

single stick is thrown on the ground, it was said, no 'tone' is heard;
but it is readily recognised if a series of sticks of the appropriate sizes
are thrown on the ground. A moment's recollection of this familiar
experiment suffices to show that in the serial part of it only pitches
are heard and recognised, not tones, unless we mean by tones merely
recognisable pitches. So too when a tone was said to be heard from a
brook. And Stumpf's test of the absence of 'tone' from subjective
(ear) noises seems to have been: how nearly their pitch could be
estimated (112, 500ff.).

With regard to theories, Stumpf's chief objection to the view that
noises consist of many simultaneous tones little different in pitch,
was that the resultant sound does not, or would not, lose "its tonal
character and its analysability" (112, 504). This double concept seems
somewhat strange. And of noises, in so far as they are said to be a
very rapid succession of very many tones of different pitch, he said,
we should still hear the "rapid change of tone." But what constitutes
'tone' when the steadiness of pitch is gone? Is it the mere change of
volume? And do not noises have volumes as well? Do not noises
show among themselves all or any of those kinds of differences which
accompany change of pitch in tones? Having rejected these two
theories Stumpf then favoured the view that noises are tones of a
definite, not necessarily changing, pitch, and are distinguished from tones
in the usual sense either by their being momentary or by their being
a rapid succession of intermittent momentary tone impressions. Here
he seems to have got rid of the tonal *phenomenon*, while still retaining
(as very brief) *real* tones in the noise. But even this theoretical device
did not quite convince him. He added: "One set of so-called noises
are intermittent tones of the highest or lowest region (growling, hissing,
etc.). Here it is by no means impossible with increased attention to
recognise the tones as such. *Still I would not maintain even in these
cases, that some scrap of pure noise is not left over*[1]." And then some
noises, as he said, are surely constant, e.g. ear noises. Noises might
therefore still be special sensations not reducible to tones, but like
enough to them to justify their reference to the same organ as a different
quality of hearing from tones. With all this, he thought, some noises
might still be more like low than high tones or conversely. Thus a

---

[1] 112, 509. Stumpf wrote as late as 1914: "That all noises contain admixtures of
tone, I should now no longer maintain" (123, 341). At the same place he spoke of noises
with a limited zone of pitch, which yet do not include 'real tones,' or do not therefore
become 'tones.'

good meaning would still rest in the oft used expression: "*a difference of pitch, but no tone, was noticeable*[1]."

Clearly the idea by which the whole of Stumpf's discussion is ultimately governed, is this: it is almost impossible to assent to any sort of reduction of noises to tones, because although noises may have some sort of pitch, recognisable under the most favourable circumstances, and some sort of volume, and any or all of the other variable features of tones, and so be classifiable with them as sensations of hearing, yet they simply are not *tonal*. Stumpf does not, as far as I am aware, anywhere give any proper analytic justification of this important implication of the tonal concept. Perhaps the clearness of pitch, or the unity of many clear attributes in tone might be referred to. But so long as noises have pitch and the other attributes at all, I cannot see how clearness could be held to divide the sensations of hearing into two such peculiar groups. The nearest approach to a justification I can find, is in Helmholtz's opening words quoted above, especially where he said: "in a noise many various sensations of musical tone are irregularly mixed up and as it were tumbled about in confusion" (29, 14; 30, 8). It is evident therefore that however much is common to noise and tone, something still remains peculiar to each, so that noises are not any more really tones because pitches can be recognised in them with special efforts, than tones are really noises because under special circumstances their pitch is often hard to recognise[2].

This outcome of Stumpf's discussion greatly confirms us in our theory of tone as a regular, probably symmetrical, system of sounds. Not the pitch, nor the volume, and still less any other attribute or feature is the essential mark of tone, but the place of the predominant pitch in the whole volume, which thus forms a regular system of sounds. That is the 'tonal' character. In order to explain noises then we do not need to attempt to reduce them to tones. We need only trace the presence of pitch and volume in them as far as we can, and by the evidence of the trend of their variations up to the point where

---

[1] 112, 510, expressed also by Hensen, *v.* 112, 500.

[2] Max Meyer discussed Stumpf's treatment of noise (76) and wrestled with the obstruction hidden in it that I have expounded, without being able to overcome it. He thought that if a chord were not analysed at all, it would appear as a noise (p. 238). He defined noise as a series (rapid changes) of tone sensation under conditions which make a determinate judgment regarding the existence of pitch impossible. The conclusion is near enough to my own to pass unchallenged, but Meyer did not get at the root of Stumpf's difficulty. So Stumpf might well reply: your opinion differs from mine, but you do not convince me I am wrong.

our observational analysis fails, make it highly probable that noises whose pitch and volume cannot be determined are required to complete the scope of the theory of the psychical constitution of auditory experience.

XVIII. Tones are regular systems of sounds. Irregular systems should occur, as should also all degrees of irregularity from the tonal ideal to complete chaos. Irregularity is produced by displacement of the predominant order from its usual position to any other condition. *À priori* this disturbance could arise in various ways. Simple displacement of the point of predominance seems normally to be more or less excluded by the nature of the physical stimulus. Certain abnormal observations will be mentioned later (p. 50 (*b*)) which seem to represent this case. The large class of pitch-blends forms for our ear a minimal departure from the ideal regularity, by which they seem rather to gain than to lose in interest. Apart from their adherence to certain more or less regular patterns already described, their 'tonality' will form the object of later consideration. The same applies to all those groupings of pitches which give more or less harmonious impressions. The 'harmony' is introspectively closely akin to the regularity of tone and is probably of the same nature as it is. Far from being anything strange in sound, as so many have held, it would then be only a development or complication of the very thing 'tone' itself. We have at this point no *à priori* method for following out the grades of harmony, but we know how to decrease this effect and make it pass towards noise.

Apart from these special cases irregularity may be got by continuity and rapidity of displacement; but this gives no decisive degree of irregularity, because the volume varies with the displacement of the pitch, and so the regularity of system—the tonal character—still remains in spite of the constant change of pitch. When sounds are very brief or momentary, there are two possibilities: either no predominant order is produced in the time allowed, but only a mass of orders in which no sort of system of intensive differences can be detected; or system and dominance do occur, but the sensory mass lasts too short a time for the characteristics of the experience to become psychically effective towards cognition, i.e. to be observed. Of the two hypotheses the former seems to be more generally accepted. At least two identical, or very similar vibrations are required if 'tone' is to be heard and recognised (1, 197 ff.). And yet it does not appear how a maximum or a system is to be produced by the second vibration if it is not already present in the first. The second is either just another first, or if the effect of the first lasts on, its hypothetical irregularity will hardly form good ground for the attainment of regularity. But it is possible that two vibrations are required only because one periodic vibration cannot be physically given or defined unless two are given. In other words the first cannot be finished off perfectly, so as to give the required balance in the sensation, unless the second is at least begun. The second or in general the last would, then, tail out irregularly.

Irregularity may also be attained by increase in the ordinal scope of the 'spot' predominant in the volume. This would mean a decrease in the definition of the predominance, and seems attainable by a rapid and irregular oscillation of the rate of vibration round about an average. Jaensch (34) claims to produce noises in this way. Of course a pitch could still be ascribed to these noises with or without the help of comparison, as in the experiment with the dropped sticks. A detectable pitch need not be strictly, any more than it is popularly, considered to be incompatible with noise. A sound might also contain two or more indefinite pitches. The greater the number, the more irregular would the whole sound be.

Following these methods of multiplication and blurring of pitches, we should attain to sequences so irregular as to produce sounds in which no trace of predominance or of system could be detected. These would be 'pure' noises. A pure noise would then be a mass of sounds in which dominance is so irregular as to be undetectable or in which no dominance occurs. The latter state in a constant form should be a possible result of various affections of the inner ear. That there are tones without noise would mean that there are systems of sound in which no trace of irregularity is to be found. That there are noises without tone would mean that there are systems of sounds in which no regularity and no approach to regularity can be detected.

We should thus have surveyed all the evidence that can be brought to bear upon the problem of noise. It is primarily psychological—the whole trend of the variations of sound away from the perfect system and predominance of pitch that constitutes tone towards multiplication and irregularity of pitch until such degrees are attained as completely baffle analysis. Parallel to this runs the evidence of the complication of the physical stimulus. These lines of evidence in conjunction with our theory of tone exclude any need for a separate being and origin in noise. The former are commonly held by those who accept the reduction of noises to tones; whereas the peculiarity of the 'tonal' experience over and above its pitch, although this peculiarity has been explicitly handled by none, is the sole reason of a psychological kind for the separation of sounds into a special class[1]. Any sort of physiological argument is, of course, irrelevant, for it could never affect the fact that tones and noises are both auditory, any more than the theory of the independence of rods and cones in the retina affects the psychology of vision. Hence with the resolution of the tonal difficulty, all may agree that tones and noises vary from one another, not in any attribute, but in the nature of the mass of auditory 'atoms' of which they consist. Of the presence of volume in noise there can be as little doubt as of the presence of pitch in noise. And what doubt there is, may be resolved in the same way, if not more easily; for in this respect we do not need to analyse the sound, but only to compare it with others as a whole.

XIX. C. *Vowels.* It is a familiar fact that in the utterance of the various vowels *u, o, a, e, i,* etc., the mouth is brought into different positions. The occurrence of vowels is obviously dependent upon these positions. How these positions actually determine the character of the sound produced in speaking is far from clear and has been greatly disputed. There are two chief views. One asserts that in the act of speaking, the cavity formed by the mouth acts as a resonator reinforcing certain partial pitches of the sound produced by the vocal chords. A special type of pitch-blend is then produced which we name by the utterance of it. The chief difficulty of this view lies in the supposition that the same sets of partials required for the various vowels can be present in all the voice-tones of the range within which these vowels can actually be produced. The other theory asserts that in the act of speaking the cavity formed by the mouth is blown by the air passing through it or past it through the nose, as a bottle is made to produce a tone by air blowing over the mouth of it. This view gets over the difficulty of the first; identical partials or sets of partials may now be admitted, no matter what may be the pitch of the voice-tones, the tones produced by the vibration of the vocal chords.

Neither of these theories would offer any new material for the special

---

[1] K. L. Schaefer (102, 17) says that, while many believe that there is in noise, apart from a more or less large number of tones, a specifically noisy element, he believes that noises like clangs (pitch-blends) are "nothing but a sum of tones, although a sum whose composition usually deviates radically in various respects from that of clangs, which rests on musical principles, and whose complete physical and physiological analysis into parts is very very much more difficult than it is for clangs." That is a tortuous way of admitting that the complete analysis of noises into tones is not possible.

study of this work, concerned as it is with the principles and outline of the psychology of hearing, not with such detail questions, which more properly fall within the scope of physics or phonetics. But in recent years a new turn has been given to the study of vowels, by which they would become of primary importance. This new turn was made possible by two things. In the first place the partials of the chief vowels show a tendency to occupy positions an octave apart from one another. This appears in Helmholtz's table to some extent ($o = b'^{\flat}$, $a = b^{2\flat}$, $E = b^{3}{}'$) (29, 171; 30, 110) and it was extended and generalised for the five vowels u, o, a, e, i, by R. König, whose set of tuning forks for the demonstration of the vowel pitches is well known, being tuned to b, b', b^{2}, b^{3}, b^{4} (or rather $b^{\flat}$, 225 vibrations). In the second place the difficulties so obviously felt in the elementary psychology of hearing, as that had grown up on the fundamental decision to look upon pitch as qualitative (with or without any reference to volume, which in any case was set aside as quasi-spatial), seemed to call for some new venture in theory. But for that, there would indeed have been room for the improvement and extension of König's results, but not for any re-interpretation of them. It was Köhler (42) who propounded the view that the vowels are the sole and primary qualities of hearing.

According to him the series of vowels lie strictly in octaves over one another, their vibration frequencies being multiples of 264, which would give the pitch of c for an 'a' of 220 vibrations. Between one c and the next higher the 'quality' of the tone changes gradually into another radically different quality, in the same way as the quality of visual sensation changes from red to yellow. And we have popular 'absolute' names for these qualities, as for red, sweet, etc. None of these things holds for the alternative treatment of pitches as qualities. These arguments of Köhler's helped to weaken the old qualitative position of pitch. The new view may be expressed diagrammatically in relation to Hering's colour system thus (123, 325; 42, 116):

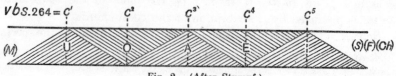

Fig. 2. (After Stumpf.)

Here, in the example chosen, the rising of the tone from c^{2} to c^{3} would bring a gradual departure from the o (*toe*) quality through the a of *all* to the a of *father*, just as red passes through orange to yellow (cf. Fig. 1).

So for the others also. It is hard to say if any given isolated tone is
the pure o or not, but after a little practice it is very easy to indicate
the point in the tonal series where the u valency just disappears and a
new quality, that of o, appears. These special points are not just
peculiarities of the mouth or of any one language, but absolute turning
points. The average values got by Köhler by the 'easier' method
appear in the following table (42, 130, 137):

TABLE I.

Obsr.	m	u	o	a	e
S.	—	261	2×261	4×263	8×261
G.	—	264	2×261	4×264	8×262
K.	$\frac{1}{2} \times 263$	262	2×258	4×262	8×264
M.	$\frac{1}{2} \times 264$	266	2×264	4×264	8×262

The value of the mean variation is never greater (and often much
less) than a quarter-tone, so that the optimal positions of the vowels
in the scale of pitches seem to be very precise. The octave law was
extended by Köhler to include M on the lower side and S and other
sounds on the higher side.

One fundamental defect appears immediately in this theory. Either
it is wrong or the meaning of the term vowel is very different from its
usual one. Stumpf claims that the sound of a powerful male voice,
contains some thirty partial pitches that can be objectively verified
by the resonance of tuning-forks. Vowels spoken by such a voice
would never be pure tones. If, then, the vowel-tone (pitch) is always
present, it can be only a partial-'tone' of the whole. As the range of
a mobile voice is limited to some two and a half octaves, it should
be able to produce clearly only as many of the vowels, or these considerably 'coloured' by the vowel qualities of the higher partials. The
theory thus loses its relation to vowels in the ordinary sense and retains
only its relation to octave differences, which we shall discuss later.

Apart from that however, the theory has received at Stumpf's
hand (123, 324ff.) very damaging criticisms. Apparently the difficulty
of recognising pure vowel qualities when they are given in isolation
is much greater than Köhler would have it appear. And for the specific
nature of the vowel qualities the introspective evidence claimed does
not exist (cf. 137, 10ff.). U and o are not as different as red and yellow,
even although they are recognisable as types, like the sounds of the
violin or the piano. Stumpf fails too to recognise any great similarity
between o, a, e, and the pitches indicated for them. Such internal

difficulties of fact, interpretation, and system make Köhler's attempt to give vowels a central importance for hearing futile. And so we may leave it, without reference to its external consistency with the wider facts of hearing[1].

An attempt has recently been made to make the vowels supply a felt want in the psychology of noise. On the basis of the method already referred to, of making the vibrating frequency of a sound vary round an average, Jaensch (34, 35) propounds the view that the vowels, far from being the qualities of tone, which they at most only resemble, are the specific and serial qualities of an older sense of noise. Thus a new line of analogy with vision is introduced. The pitch series is like that of the series of colours because the stimulus of each is a definite rate of vibration; the noise series resembles the series of neutral brightnesses from black to white.

Apart from all the difficulties that arise when we try to work out this analogy, Jaensch's experiments by no means warrant the theory built upon them. The only difference in the stimulus for tones, vowels, and noises shown in his experiments is an increase in the mean variation of the individual values of the vibration frequency about one and the same average. That alone would suggest the question whether the introspective difference between the three is not a decrease in definiteness of pitch. Introspection affirms this. Thus Stumpf says noises have a pitch, but it is not so well defined, and always fills a certain stretch of the line of vibratory frequencies; that, he says, probably explains their phenomenal character (123, 341). It is hard to see from Jaensch's experiments why vowels should be held to be the qualities of noises rather than of tones, for they are said to resemble tones, but not noises; or why we should not assume the existence of three senses in hearing for tones, vowels, and noises, severally. But taken at their face value Jaensch's results offer a very acceptable confirmation of our view already developed that tones and noises are both complex auditory experiences, auditory molecules, as it were. We may therefore place vowels between them, so that the study of vowels serves to extend and confirm our previous studies.

XX. D. *Octave qualities.* Another direction remains in which new material has been sought for the elucidation of the elementary

---

[1] An excellent account of the work on vowels in relation to the assumption of Köhler's vocality as a quality of tones is to be found in 51. For a good example of the rather uncritical determination of that theory see there, p. 746, where it is held that vocality can be determined by a partial that is inaudible when presented alone.

psychology of hearing. Although the great series of auditory qualities taken from the whole range of pitches, as expounded e.g. by Stumpf in 1883, appealed with satisfaction to the great majority of psychologists, doubts kept recurring to a few. The chief trouble of all these qualities is the great number of them, which does not seem reducible to a few, like those of vision. Of course the smallest number of qualities to which any single series of differences is reducible is two, those that occupy the extreme ends of the series. This merely possible view was actually propounded by Mach (60, 122; 2nd ed. 1900, 181). He compares the pitch series with the series of colour differences leading from red to yellow. A comparison with the black to white series would be equally effective of course. Mach's proposal received hardly any support. The chief difficulty was that a leading physiological theory like that of Helmholtz offered no warrant for it whatever.

F. Brentano[1] alone adopted the suggestion made by Mach, but with considerable modifications for its improvement. He reduced the number of qualities of the pitch series by recognising as primary only those differences included within the range of an octave. The differences given by the repetition of octaves were explained by the assumption of a brightness component of sound increasing from one octave to the next above. A view very similar to this was stated summarily by W. McDougall (153, 73) as early as 1899. He suggested that "all the elementary qualities (of tone) are contained in a single octave, which might be likened to the complete colour series, and that the differences of pitch that distinguish the same qualities in different octaves...are of the same order as differences of extensity or voluminousness in the case of visual, tactual or temperature sensation, and are due to differences in the number of sensory neurones excited."

The strength of this theory lies in the powerful appeal it makes to one of the special interests of hearing—the similarity or at least equivalence of the tones of successive octaves. The interests of theory were bound to be influenced by this peculiar phenomenon so long as the elementary psychology of hearing was not perfectly satisfactory and no convincing explanation of the phenomenon had been given which would make a transference of it into the elements impossible. The latter explanation, as we shall see later, was never given, so that the transference was at all times possible. The only serious objection to the transference was the immanent incoherence of the theory itself, which,

---

[1] 8, 101 ff. For a much earlier report of Brentano's views by his pupil Stumpf, v. 112, 199.

although satisfactory as far as the octave is concerned, is unable to do justice to the other degrees of similarity and musical relations within the octave and to the perfectly relative nature of the octave itself. These and other objections led Stumpf (112, 196 ff.) in 1890 to reject Brentano's proposals entirely. Stumpf was satisfied in accepting the octave relationship and the other facts of fusion as ultimate facts of hearing, preferring his already discussed theory of the elements to any remodelling of them on these lines.

But the poverty of Stumpf's elementary psychology of hearing as a source of fruitful explanations[1] led him comparatively soon to the acceptance of Brentano's distinctions. He gives himself the date 1902 as that of his conviction, 1912 as that of public admission[2]. And his reasons are: "not the analogies with the colour sense, which are a nice illustration, but no proof, but reasons taken from the experiences of hearing itself, especially the common deviation by one and even two octaves in the determination of absolute pitch, the ease of the octave transposition, which is often done quite unwittingly, and the harmonic equivalence of the octave in chords (inversion of intervals and chords)" (123, 311). All these reasons were present to his mind in 1890, but were rejected as being mere consequences of fusion.

Recently a series of papers has been published by Géza Révész in which both broad and special foundations are sought for this distinction between octave-quality and height-brightness. It is hardly possible to use the word pitch to represent the latter concept, because so much of the ordinary meaning of the word pitch has been absorbed by the term quality, and it is not easy to say just what remains over. But the remainder includes at least the rising aspect; probably almost what Stumpf thought of under 'volume,' when he distinguished it from pitch-quality in 1890 (112, 203 f.). In order to distinguish this new attribute from quality, it is well to use the word 'height' for it, in order to avoid clashing with the meaning of the word pitch, as it is used both in ordinary speech and in psychology. After all pitch is what we begin to theorise about. So if we cannot take over the ordinary meaning of that term into our psychology, let us use another word. In referring to Stumpf's quality of 1883–90 I shall say pitch-quality, in referring to his recent quality, I shall say octave-quality. Let us now consider closely the arguments for and against octave-quality.

[1] Cf. 123, 314, where Stumpf admits this as the "Undurchführbarkeit der psychologischen Konstruktion."
[2] Cf. 121, 334, note, where the question was still left open.

1. *Direct.* Trained and untrained observers have long noticed a great similarity, if not identity, between tones an octave apart, whether they are of the ordinary musical kind or are perfectly simple in pitch (cf. 123, 309 note, 312; 94, 248). There is no need to urge the point. It may be granted at once. There is something which links a tone to its octave very closely. But the question is: what is it and what is its psychological status? The mere fact of similarity or whatever else one may call it, indicates neither identity, nor simplicity, nor psychological status.

In this connexion it is important to notice a recent remark of Stumpf's in which he says: "Statements about the fundamental properties of our sensations should in general be based only upon the observations of those who by long practice are at home in the province referred to, and have also tested their single observations time and again" (123, 307). That is true as it stands for any province of facts. But if it means that no one is to have a voice in the discussion of the primary attributes who has not an absolute ear and the practice in experimental observation of sounds that Stumpf and his important co-operators Abraham, v. Hornbostel, and others have, it is plainly absurd. For, as I have already shown, judgment upon the psychological status of an attribute is a matter of wide theory; it has, therefore, no relation to the fineness of discrimination of that attribute or to the ability to name its varieties. This is surely the only sort of explanation that can be given to the fact that so highly qualified an observer as Stumpf himself could in the course of time uphold diametrically opposed sides on one and the same question, without having any new weight of argument on the side now taken and without being able to demolish any of his previous objections to it (*v.* 112, 196–204).

Stumpf himself offers an objection of a direct kind; if octaves are identical qualities, we should expect the identity of c' and c^2 to be as easily recognisable as that of a stronger and a weaker c'. This sound objection may indeed be pushed farther. If c' and c^2 are the same except for their accompanying brightness or height, we should expect the octave partials of a musical tone or octaves in a chord to be indistinguishable, as Stumpf himself very properly said in 1890 (112, 200), and, if anything at all, only differences of brightness or height to be left in it. But the opposite seems rather the case: the pitches c' and c^2 are distinguishable, but in a perfectly steady tone the brightness or volume components of each are no longer traceable (137, 36 f.). Where such close fusion of tone is attained as in pitch-blends, we should at least expect identicals to lose their distinction (cf. 112, 200).

Of course, if we are determined to keep octave qualities at any cost, we may plan the matter out in various ways. We may say that, besides octave quality, tones have both pitch and volume, or that what distinguishes c' and c^2 in a pitch-blend is their pitch or height alone. But the latter view would imply that the 'similarity' of c' and c^2 is not detectable in a pitch-blend, which would hardly be admitted. Thus at least the assumption of identity of octave-qualities seems to be untenable. The most we can say is that tones an octave apart are similar or equivalent, but always distinguishable under favourable circumstances.

More direct still is perhaps an objection originally held by Stumpf (112, 197). Octave resemblance is undetectable in fast chromatic scales or when the pitch of a tone is raised continuously, as is possible on the violin or on Stern's piston-bottles. Here, "emerges clearly the uniform qualitative withdrawal from the starting tone, because such motions let no consciousness of a definite key, of a tonic, dominant, etc., appear, or at least immediately destroy the beginnings thereof." Octave resemblances could then hardly be reckoned amongst the primary irremovable attributes of tone. Where so much tone is given, surely all its attributes will emerge. What cannot emerge, is any relation that requires a special setting or favourable circumstances.

2. *Indirect.* This we have already noticed: the common error of one or even two octaves in the determination of absolute pitch, the ease of octave transposition, which is often done quite unwittingly, and the harmonic equivalence of the octave in chords. But the issue of this evidence is by no means clear; for it is functional evidence ('equivalence,' cf. 121, 334 note), not introspective. The facts referred to contain or presuppose no insuppressible differences, such as are whatever differences of pitch anywhere occur throughout the tonal series, but only imply some sort of 'similarity.' The latter as an argument for the primacy of octave qualities is of the utmost weakness compared with the former, which lie behind pitch-differences, whether an attempt be made to hide them under the name of height or brightness or not. This indirect evidence carries us no farther than the direct— there is a great 'similarity,' whatever its nature may be, between octave-tones, so that we often apply the same names to both, and in whistling and the like give one for the other, while in harmonies they are also largely equivalent.

Stumpf again offers certain contrary evidence of an indirect kind. Why, he asks, is absolute ear not much more common than it is, if

each octave offers a repetition of one and the same set of qualities?
Why is the octave sung too high from simple tones? The answer to
the former query should be: it is easy to recognise the 'similarity'
of octave tones when given together or in succession, because they
are 'similar,' as we have admitted; but absolute ear is quite another
thing. In it either (1) we have to name the octave quality of a single
tone, and for that we must have adopted a definite octave basis. There
exists no natural octave basis, in spite of Stumpf's attempt to impute
one to unmusical observers, whose judgments are here for once admitted
as influential (123, 337). Or, (2) we have to give a tone the quality-
name it would assume on a definite instrument, e.g. a certain piano,
and for that we must have adopted a definite brightness-pitch basis. In
either case absolute ear rests, not upon absoluteness of octave qualities
which are notoriously purely relative and movable, but upon something
else. In other words absolute ear is not absolute in so far as octave
qualities are named; these are only our conceptual means of naming
the absolute differences, i.e. brightness-, height-, pitch-differences, upon
which octave similarities are traced out. On Stumpf's theory, however,
it is certainly true that no one should have absolute ear for one octave
without also having it for the other musical octaves. But such cases
do occur. The answer to the second query is not clear on any view.
But neither query has any more significance for the octave quality
view than it had for the older pitch quality view.

3. *Independent variability.* The evidence here falls into two
parts: first, the nature of hearing in the extremes of the pitch series;
second, the abnormal hearing of Dr v. Liebermann.

(*a*) Discrimination of pitch, as we have already seen, is less keen
in the extremes than in the large middle part of the series. Very high
tones are indistinguishable in pitch. They lose their octave quality,
as it is said (94, 250). Stumpf gives an excellent example. Appunn the
younger sent him in 1899 four pipes alleged to be exactly tuned to
c^5, c^6, c^7, and c^8. But their vibration frequency was found to be 4000,
5120, 6400, 7450, i.e. approximately c^5, e^5, $a^{\flat 5}$, b^5. Thus Appunn's
claim to be able to recognise the qualities of highest tones directly was
shown to be illusory (123, 317f.).

As we pass from the middle reaches of pitch to the higher, especially
in the second half of the fourth accented octave and in the first half
of the fifth, a judgment on musical quality and interval is still possible,
but the pitches are given too low and the intervals too small. For double
the number of vibrations of c^4 we get not a c, but a b approximately.

This looks like a natural approach to the alleged great weakness of octave quality in the higher regions. But Stumpf points out that it is possibly to be accounted for in other ways, especially by the tendency of even musical people to enlarge the octave in singing it from simple tones. In transposing from very high tones over several octaves this error would of course be increased, and might so account for the lowering of c to b. And then this octave error is not permanent but disappears when the two octave tones are taken often in immediate succession. But in spite of these things, we may conclude that there is little reason to believe that this octave error is not a stage on the way to the great depreciation of octave quality in the highest regions. I shall return to the subject again (*v. infra*, Table V).

The same sort of thing is found in the lowest reaches of pitch. These tones however are still more or less distinguishable, probably on the basis of differences of height or brightness, although Stumpf now prefers to leave this point unsettled at present. Previously, as we have seen, he ascribed this difference to changes of volume. The converse of this change of brightness without change of quality is found in the middle, musical range of pitches, where very slight changes of pitch, i.e. of octave quality, are detected without any sign of a change of brightness (94, 248).

Of this first part of the evidence it may be said that it is relevant only in so far as the assumption of octave qualities has already been made. It cannot show any ground of preference between pitch qualities and octave qualities. In fact the latter have all the difficulties to face; these arise from the very assumption that qualities run in octaves, whereas octave relationships must somehow be imposed upon pitch qualities. The irregularity of musical relationships in the extreme regions would then be due to these relationships themselves, whatever their basis may be, and not to the primary pitch qualities, which may therefore be presumed to be regular. If we are to have difficulties, let us put them for want of any better reason amongst the complications of hearing where we may hope to find a cause for them rather than midst the elements, and above all the qualitative elements, where explanations are by the nature of the case excluded.

(*b*) The second part of the evidence claims that within the ordinary musical range in abnormal conditions octave quality may vary independently of brightness-height. Octave quality may remain constant over considerable variations of the latter, and one and the same brightness-height may have two octave qualities, one for each ear. The facts are reported by Dr v. Liebermann and G. Révész from observations by the former on his own hearing (52, 52a, 53, 54, 55, 94, 95, 96). It is unnecessary to enter fully into this complicated case here[1], because it is already clear that even the facts alleged would in no way strengthen the cause of the octave qualities. All the facts may be accepted, in so far as they seem probable, for the study of the relation between order-pitches and order-volumes. Our main conclusion from them would be that, while the volume of a tone does not seem to be affected by the pathological processes of the case, the predominating order is influenced thereby. The order that predominates pathologically, is not always identical with that which normally predominates for the same stimulus, so that the pitch of the tone heard seems to be changed. But a certain estimation of the true nominal pitch of the tone can be made on the basis of the unaltered volume alone. In v. Liebermann's case the change of predominance appeared only when the stimulus was briefly and not too intensely given, or when special attention was directed towards its pitch in chords. Otherwise the predominant pitch was the normal one. These facts call for special study in connexion with the processes of attention and with the physiological processes of hearing. Evidently the attention is able under suitable conditions to bring about by its special insistence a change of predominance in tone, which then departs from its usual parallelism with the stimulus.

In unmusical people we find such degrees of failure of discrimination as might be held to point to the absence or great indistinctness of the octave qualities without any impairment of the brightness aspect of tones (123, 316f.). But if octave qualities can suffer thus, so surely can pitch qualities also.

4. *Failure of psychological construction.* Obviously the decision regarding these things cannot be made on the basis of the facts themselves, but only on the basis of the solution which may independently be offered for the musical relationships of the octave. There is no direct call to take octaves as the index of qualities. There is only a motive thereto in the failure to explain musical relationships otherwise and in the unsatisfactory nature of the previously prevailing psychology of the elements of hearing. Psychological construction has not succeeded on the basis of pitch qualities. And the hope is, that it may be more successful on the basis of octave qualities. But the outlook can hardly be said to be hopeful. It does not appear how the problems of noise are to be solved, unless it be by the assumption of a vanishing power

---

[1] A detailed account and discussion of it will be found in 137, 14 ff.

in these new qualities, taken in view by Stumpf (123, 318) for tones above c^5. Surely it would be better to rest without any explanation of musical relationship than to have to reconstruct the foundations of the psychology of hearing upon such shifting sands. Such a weak-kneed hypothesis cannot compete with the conclusions drawn above regarding the *rôle* of pitch in tones, vowels, and noises. For unmusical persons a natural explanation offers itself at once, which will fulfil the utmost demands. We need only suppose, as is very probable, that such variations in the texture of the organs of hearing occur as prevent the stimuli of sound from producing in every person that clear predominance of pitch and that regularity of ordinal system in tone which characterises the best observers. All degrees of deterioration of predominance and regularity of system should be possible and would immediately form an adequate expression for all possible degrees of unmusicalness. Psychologically this explanation is perfectly acceptable.

In the theory of octave qualities we can see no prospect of a proper and adequate account of the various degrees of fusion throughout the octave. Indeed this qualitative classification admits only of a direct description, and it must be evident at a glance that no direct reading of the octave will yield a regular expression (cf. 123, 323 f.; also 112, 200 f.). In fact all sorts of suggestions have been made: circle, regular spiral, zig-zag spiral, straight line with sudden recurrence of quality, and want of all order. Regularity here can only be indirect or real, not phenomenal. And what hope is there of discovering this real underlying regularity in the qualitative region? Stumpf (123, 322 f.) attempts a solution by distinguishing between original qualities and the qualities of our musical system or of any other. But this would only reintroduce the whole range of problems that the octave qualities ought presumably to have solved, with the exception of the octave itself. So much trouble for so little result! Psychological construction is now no better off than before. No explanation of fusions has been given; they have only been differently named and put well nigh beyond the reach of any solution. No benefit accrues to the system of the attributes and of the senses as a whole by this new treatment of sound, unless it be the demonstration of a certain analogy with the octave of colours. And no new conviction or explanation is got thereby, for the analogy is far too weak and irregular. The psychophysics of hearing becomes more mysterious than ever. How are the organs of the ear to be linked up with a recurrent series of octave qualities?

5. Finally we have to urge that a direct and satisfactory statement

of the fusional relations of tones, especially of the octave and the fifth, can be given which makes any transference of the former from its natural position to the elementary properties of sound unnecessary. The statement given for the other degrees of fusion is less satisfactory; but so it is in the octave quality theory and in the nature of the case itself. Nevertheless it is sufficiently good to appear both sufficient and highly probable as of a piece with the explanation of the octave fusion. This is then the chief argument against the octave quality view, and a valuable support to our own ordinal classification of pitch. The former view loses its *raison d'être*, while the latter's efficiency is confirmed.

CHAPTER II

THE ANALYSIS OF BI-TONAL MASSES

XXI. Bi-tonal masses can be produced in a methodical way by the simultaneous use of two sources of sound. These are brought first into perfect unison and then one of them is gradually raised or lowered in pitch until at least the next octave is reached.

The first change to strike the attention is the appearance of beats. Stumpf's account of them (112, 450 ff.), from which the following observations are taken, may be accepted as a standard. Following Helmholtz he defines beats as "regular fluctuations of intensity of tones," in no way different from any ordinary fluctuation of intensity, although their physical origin is different, and although there is a difference in the "tonal material" involved in the sensation. When beats are made more frequent by the further raising of one of the two physical sounds, they become pulses or jerks separated by pauses, without thereby losing their nature as intensive changes. So too even when they are so frequent as to appear to roll or rattle or whir or chirrup. But in the latter case other features appear, such as very high pitches, and more especially noises, and even touch sensations from the violently moved drum of the ear.

Apart from these intensive changes the pitch of the original unison is also affected. With very small differences only one pitch is to be observed and it is beating. It is hard to tell whether this pitch lies midway between the separate pitches of the two sounds. When the primary sounds are about half a tone apart, e.g. $g\sharp$ and a, pitches corresponding to both are heard, and besides a third pitch lying between them somewhat nearer the lower than the higher[1]. With differences of a whole tone, e.g. g' and a', only the two primary pitches are heard and these both seem to beat. If the attention is turned specially to one of them, that always seems to be the beating one. The seat of the beating seems to follow the direction of the attention (112, 490), according as that is spread over the sound as a whole, or directed to the mid-pitch, or to both or either of the primary pitches, when all these are distinguishable. If one of the two pitches is more prominent, it draws the attention upon itself and it seems to beat (99, 88). In larger groups of pitches at first the whole seems to beat, but as soon as the several pitches are singly heard, the beats attach to the proper pitch, i.e. to the physically beating pitch.

The first effect of the departure from unison of tone is therefore to introduce into its perfectly regular system irregularities of various kinds, chiefly fluctuations of intensity, noises, and multiplication of pitches. But no new feature is thus added to our auditory experience, although the mode of origin of these changes is new. Such relations are of importance in the physiological study of hearing, but they do not affect the main psychological scheme of hearing, which sets the problem for physiological solution. The physiological problems of beats are therefore special questions which must follow the main lines set for physiology by psychology.

XXII.   The same applies to the next group of changes that appear upon further raising or lowering of one of the two primary sounds, namely difference tones or difference pitches. Consideration of the physical changes by which these are produced makes them appear to grow out of beats. The beats grow in frequency, there being one beat for every vibration per second by which the rates of vibration of the two primary sounds differ from one another; and gradually therefrom emerges the first difference pitch whose height also corresponds to the latter difference of rates of vibration. But this logical and physical continuity is not confirmed in the experience. For one thing, within a certain range of differences of vibration both beats and difference pitch are heard together. For another, whereas beats attach as we have seen, either to the whole sound or to the mid-pitch or to either or both

---

[1] Regarding the first observation of the mid-tone see 119, 5.

of the primary pitches, the difference pitch lies far away from them all in the lower regions of the pitch series. No doubt difference pitches originate in the same mass process as evokes beats, but they must be due to quite a different aspect of it, which becomes effective upon hearing only with a considerable increase in the difference of vibrations.

There are two chief difference 'tones' whose pitches follow the formulas: $D1 = h - l$; $D2 = 2l - h$; where h and l are the rates of vibration of the primary sounds. These and other less easily heard pitches, which may be reckoned from similar formulas, are indicated in Figure 3, which shows these adventitious pitches for all differences between the primary sounds from unison to the twelfth above. The prominence or audibility of these adventitious pitches in the tonal mass is indicated in the figure by the heaviness or continuity of the various lines.

There is in recent years a growing trend of opinion towards the belief that the secondary tonal phenomena of combination tones, variation tones and interruption tones, not to speak of beats, are not subjective, but rather, like all audible tones, due to pendular components of the sound wave as it enters the inner ear (cf. 102, 12f.; 101, 532, 568f.; 90, 317; 44, 304; and perhaps especially 150, 306ff.).

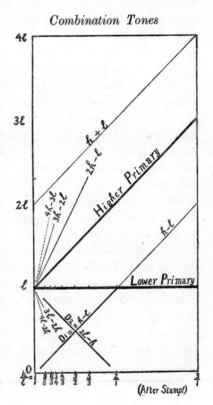

Combination Tones

(After Stumpf)

Fig. 3 (119, 135).

XXIII. The multiplication of pitches by means of difference tones and the like offers us no new psychological problems; for we have already encountered that multiplication in pitch-blends. But the general problem of multiplication is perhaps one of the most important in the psychology of hearing. Its special interest lies in the connexion so readily formed between the problem of the multiplication and discrimination of pitches and that of the multiplication and discrimination of tones. So readily has this connexion occurred to the minds of those who have made a special study of hearing that none of them has ever hesitated to write down the problem of multiple pitches as the problem of multiple tones[1]. We have already seen that there is a sufficient difference between pitch and tone in the strict senses of these terms (predominant order and regular system of orders) to call for great caution in identifying them at any point. Thus far we are certain only of the presence of several pitches in the sound evoked by the simultaneous presentation of at least two sources of sound, such as tuning-forks, notes of piano, etc.

But the other problem is a legitimate one. The most characteristic difference between tones is undoubtedly given by their pitch, and it is more or less natural to think that hearing several pitches means hearing several tones. Only it at once appears that, when several sources of sound are played at once, we never hear their 'tones' quite as clearly and properly as we do when they are played one after another. A little reflection reminds us however that such fusion of sensations occurs in other senses; smells mix up with one another and even with tastes so that we can hardly distinguish them. For those who classify pitches as qualities this example is obviously an excellent parallel (112, 65 f.). But further consideration shows that the fusion of 'tones' is an 'extra-special' case of fusion. So it is specially treated as the clearest example of a generally prevailing fusion, or as a special peculiarity of tones, generally known in either case as the problem of tonal fusion. Stated explicitly the problem is a study of those features of the tonal mass evoked by two simultaneous sources of sound which prevent us from hearing two tones together in the same kind of independence and integrity as appears on their successive presentation.

Obviously this problem is the problem of partial 'tones,' difference 'tones' and other varieties of adventitious 'tones' as well. But we shall direct our attention primarily upon the problem as it affects the tones evoked by each source of sound separately. The reasons for this course are twofold and decisive. In the first place the musical observer usually ignores, or is even unaware of, the presence of partial and differential pitches. He concentrates his attention on the pitches of

---

[1] But compare Stumpf's discussion of the point 112, 66 f. There is more methodical importance in speaking first of the discrimination of pitches rather than of tones than would appear from Stumpf's attitude. It is the aim of our exposition to reveal that importance.

the primaries, as these are the pitches actually set for him or thought by him in the music or played by him on the instrument. They are his primary interest because he produces them and because the nature of the sound as a whole depends to a large extent upon how he produces them. In the second place any determinations regarding the discriminability of the primary pitches must hold still more for that of all other pitches.

It is easy to see that some confusion of the issue could not but spring from the historical origin of the problem of fusion. What are we about to study? Is it the fusion of pitches or the fusion of tones? One might say: fusion of pitches, because the discrimination in a tonal mass of the pitches corresponding to the two sources of sound is taken as equivalent to the hearing of the 'tones' of these two sources, while those who do not discriminate the pitches do not discriminate the tones either. Or one might say: fusion of tones, because every musical observer knows that the pitches can be distinguished, but that they (or their 'tones') seem nevertheless not to be properly separable. We must keep this source of confusion in mind, if we are to appreciate properly the methods devised for the examination of fusion and the difficulties encountered in defining fusion itself.

XXIV. After direct examination of the tonal masses given by sounds standing to one another in the ratios of the intervals of our scales, Stumpf (112, 127) asserted the existence of five grades of fusion between 'tones,' differing according to the ratios of vibrations of the primary sounds: (1) the octave (relative rates of vibration are $1:2$); (2) the fifth ($2:3$); (3) the fourth ($3:4$); (4) the natural thirds and sixths ($4:5, 5:6, 3:5, 5:8$); lastly all other pairs of pitches, which have all the lowest grade of fusion, except perhaps the natural seventh ($4:7$), which may be a little better than the rest. This account is corroborated not only by the musical practice of all times in which singing in octaves is considered equivalent to unison, but also by the frequent occurrence of continued parallels of fifths and fourths in the music of various peoples (120, 44). These parallels evidently give some impression of unity (112, 179).

Indirect confirmation is also to be gathered from the judgment of unmusical persons. Tones may be held to differ in fusion according to the percentage of correct judgments regarding the presence in a sound of one or more pitches ('tones'). Of course material for these judgments is not sought in the difficult discriminations of pitch-blends, but in reference to the more obvious pitches emanating from independent sources of sound. Stumpf's experiments showed the following (approximate) percentages of correct judgments[1]:

TABLE II.

Octave	Fifth	Fourth	Minor third	Major third	Tritone
20	50	65	70	73	77

This list agrees with the results of direct observation at least in its upper values. In 80 per cent. of cases two simultaneous sounds an octave apart were held to be one sound. It was 30 per cent. easier to distinguish as present together two sounds a fifth apart. Another distinct step leads down to the fourth, after which there was little difference between the different intervals[2]. With approximate certainty for all cases one may say there are three distinct grades of fusion: the octave, the fifth, and all the others. Only the former pass without discussion. The others probably differ among themselves, but it is not always clear that their differences are really matters of fusion[3]. For we have so far only got the differences in the mass, as it were. The question is: what are precisely differences of fusion in psychological terms?

XXV. At one point (112, 127) Stumpf calls fusion: "a special relation in the sensation which makes the analysis of tones difficult." That is a preliminary or passing definition which would remind us most of the tests made with unmusical persons, and would imply that fusion is primarily a matter of pitches, as it is chiefly with unmusical persons. Fusion then makes the analysis of tones difficult from the outset. Other circumstances, it is true, affect the ease of analysis, such as practice, beats, smallness of 'distance' between pitches, etc. But these can be distinguished from the difficulty consequent on fusion.

[1] From 112, 168, value δ. The octave I obtained by proportion from page 145, where the values for thirds and fifths are of about the same proportion as they are on page 168.

[2] Faist (19) performed similar experiments with six scholars; their result was (in similar percentages): 0=33 %, 5=60, 4=80, 6 (minor)=81, III (major)=81, VI=83, T (tritone)=85, 7=88, 3=88, VII=91 (pp. 108, 121). The three first clear steps are well shown; also the little difference between the fourth and the rest. Each interval was judged 480 times. Individual differences were not displayed. Other series of experiments by Faist showed other irregularities below the fourth (pp. 119, 121). Cf. 114, 283 ff.

[3] Cf. 112, 152 f., where Stumpf admits that his direct judgment about the fourth was greatly influenced by the result of his experiments with unmusical observers! Cf. 112, 170, 177; 40, 29.

But Stumpf was quite well aware that fusion is not merely a matter of difficulty of analysis; certainly not merely of analysis of pitches, though that too becomes prominent in unmusical persons and is interesting indirect evidence and confirmation of the direct observation of fusion. Stumpf followed up the above preliminary definition with a fuller one: "fusion is an unalterable peculiarity of sensory material which always remains over when all other hindrances to analysis have been removed and which can be recognised as such only after the analysis has been completed and the tones have been clearly recognised as two" (112, 128). This definition implies that fusion is primarily a matter of tones and not of pitches. Complete analysis of pitch is always possible and is even a matter of course for the best observers of sounds. The tones form together not a sum but a whole (*ibid.*) It is merely a consequence of this that the total impression in the higher grades of fusion approaches that of one sensation and is hard to analyse.

XXVI. It cannot be said that Stumpf's conception of fusion is perfectly clear. But the main motives determining it are evident: the classification of pitch as quality, the fact of the varying difficulty and ease of pitch analysis for different persons, the lack of any definition or discussion of tone in distinction from pitch, the seeming adequacy of the terms 'not a sum' (= not a matter of qualities or pitches), 'but a whole' (= a fusion). In his conclusion, however, Stumpf was quite explicit. In 1890 he decided that every appeal to psychological laws for a solution of the problem of fusion is fruitless. Fusion is a primary fact of hearing; it is inexplicable by reference to habit[1], or to feelings, or to upper partials (29), or to difference-tones[2], or to any other psychological adjuncts of the tones involved in the fusion[3]. The "direct

[1] Cf. 112, 208 ff. C. S. Myers, however, supports this 'natural basis of association' (82, 55). Also R. M. Ogden (88), who tries to rescue the theory by pleading racial, rather than individual, experience. But Stumpf himself suggested this racial derivation as a possible source of fusion (112, 215 f.). Most recently H. T. Moore (79) has tried to provide the theory with an experimental basis in records of individual practice with dissonant intervals. I do not think that any of these or other writers have put forward any real grounds for a belief in any such effect of habit or association. Arguments from habit can always be inverted, unless actual evidence of the *intention* of the habit can be provided. And that is absent in this case; or rather it is as probable that habit leads to perpetual discrimination (hearing as two or dissonances) as that it leads to hearing as one (or consonance).

[2] Cf. 118, 122, in which Krueger's attempt to found a theory of consonance and dissonance upon difference tones is shown to be in fact and principle a complete failure.

[3] Cf. Stumpf's special paper on the subject (115).

ground of fusion" can be given only by "a physical apparatus in the central organ" (112, 184). Such a conclusion is really equivalent to the admission that all attempts to give a direct statement of its nature and all comparisons of it with the phenomena of other senses have completely failed.

But, apart from that and from the confusion caused by the failure properly to distinguish between pitches and tones, Stumpf's treatment of the problem of fusion is so sound that it has been accepted as authoritative by most psychologists, although various attempts have been made to improve upon the general setting given to the special notion of tonal fusion. No one has yet shown Stumpf's methods and results to be wrong, and no one has made any essential advance beyond his conclusion just stated. But advance beyond it must be made. We cannot tolerate new primary facts at this stage, facts which leap over all the already exhausted primary facts of the attributes direct to a special physiological basis which does not reveal itself in these attributes at all. We feel such a leap in the dark to be an offence to our sense of continuity of action, and we must urge that a search be made amongst the attributes for a proper psychological basis of fusion. A reason for Stumpf's recent conversion to the belief in octave qualities may well have been the feeling that his primary facts of fusion should be brought to rest nearer to the real primacy of the attributes.

As the aim of this exposition is the establishment of a new analysis of hearing, it can use historical exposition and criticism only in order to prove itself by showing how difficulties have arisen and how the analysis to be established is latent in these difficulties and in the solutions already obtained. I shall therefore use Stumpf's results as a basis from which to obtain a true psychological theory of fusion, not stopping here to discuss any criticisms and restrictions applied to his view. We must remember that, as no later view has made any essential advance beyond Stumpf's conclusion, their criticisms may be irrelevant or trifling. If important, they can be recognised as such only from the vantage point of a more advanced and successful analysis.

XXVII. Let us therefore apply my method of dealing with the attributes to the problem and see whether it will not carry us beyond Stumpf's first conclusion. It will be observed that in it his general remark about the fruitlessness of appeal to psychological laws applies to any reference to the psychical *adjuncts* of the fusing tones—feelings, partials, combination pitches, habits, etc., apart from the explanation by the inherent similarity of tones, which at that time he rejected. The last of these is after all methodically the best explanation, for it looks downwards, not upwards for a cause. We shall follow it in looking downwards to the attributes for a cause. This method, as I have already pointed out, was practically closed to Stumpf and others by the qualitative classification of pitches and by the consideration of volume as quasi-spatial.

Stumpf's laws of fusion (112, 136) provide an excellent basis for our method. No. 1 says: " the grade of fusion is independent of the tone-region," i.e. of the pitch-region[1]. The octave, fifth, and fourth show the same grades throughout the whole musical range of pitch. The extremes of pitch, especially the upper reaches of it, present a difficult problem for any theory; but we may neglect them at present and proceed as best we can from whatever sure ground we find. Within the musical range, then, we can say: fusion is independent of pitch. And direct evidence confirms this: fusion is not altered by our discrimination of the pitches of a sound. The difficulty of analysis which is a characteristic consequence of fusion therefore does not apply so much to pitch as to some other feature of the sound to be analysed; for it survives the highest practice and the greatest ease in detecting the pitches present in a sound, shown by certain persons specially gifted in the observation of sounds. Stumpf admits this implicitly when he says (112, 128) it is the *total impression* which in the higher grades of fusion approximates more and more to that of one sensation. Fusion, we may then conclude, is not primarily a matter of pitches, i.e. it does not primarily concern the predominance of order that constitutes pitch in the strict sense.

XXVIII. Law No. 2 says: fusion is independent of intensity, both relative and absolute[2], although analysis is impossible with great differences of intensity of the primary sounds. Why that should be we shall see later. For the present this law clears us of another attribute.

Two attributes remain: quality and extensity, or as we find it in tones—volume. Now quality drops out of itself, for there is only one auditory quality. The inevitable conclusion then is: fusion can only be a matter of volumes. For those who will accept my method of dealing with the attributes, this conclusion may be sufficient. But

---

[1] Admitted by Kemp (40, 159).

[2] *Restricted* by Kemp (40, 159). We shall discuss Kemp's objections later. For the present we shall accept Stumpf's law and discuss Kemp's points in the light of our conclusions.

we shall consider all other available evidence. At any rate pitch in
the strict sense (as against the loose sense in which it is often used
as equivalent to 'tone') and intensity are definitely excluded. Is fusion
then a matter of volumes?

XXIX. We have already seen that the volume of tone decreases
as the pitch rises. We cannot say offhand that this change is a regular
parallel to the change of pitch, as would be the case if equal diminutions
of volume accompanied equal increases of pitch. For we do not yet
know how to establish the presence of equality in these variables. But
one thing is clear, that between the volumes of the lowest tones and
those of the highest there is continuity of diminution. The decrease
of volume can therefore be represented by the perspectival projection
of two parallel lines meeting at the horizon (cf. Fig. 7 below). We
have also agreed that the predominant order of the volume by which
pitch is constituted is probably central to the whole volume. No
asymmetry of the volume is detectable. And all higher pitches lie on
one side of any given pitch.

When two pitches of no great distance from one another occur in
one tonal sound, we should then expect the upper pitch to lie imbedded
in the volume of the tone which would exist if only the lower pitch
were present in predominance. If the volume of the whole tonal mass
is in any way made up of the volumes which each sound would produce
separately, it would follow that in the tonal mass the volume of the
higher sound must overlap or coincide with a part of that of the lower
sound. All this follows directly from the facts of volume, predominance,
and continuity of the ordinal series in sound.

XXX. But simultaneous sounds never seem to lie completely
apart from one another, no matter how different or distant their pitches
may be. They are always heard through one another, as it were. That
would seem to indicate that the volume or at least the predominant
order of any tone always falls within the volume of any other lower
tone, no matter how distant their pitches may be. But if orders existed
beyond the extreme upper[1] order of the lower tone, it is not evident
why these outlying orders should not be the predominant orders of
some high tone of a very small volume. Thus we seem to be forced
to the conclusion that the predominant order of the absolutely highest

---

[1] 'Upper' may here be defined as 'on the side of the pitch of a (pure) tone towards
the pitch of any higher tone.'

tone is the extreme upper order of any and every lower tone[1].   For if
it were not, two tones could be got which would lie completely apart
from one another, which is not the case.   Thus the extreme orders
involved in the volumes of all tones would be identical on the upper
side.   But it would then follow that the volume of the highest tone would
be minimal.   For as its predominant order is the extreme (upper)
order of all and is presumably central to its whole volume, the range
of its volume on both sides of its predominant order will be equal and
be twice the minimum, i.e. the minimum itself—the spot of tone, as
it were.   This deduction is sufficiently stringent to be convincing.
But if it be urged that it is not completely stringent, we may reply
that the error possible within it must be so small as to be negligible.
That is to say, parts of the volume of the highest possible tone might
conceivably lie a little beyond the upper limiting order of a lower tone,
without these two tones yet being heard apart and separately from
one another.   That is logically possible within my proof.   But it does
not thereby become probable.   Before it could be deemed noteworthy
as an objection, some probability would have to be shown for it.   We
shall see later on that inferences from the chief grades of fusion make
it highly improbable and so consolidate the present argument.

XXXI.   Further light comes from certain obvious facts.   One of
these is the standardisation of the whole range of musical pitch on the
basis of the octave unit.   The whole range is plotted out in portions
of one octave.   At the same time the octave is the highest grade of fusion.
Thus the musical range of pitch is stated in terms of the highest grade
of fusion.   The octave is the standard.   We may be quite certain that
the octave as a unit and as an interval is based upon the octave fusion;
for the octave as a difference of pitches or orders is not by any means
equal throughout the musical range[2].   The distance between the pitches

[1] K. Dunlap (11, 292) seems to have conceived an idea like this, when he speaks ana-
logically of "making one end of each streak coincident with the corresponding ends of all the
others."   Indeed Dunlap seems to have come within an ace of conceiving the basis of the
theory of this book.   But if he ever thought of working out this theory fully, that was inhibited by his rejection of local sign as the nearest attributive relative to pitch (cf. above,
p. 21).   Cf. also 12, for summary indications of Dunlap's applications of his theory.

[2] It need hardly be mentioned that the octave standard is not based upon the ratio
of physical vibrations which usually characterises its stimulus; v. Stumpf (121, 325):
"If e.g. we hold one tuning fork a^2 very near the ear, another physically exactly an octave
lower, further from the ear, but so that they are still distinguished, we then hear a^2 considerably flattened, as much as a semitone, and the octave out of tune, and must therefore sharpen this fork correspondingly, in order to get a pure octave for the ear."

involved in an octave, or indeed in any other interval, e.g. the third, is very different in the extremes of the pitch range, where it is only just detectable as a distance, from what it is within the musical range, where many smaller intervals are distinguishable. Within the musical octaves, the distances included in any interval differ very much. We shall consider this more fully later.

If fusion then is a matter of volumes, and if the octave fusion is a constant standard, we should expect the overlapping of volumes in an octave fusion to be constant as a type. Only one natural pattern offers itself as obvious: that in which the extreme order included in the volume of the higher tone on its lower side coincides exactly with the predominant order of the lower tone. As the extreme orders of all tonal volumes on the upper side may be presumed to be identical, the predominant order of the upper octave pitch should lie just half way between the predominant order of the lower octave pitch and the common extreme on the upper side. No other pattern, proceeding for example by thirds, quarters, etc. of displacement of the upper predominating pitch, would give any feature of coincidence of volumes which could be used as a natural standard, except in so far as the 'half' pattern merged from each. Nor would any such natural standard emerge unless the upper limiting orders of all tones coincided exactly. The existence of the octave fusion speaks for some process of exact interlinking of volumes; and as an approximate coincidence of upper limiting orders was made highly probable above, we may now accept the identity of upper limiting particles as most probable. In the octave, then, the upper 'tone,' fits most perfectly into the volume of the lower 'tone,' exactly filling that half of the latter upon the side of which it lies, i.e. the 'upper' half. It thus merges into the lower 'tone' and forms a part of it. It is distinguishable from the lower tone only by the pitch it adds to the latter, unless it be by the extra 'weight' which the volume of the lower tone receives on the upper side owing to its being induced from two sources, i.e. more intensely. But without the new predominant pitch, such a change we may presume would be hardly detectable alone.

This 'deduction' of the psychological nature of the octave fusion receives confirmation from the fact that the rate of vibration of the octave is, in all regular cases, double that of its relative tone. We should thus have established a parallel between the psychical and the physical to which the intervening physiological must undoubtedly conform.

I have no doubt that the whole argument of this 'deduction' will meet with the liveliest opposition from many. It will be considered grossly material, the application to psychical states of categories that are fit only for material objects. But that sort of objection rests solely on the fact that sensations have never been held to be ordinal, but only to be localised. They are held to be localised, but at the same time they are said not to be out in space 'at' the objects they refer to, but to be only psychically localised. This kind of localisation stands for or means practically the same as material localisation, but is of course really quite different. But we must urge in reply that in a certain aspect material and psychical localisation are quite the same—they are both ordinal systems. Their essence, the stuff in which the orders are imbedded, is different, but otherwise they are quite of a kind. The same remark applies to the orders of hearing. If the orders of matter can be treated in a certain way, as far as the known facts regarding matter allow, why should the orders of sensation not be treatable in the same way, if the known facts of hearing (or any other senses) allow it?

XXXII. Let us continue with our deduction. There are in any tone three characteristic orders which define its being—the two extremes and the predominant order. Of the former the upper one is identical for all tones. There remain then only two orders available for the determination of fusions. The only possible form of coincidence, where the other extreme order of the upper tone coincides with the predominant order of the lower has been allotted to the octave fusion. Another arrangement, this time of balance, is possible. In it the extreme lower order and the predominant order of the upper tone lie each equally far from the predominant order of the lower tone on either side of it. Thus we should get a new form of symmetry: not indeed the perfect symmetry of the tone of simple pitch, but nevertheless a very good balance as far as orders are concerned. The predominant order of the lower tone must be the predominant order of the whole, for it occupies the usual central position of predominance. In a constant tonal mass in fact this will always be the case: the pitch of the whole mass must be the pitch of its lowest component, as it is actually[1]. On either side of this all-important point lie the two points brought by the higher

---

[1] 112, 384, 407. C. Valentine (128, 192) thinks "the pitch of the higher note in any combination near the centre of the piano is likely to be an influential determinant of the apparent pitch of the combination." Of course it may be so for some persons. It is all a matter of the most frequent attitude of observation. Those whose observation has taken its nourishment almost solely from melody—which in simpler musical works of the present day is usually the highest voice—will doubtless oftener find the higher pitch first. That would not be inconsistent with the general predominance of a natural attitude directed towards the centre of any tonal mass, i.e. to its lowest pitch; but not, of course, if that lowest pitch is very weak and some higher one is very strong. But Knight Dunlap (11, 291) endorses the view of the text from his theory.

tone,—its predominant point and the point where the departure from the usual 'outline of predominance' of the lower tone begins. We have already seen reason in the vagueness of the pitch of certain tones to suppose that the predominance that constitutes pitch is often of some extent. We may well suppose that it decreases in some manner, rapid at first, towards the extremes. This is contained in the mere notion of predominance. The manner of decrease will be decisively altered if simultaneity of sounds means in the least degree an addition of volume values. That it does so is evident from the fact that the higher sound brings a point of predominance into the total sound mass.

This arrangement of balance would not be so close an approximation to the perfect symmetry of the tone of simple pitch as is the octave. For whereas in the latter there is only one point within the extremes where a departure from the perfect system of tone occurs, within the former there are two. This arrangement would therefore constitute only a second grade of fusion and may be ascribed to the interval of the fifth. It agrees with this deduction that the rates of vibration of the fifth are relatively $2:3$. For as the pitch is central in any volume and the lower half of the volume of the higher tone is supposed to be divided into two equal parts by the pitch of the lower volume, there will be three out of four parts of the upper volume within the upper half of the lower volume. Hence the volumes are as $4:6$, i.e. $2:3$.

XXXIII. From these two volumic coincidences of the octave and fifth we can obtain the proportions of any other interval by indirect means. For this purpose we do not need to leave the ground of psychical comparison and relations. The evidence of the octave shows, as we have noticed, that the volume of tones changes proportionately to the pitch. Or perhaps, as we should rather say, volume changes continuously from lowest to highest tones, and the octave units mark it out into stages, which then read as a natural proportionateness to pitch only so long as one does not see that this pitch is not the 'natural,' but only the nominal pitch. The measurement of volumes by means of the octave and fifth, for measurement it surely is, is as direct as any measurement could be. It is in principle quite the same as measurement with a foot-rule[1], although it is hampered in practice by the

---

[1] I may refer here to my discussion of the question: are the intensity differences of sensation quantitative? (136). No doubt the position I took up may have seemed to many unnecessarily extreme. I have seen no reason since to doubt its validity. My measurement of volume now comes as an interesting confirmation of what I said, *loc.*

impossibility of getting a large number of units of different size on to one measuring unit. So for our present purposes we may simply take over the ratios from present knowledge without further inquiry into their origin and apply them to psychical volumes.

For the interval of the fourth the 'lower extreme' and the 'predominant' points of the upper tone would lie respectively one-fourth of the whole length of the lower tone towards the lower extreme order of it away from its predominant order, and one-eighth away on the other side[1]. Similar values[2] for the other grades of fusion and the intervals included under each by Stumpf and Kemp (v. below, Table VI, p. 104) are given in Table III. The line separating the columns 'Lower extreme' and 'Pitch-order' may be taken as representing the predominant point of the lower tone. The values in each column then give the distance, in terms of the volume of the lower tone, between the latter's predominance and the *lower extreme* order of the higher tone and between

cit. p. 181 f. If my method and results are correct, I have now measured real volume by superposition. I have not however measured the mode or *Gestalt* 'volume,' which must remain in its psychical essence, as it has always been, a mere magnitude. For a clear assertion of this—that volume is an immeasurable magnitude like intensity—see Stumpf (112, 53). Those who hold that magnitudes are somehow measurable—on the distance method, for example—may not now turn upon me and say: you have just succeeded in measuring a magnitude. For I have not measured volume by the distance ritual, nor have I measured it as a magnitude: but I have measured its real basis by an inferential process, by superposition, the same inferential process by which real physical distances are measured. As I said in my paper, some day the real psychical basis of intensity—if it has one—may be measured in this way. But that will not be a measurement of intensive magnitudes. Are those who still differ really ready to accept the ultra-sensationalism implied in the denial of my argument? I doubt it very much. If volume and interval are really in psychical essence something more than their psychical basis of auditory atoms, they are essentially immeasurable, although they are magnitudes. But their real psychical basis is measurable. I do not deny the possibility of psychical measurement. But I do deny the possibility of measuring psychical magnitudes as such. In strict logic it is the 'as such' that matters. If any one cares to omit it and to substitute for the magnitude in question some other in order to be able to say he has measured that magnitude, I suppose he will. But in that case all discussion is at an end.

[1] The predominant point of the fourth therefore divides the distance (in the strict sense) between two pitches an octave apart into two equal parts. Generally, the half-distance pitch is got by subtracting the inverted ratio of the two tones from unity and dividing by four. If the resulting fraction is found in the fourth column (x) of Table III, the required tone is given by the interval of the first column; otherwise by simple calculation, e.g. $c:a = \frac{5}{3}$; i.e. $1 - \frac{3}{5}$; $= \frac{2}{5} \div 4 = \frac{1}{10}$; i.e. III or e; e divides the *distance* $c - a$ into two equal parts. On distance compare below, p. 75 ff.

[2] Cf. 137, 34. There by mistake the values for the natural seventh (4:7) have been given instead of those of the tritone (32:45).

the predominances of the two tones ('pitch-order'). The values for the intervals beyond the octave are set alongside. In these, *both* the special defining points of the upper tone fall above the point of predominance of the lower tone. It is important to notice that the lower extreme point of the upper tone falls in the intervals beyond the octave exactly where the predominance of the upper tone fell within the octave.

TABLE III.

Interval		(In terms of the lower's volume) From the pitch-order of the lower to the higher's:			Interval	
		lower extreme	pitch-order (x)	lower extreme		
0	$1:2$	0	$\frac{1}{4}$	$\frac{1}{4}$	$0+0$	$1:4$
5	$2:3$	$\left(\frac{2}{6}\right)\ \frac{1}{6}$	$\frac{1}{6}\ \left(\frac{2}{6}\right)$	$\frac{1}{6}$	$0+5$	$1:3$
4	$3:4$	$\left(\frac{2}{8}\right)\ \frac{2}{8}$	$\frac{1}{8}\ \left(\frac{3}{8}\right)$	$\frac{1}{8}$	$0+4$	$3:8$
III	$4:5$	$\left(\frac{2}{10}\right)\ \frac{3}{10}$	$\frac{1}{10}\ \left(\frac{4}{10}\right)$	$\frac{1}{10}$	$0+$III	$2:5$
3	$5:6$	$\left(\frac{2}{12}\right)\ \frac{4}{12}$	$\frac{1}{12}\ \left(\frac{5}{12}\right)$	$\frac{1}{12}$	$0+3$	$5:12$
VI	$3:5$	$\left(\frac{4}{10}\right)\ \frac{1}{10}$	$\frac{2}{10}\ \left(\frac{3}{10}\right)$	$\frac{2}{10}$	$0+$VI	$3:10$
6	$5:8$	$\left(\frac{6}{16}\right)\ \frac{1}{16}$	$\frac{3}{16}\ \left(\frac{5}{16}\right)$	$\frac{3}{16}$	$0+6$	$5:16$
T	$32:45$	$\left(\frac{26}{90}\right)\ \frac{13}{90}$	$\frac{13}{90}\ \left(\frac{32}{90}\right)$	$\frac{13}{90}$	$0+T$	$32:90$
II	$8:9$	$\left(\frac{2}{18}\right)\ \frac{7}{18}$	$\frac{1}{18}\ \left(\frac{8}{18}\right)$	$\frac{1}{18}$	$0+$II	$4:9$
7	$9:16$	$\left(\frac{14}{32}\right)\ \frac{2}{32}$	$\frac{7}{32}\ \left(\frac{9}{32}\right)$	$\frac{7}{32}$	$0+7$	$9:32$
2	$15:16$	$\left(\frac{2}{32}\right)\ \frac{14}{32}$	$\frac{1}{32}\ \left(\frac{15}{32}\right)$	$\frac{1}{32}$	$0+2$	$15:32$
VII	$8:15$	$\left(\frac{14}{30}\right)\ \frac{1}{30}$	$\frac{7}{30}\ \left(\frac{8}{30}\right)$	$\frac{7}{30}$	$0+$VII	$4:15$

All these arrangements are obviously devoid of the coincidence or balance that is so obvious in the first two—the octave and fifth. All of them are irregular, but to some extent this irregularity gets worse as we proceed, while one of the two defining points of the upper tone comes closer to the predominance of the lower. All these fusions will therefore naturally belong to a lower grade than the fifth, whether our conceptual estimation of their balance is as graded as our auditory apprehension of them or not. We shall consider these details more closely in another connexion. For the present our deduction agrees sufficiently with the introspective and indirect determinations of fusion expounded above.

Our study of the tonal mass produced from two different sources of sound thus teaches us that in almost all cases pitches can be found in it that correspond exactly to the pitches of the original sounds produced separately. In this sense analysis is perfect. In the case of slow beats, as we have seen, the original pitches cannot be recovered. But of the other attributes of tone neither volume nor intensity can be recovered in their original forms by analysis. Fusion, we have concluded, is to be defined as the coincidence and inseparability of volumes which remains over even after pitch has been perfectly analysed. The merging of intensities in one another is proved in general by the familiar fact that a sound can be heard in the silence at an intensity far lower than that required when another sound is being made[1]. One sound seems to drown the other to some extent. This is again a sign that sounds coincide at least to some extent in their 'stuff' as it were[2]. Some of the 'atoms' or 'spots' of sound of which they are composed, are identical, as we have seen in the study of fusion.

XXXIV. Let us illustrate these things with a diagram. Let the two primary sounds have the pitches c' and c^2. The diagram of c' alone would be as in Fig. 4. The line Vh–Vl represents the total volume of the tone, Vl being the lower extreme and Vh the higher. P represents the predominant order that constitutes the pitch, while the perpendicular Pi represents the relative intensity in which that predominant order is present. The relative intensities of the other orders that make up the whole volume are found by perpendiculars parallel to Pi. But the diagram does not claim to represent these differences truly, but only to indicate them in principle. Their exact relations are a matter for difficult special research.

The diagram for c^2 looks in principle exactly like that for c'. In actual fact the rise of its intensities may be somewhat different especially about the point of predominance. Only the dimensions of the whole are half as large.

[1] Cf. 112, 220 f., 420. Weber's law alone would suffice to explain this if a coincidence of volumes is admitted.

[2] A remark by W. James (36, 84) is of interest in this connexion: "At most, the high tone is felt as a thin, bright streak on a broader, darker background." Cf. however, Stumpf's denial of all the implications of this suggestion (112, 53). Cf. with this, Dunlap (11, 291): "the higher note is contained in the lower note both psychologically and physiologically, just as if a short streak of light were superimposed on a long one."

In the combined diagram of the sound heard when both sources of sound are played at once, the lower half is identical with that of c'. A second point of predominance appears in the upper half. But what exactly are the intensive relations of the curve of the upper half we cannot say, except that they must be somewhat greater than are those of c' for the simple reason that a second point of predominance appears.

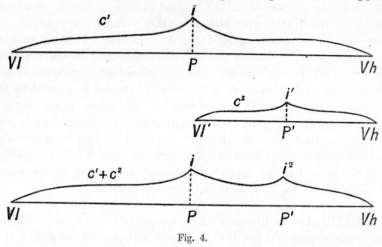

Fig. 4.

A similar diagram is given in Fig. 5 for $c' + g'$. There the curve of g' overlaps two-thirds of that of c'. A point of predominance is not created at the end point of coincidence Vl'. Evidently more is required for predominance than just an increase of intensity. But this increase is not so good as absent or ineffective, any more than it is at the extremes of a tone of simple pitch. It is effective in so far as it marks out the

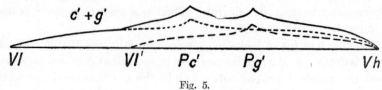

Fig. 5.

balance in the whole tonal mass that is characteristic of the fifth and that makes the fifth so like a perfectly balanced tone of simple pitch that it is often taken for one. The common difference tone c^0 will in this case bring out a third point of predominance at Vl, the rest of the volume of that low tone stretching away out as far as the whole length Vl–Vh on the left of Vl.

Certain other phenomena are now readily deducible from our diagram. In low tones and in simple mild tones the curve of predominance may be much rounded or flattened[1], so that the pitch seems indefinite and to a certain extent displaceable at will. Such rounding may be produced by the interaction of sounds. Or by the same influence the addition of a second sound may seem to pull the pitch of the first sound towards the new pitch (112, 396 ff.). But this shift of pitch is evidently only due to the rounding of the predominance. For the true pitch or the real point of predominance is always to be got by attentive observation.

The theory represented by our diagram provides a basis for a detailed study of the relation of sounds of different intensity to analysis. Stumpf's conclusion "that the higher tone must possess a greater excess of intensity if it is to cover the lower one than conversely[2]" seems to be deducible from our diagram. For the volume of the lower tone always encompasses completely the volume of the higher, which can then only suppress the former if its predominant part lies near that of the lower tone and if its intensity is great enough to swamp the predominance of the lower tone. The lower tone on the other hand has the advantage of being the only clearly defined volume, which can be flooded by higher tones from one side only. If the higher tone is more than an octave above the lower, the latter can be flooded only on the upper side. Any sort of mutual flooding of volumes will be much less likely with considerable differences of pitch (cf. 112, 229). In fact the intensive relations within the tonal mass from two sources of sound might yield a fairly good statement of the relative volume curve of a single tone, if one tone were plotted out in terms of the minimal audible intensity of all other simultaneous tones within an octave on either side[3].

XXXV. Concluding our consideration of the mass of sound evoked by two sources of sound at once we may say that the whole nature of the mass is continuous with that of a tone of simple pitch. In fact

---

[1] Cf. 112, 114. The greater threshold for discrimination of simultaneous pitches in the lower regions also suggests this. v. 103, 94 f.

[2] 112, 228. On this subject in general cf. 102, 16 ff. The tones considered must be of comparable intensity. Of course a weakish low tone is obliterated altogether by a loud or shrill high tone, from which the ear (i.e. the attention) cannot free itself. Schaefer and Guttmann (103, 87 ff.) have shown that in the middle parts of the scale of pitches two pitches are not discriminated until they are some 10–20 vibrations apart.

[3] Other details on this subject will be found in 112, § 21. We cannot pursue it further now. It must at present suffice to have indicated the chief lines of theory in this region.

the theory of the mass of two sources is just a modification of that of the 'pure' tone. Both are masses of elementary auditory 'atoms.' Both are regular and balanced and therefore admit of the predicate 'tonal' applied specifically to the sound of simple pitch. No complete analysis is possible except of the aspect of pitch, where predominance is equivalent to discreteness. These pitches are not tones, in spite of the prevailing tendency to identify the two notions. But in view of the fact that not only the whole mass of sound but also the parts surrounding each pitch are so regular and balanced as to admit of the predicate 'tonal,' *it is permissible to speak of the analysis of the whole mass as an analysis into tones.* Yet we must not forget that tones cannot be separated completely from one another. The separation is much less good than is that of two neighbouring patches of colour; for the contrast effects on the area surrounding a patch of colour do not really belong to that patch as a unit.

Every tonal mass, in fact every sound, is then a unity except in so far as it can be analysed (cf. 112, 77). Unity and fusion are primary and ineradicable, analysis is only possible so far as the discreteness of pitches and other favourable circumstances, such as the movement of tones in a mass, permit. There is then after all no new problem in the unity of pitch-blends, or of fusions of the octave, fifth, fourth, etc. Their problem is the one problem of tone in the strict sense. And all analysis is a consequence of the predominance of pitch. But analysis goes only so far as it is induced by favouring circumstances or is pushed by will. And then of course all attitudes or habits of attention are in a sense artificial. Attention falls back from them under ordinary circumstances into an easy posture which corresponds roughly to the mass-nature of the experiences in question. And in the case of sound that mass-nature is fusion with a central predominance of the fundamental pitch (cf. 112, 384 ff.).

We thus obtain a central point of view for the most varied series of phenomena and many standing conflicts of theory are allayed. The comparative smoothness or roughness of pitch-blends depends upon their approximation to the balance of the ideal pure tone. So does the grade of fusion of two tones. We cannot, therefore, explain consonance by agreement or disagreement of partials; but we can reduce the similarity of both to the same basis in principle. The same holds for any other adventitious accompaniment of tones which might be invoked as the basis of fusion, e.g. difference-tones. Any smoothness or fusion-like character which may appear in groups of difference tones must be due to the approach made by the mass to the balance and smoothness of a pure tone. But each group of pitches (volumic predominances) has its own balance. We do not need to appeal to one group for the smoothness or roughness that we cannot find theoretically in another group. Here we touch again on the principle of nativism. Theory shows that we do not need these transferences of properties between experiences, just as principle urges us to decline to accept such an irrational and uncontrollable process. Even the roughness of beats is but a further instance of departure from the ideal smoothness of the pure tone. Beats undoubtedly do sound rough, if at all frequent; but they could be so theoretically rough as they seem to be to everyone since Helmholtz, only because the basis of the resonance theory passes over in the region of beats insensibly into a series of small volumes, blending and oscillating with one another, even although no volume was explicitly attributed to the tonal element in that theory. We involuntarily think of a parallel like visual flicker—and that is a volumic parallel. A non-volumic theory of hearing has no right, strictly, even to the rationality of the roughness of beats. All the theories, then, like all the facts, lead to, and ground in, the volumic differences of tones and the ordinal differences that are implicit in them and are made explicit in pitch.

CHAPTER III

DISTANCE AND INTERVAL

XXXVI. The further psychology of hearing must naturally build upon the results of the study of simple sounds. Whatever success we may have in carrying on our early conclusions will help to confirm their validity. Then the psychology of hearing will be continuous in its principles and explanations. We have already seen how the psychology of the attributes provides a basis for the adequate study of fusion and tonal complexes. We shall now see how the same basis suffices for the study of distance and interval that in the ordinary psychology of sound appear so mysterious and peculiar.

In the senses of vision and touch, distance is known to everyone. We can feel the distance between two points or the thickness of a book very accurately with the thumb and first finger. We can compare the distances between two pairs of stars or between two pairs of dots on a page with great exactness, quite apart from any measurement of these distances. Of course a small and somewhat variable error is made, but that does not detract from our ability to compare distances very rapidly and efficiently. A great deal of our ordinary practical work involving appreciation of distances can be done quite well without any measurement.

Although we are all thus familiar with distances, using them and speaking of them constantly, psychologists have been of very different opinions regarding their psychical nature. At present many incline to regard distances as special parts or kinds of experiences, something other than the attributes of elementary sensations, an addition to them which supervenes only when two or more elementary sensations are given. Apart from theoretical objections, a moment's consideration will make this seem very probable. The distance between two visual points is quite another thing than the two points themselves. One might reply that between the points there is a continuous stretch of visual sensation, since the whole field of vision is always full of sensation. But that mere fact would be no reason for our selecting the stretch of sensation between the two points as of special interest, except as a stretch or distance. Besides, when we speak of distance, we do not mean more or less the sensation lying between two points. What interest is there in that vague sensation, undistinguished as it is from its surroundings? What we mean is the specific experience of distance. All this is no explanation, but only an attempt to point out what is meant.

Moreover if we refer to the sense of touch we find that we have distances without any continuous background of sensation. If two points are touched at once some inches apart on the forearm, we feel a distance between them. We can also feel distances with the tip of the finger or tongue.

When we reflect on the relation between distance and the attributes in these senses, we find that distance is dependent on the occurrence of two sensations of different order. Thus from senses in which the facts are easily distinguished we get a pattern by which to test all the senses. And this procedure leads to a general rule in the same terms, which is supported by another rule saying that distance is only found in those senses in which suitable variation of the attribute of order occurs. There is no distinct trace of distance in the olfactory and

muscular senses. In those senses in which only unrelieved masses
of sensation occur, especially the organic, and also cold and warmth,
no distances can emerge properly. In articular sense distances are
very important. Here we see further confirmation for our classification
of the variations of position in this sense as primarily ordinal (cf. 133,
172 ff.; 135, 250 ff.).

Such agreement amongst the senses must lead us to expect to find
in hearing an experience similar to distance, founded upon differences
in the attribute of pitch; and its presence is admitted by a number
of psychologists.

XXXVII. The amounts or sizes of the distances between pairs
of pitches can surely be compared with one another, like visual distances,
especially if we compare the distance between one pitch and two others
above or below it, e.g. *c–e* with *c–f*. Anyone who is not quite unmusical,
will notice an increase in the distance between these pitches. However,
even for these more or less obvious cases doubts may be raised. Stumpf,
for example, is inclined to think that then our judgment is based on
the difference of pitch of the upper tones and not directly upon the
difference of distance between the pairs of pitches (111, 248). But he
is quite sure of our ability to judge very small tonal distances, smaller
than a semitone (111, 252 f.). That much is at least comforting and
forms a beginning. But in different parts of the musical range of
pitches, e.g. *c–e* and *g–a*, it is much more difficult to compare distances.
In fact we seem sure only when we make rough comparisons. These
again hardly do more than assure us that distances exist throughout
the range of pitches and are comparable as to size. It is said
that the distances given by one and the same ratio of pitches
are not the same in different parts of the tonal range. According
to Stumpf, who admits the difficulty of judging[1], they increase from
the depths up to about the third accented octave. In the lower part
of the great octave (*C–c*) the interval of a third (4 : 5) is just recognisable
as a distance; i.e. it is a minimal distance. The fifth then also seems
hardly greater than a third in the middle musical range (112, 403 f.).
In the upper ranges of pitch a similar contraction of distances over
against one and the same ratio of vibration is also to be observed.

[1] Cf. his criticisms (113) of Lorenz's attempts (58, 26 ff.). At p. 455 Stumpf speaks
of judgments of tonal distance as a field "in which clear results are clearly out of the question." On p. 459 he gives a few approximations of his own: the middle between *c'* and *c³*
is about *d²*; between *c'* and *g²* about *b'*; between *c'* and *d²* about *g'♯*.

These things hold whether the sounds that form the interval are given simultaneously or successively (112, 406).

XXXVIII. Compared with the ease with which we handle distance in the other senses, especially vision, such helplessness in hearing seems mysterious. We might have expected to be able to say with great precision whether the distances between two pairs of pitches were equal or not, no matter how far apart these pairs of pitches were, just as we do with visual distances, looking first at the one distance and then at the other. But, as it is, unless the suggestion had been given to us in various ways[1] from the other senses, we might hardly have thought of looking for distance in hearing at all, were it not that it seems so to contract in the extremes of the pitch range.

But we must be careful not to be misled by the constancy of physical ratios. How do we know that one ratio offers the same possibility of distance in the various parts of the range of pitches? Surely it gives no such guarantee, any more than the number of inches between two points on the skin gives an index of the comparative size of the distance we shall feel between them. On the theory of pitches above developed this parallel is quite true and exact. The only proper basis for judgments of distance is distance itself. And we can only ask for a reason why we apparently judge auditory distances so badly.

One obvious reason is that every one finds it so much easier to state the relations between pitches in forms of interval (111, 249 ff.). For interval is not only a constant ratio of vibrations, it is also a constant experience. All the ease that we should expect to find in our dealings with tonal distances, we actually find in our work with intervals. We trace their equalities in the same and in different parts of the musical range very easily. We can do with intervals what is hardly possible even with visual distances, at least with such accuracy; we recognise them in isolation without comparison. We must therefore examine intervals carefully in the hope that we may then throw some light upon the obscurity of tonal distance.

---

[1] I refer not only to my own rule of the relation between orders and distances, which is too new and revolutionary yet to have been accepted by others, but also to the curious classification of all differences between sensations, whether qualitative or not, as distances (cf. 111, 122 f.; 125, xxiv ff.). This classification is of no direct importance for our discussion, but it seems dangerously confusing. There may be a degree of 'distance' between red and orange that can be stated in figures, but there is no distance in the ordinary ordinal sense of that word.

XXXIX.   Interval is physically defined as the special feature of auditory experience that is common to all tonal complexes evoked by two sources of sound vibrating in a certain fixed ratio at any part of the musical range of pitches. It is not identifiable with degree of fusion, for, as we have seen, intervals like thirds and sixths, or seconds and sevenths, are not easily distinguishable amongst one another in terms of degree of fusion, although they are readily distinguishable as intervals. Fusion considers only the degree of disruption or disorder in the whole mass, the ease with which it could justify the judgment that it is evoked from two sources of sound, with or without simultaneous attention to the discriminability of the pitches it contains. Interval applies to the whole experience, not before or after the analysis of its pitches, but both before and after, at all times, as a characteristic whole especially in reference to the setting which the whole mass provides for the primary pitches it contains.

That whole setting must be a characteristic thing. And on our theory of fusion it is so. We may at once state interval as the outline of the whole mass of sound which, within the musical range, is characteristic of any ratio of vibration, especially such ratios as are already characterised by fusions, e.g. octave, fifth, fourth, or by any other features such as we shall indicate later.

In the case of fusion the character of the whole mass of sound given by any ratio of vibrations was set into special relations to its unitariness or balance. Or, in practical terms, to the ease with which it could be correctly judged to have been evoked by two sources of sound. The discrimination of pitches in fusion is only a secondary matter or a parallel indication of its unitariness. The fusion proper is there equally before and after discrimination of the pitches in the sound. In interval, not the unitariness, but the characteristic volumic outline— the ordinal incidence of its variations in intensity and predominance throughout its whole extent—is set into relation to the pitches and their difference.

It is a fine point of analysis to say whether this difference includes or excludes the distance between the pitches. Which do we actually mean when we hear an interval? Do we mean that these two pitches stand in a characteristic mass and so fall into one class with all other pitches which also occur in a mass of the same character; or does the reference hold for the distance between the pitches? Distance might perhaps be less involved than are the pitches, in so far as we do really ignore all the differences of distance that occur in the same intervals.

Pitches are not ignored; for, being predominant in tonal masses, they are in all practical senses, and in some others too, the chief object of interest in sounds. Probably, in interval as such, neither distance nor pitches are the chief concern, but only the interval, the characteristic volumic outline as such, while the pitches it contains stand for other reasons well forward for attention. Of course the accompanying distance may be ignored as of no special interest, but it cannot be suppressed.

XL. However fusion and interval are distinguished from one another in careful reflection, there is no doubt that they are really very closely connected with one another. In a sense they are merely diverse aspects of the same thing—complex tonal mass—although interval owing to its special interest or 'intent' naturally carries us further in distinguishing and recognising these masses. Probably both are in varying degrees responsible for the standardisation of the range of pitches. Fusion perhaps leads the way in so far as owing to its influence octave parallels pass in unreflecting minds as identicals. But wherever the reflecting and observing consciousness sets to work with sounds, interval must take the first place. Then the characteristic mass volume of the octave, so perfectly balanced, so easily repeatable, and so little affected by reduplication, must inevitably give an ineradicable 'set' to the whole attitude of observation towards the range of pitches. No other interval is so little affected by reduplication. If, for example, two fifths are given at once, the second is not a perfect repetition of the first: for neither of the two new points (the extreme of the top volume and its predominance) coincide with any of the points of the first fifth; they merely upset its balance a little. But in the octave the lower extreme point of each new volume always coincides with the predominance of the lower one (v. Fig. 6).

The fifth might therefore be used as a unit, but it would not be able to maintain itself as a unit in spite of simultaneous duplication as the octave does. This holds, in fact, for any other interval than the octave. The incompatibility of two identical intervals, e.g. c, e, $g\sharp$ is, therefore, by no means mysterious. c–e and e–$g\sharp$ separately are good thirds, but together they create an unbalance, otherwise that of c–$g\sharp$ separately. Of course, theories that can show no inherent connexion between tones of different pitch, cannot account for this— to them, erratic—behaviour of two-tone fusions in triads[1].

---

[1] Cf. Riemann's criticism of Stumpf's theory of consonance (69, 419 ff.).

The law of the octave is then the supreme law in the reflective use of the range of pitches, or, in the more usual term, in music. If any other intervals are used, their presence and peculiarities must be entirely subordinated to the limits imposed by the octave. Under these circumstances it is only natural that the standpoint of the octave should in the course of time work itself ineradicably into our dispositions of observation. For after we have run through all the intervals that we admit between any two pitches an octave apart, the same intervals recur in the next octave without any change of standpoint. But it is clear that if we wish to change our octave basis, for example from c to d, it cannot be done without intermediation. For the volumic

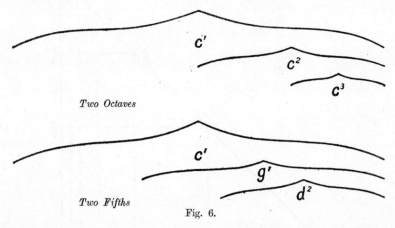

Fig. 6.

relations of c as an octave and of many of the other intervals admitted as compatible with the octave c, are not coincident or continuous with those of d.

We can now understand why octave relationships come to be so prominent[1] in the pitch range that they could be thought to be based upon identity of quality (cf. above, p. 44 ff.). And we can see too why we must take special means to confuse and suppress our ready disposition towards the octave attitude, if we are to appreciate fully the original continuous pitch differences of all tones. We need to play chromatic passages rapidly in order to baffle the octave disposition. We can hardly exaggerate the strength and readiness of that disposition in modern minds that are familiarised with it from the first contact with music or even with the most accessible musical instruments such as piano or organ, apart from the natural inevitability of the phenomenon

---

[1] Of all intervals the octave is far the most easily recognised. v. 117, 168.

itself. The whole range of pitches is made manageable by it. Pitches are standardised then in relation to their volumic outline. We might represent the whole musical range by a convenient diagram[1] (Fig. 7). The lines v^0, v', v^2, v^3, etc. represent half the volumic proportions of the tones of the pitches c^0, c', c^2, etc. The letters p^0, p', p^2, etc. stand, therefore, at the points of predominance, or at the pitch-points, of these volumes. On the other side of p^0 from v^0 there would be as much volume again as is indicated by the bottom line of the diagram. The diagram represents the relations of the tones of the musical scale truly,

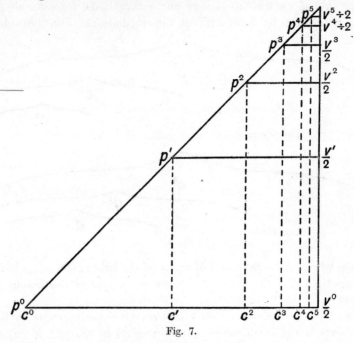

Fig. 7.

but it does not necessarily indicate correctly the real relations which may subsist between the pitches as orders. We do not yet know for example what relation the number of orders in the lower stretch of volume of c' bears to the number in the lower stretch of c^2. This

[1] The only diagram of pitch-volume I have met with in psychological literature is Titchener's (126, 94). "This attribute [of size or diffusion]," he says, "runs, in general, parallel with the attribute of pitch; but at the ends of the scale it changes more quickly, in the middle region more slowly, than pitch, so that deep tones appear very large and diffuse, and high tones very small and concentrated, while the intermediate tones seem all to be more or less of the same size." I am not aware that this view has received wider acceptance.

problem can only be settled by a direct examination of the discriminability of pitches.

XLI. Such an examination shows that the differential threshold of pitch does not conform to Weber's law, as was naturally expected on the hypothesis of the qualitative classification of pitch, or as would be expected also upon a quantitative interpretation of pitch, such as that suggested by K. Dunlap. We do not need to multiply the rate of vibration of a given tone by a fixed ratio in order to get the tone just distinguishable from the first in respect of pitch. The increment is very nearly an absolutely constant quantity. It increases absolutely (not relatively) slowly with the rise of pitch within the musical range, as the following figures show: D_1 (ca. 70 vbs.) + 0·4 vb.; c^0 (125 vbs.) + 0·4; c' (250 vbs.) + 0·4 vb.; a' (417 vbs.) + 0·65 vb.; a^2 (834 vbs.) + 0·9 vb.; a^3 (1668 vbs.) + 1·1 vbs.; g^4 (2965 vbs.) + 7 to 10 vbs.; c^5 (4000 vbs.) + 10 to 40 or more vbs.; after this point the threshold soon rises enormously (cf. below, Table V, p. 96). These values are averages taken from tests made by Stücker (110, 396f.) upon some 30 professional musicians, 14 of whom belonged to the K. K. Hofoper in Vienna. In reckoning the values I have omitted a few abnormally high values (poor discriminations). Meyer (67, 358) working with the special training in observation possessed by Stumpf, got for an increase of 0·35 vibration per second on the tones of 100, 200, 400, 600, 1200 vibrations respectively 71, 83, 80, 84, 67 per cent. correct judgments. These sets of results show great similarity. They are the only apparently reliable and uniform results I have been able to find. Determinations of the threshold of pitch differences made by unmusical and untrained ears are almost worthless; they are erratic and irregular and unless got by strictly incognitive methods, probably illusory. A grouping of them is given by Vance (129, 133): for 64 vbs. some 3 vibrations give the threshold; for 128, ca. 1·5 vb.; for 256 ca. 1·5 vb.; for 512, ca. 2 vb.; for 1024, ca. 3 vb.; for 2048, ca. 6 vb. Practice has of course a marked effect upon them, as F. O. Smith has shown (107). The simultaneous threshold for pitches shows somewhat the same differences of relation to pitch (102, 25). Absolutely it is much bigger, some 10–20 vibrations in the middle range.

No doubt the size of this increment at any pitch depends upon the spread of excitation round the point of predominance and upon the displacement consequently necessary if a noticeable shift of the centre of predominance is to be got. And as the volume of a tone is the smaller the higher it is, we may suppose that its volumic outline is proportionately smaller all over, as it rises. This would mean a greater pointedness of predominance in direct proportion to the rise of pitch or in inverse proportion to increase in the number of vibrations per second. Apart from slight differences due to rounding, and apart from the desire to extend the range of predominance, which gives a tone a certain elasticity of pitch as we have seen above (p. 31), the displacement required for discrimination under the best conditions of attention might therefore well be about the same fraction of a vibration per second.

This analysis however would not imply that the numbers of orders which compose a volume are anything but proportionate to the magnitude of that volume. Indeed how could we expect it to be otherwise? The very notion of volumes implies a reference to the original multitude of orders constituting it. Although this inference receives no support from matters of fusion, which rest upon the coincidence of volumes, nevertheless it seems natural that apart from the measures of coincidence volumes should really decrease evenly with rise of pitch, as they seem to do, especially since the predominance of pitch seems to be central to each volume. We can only assume that both volume and distance are proportional in magnitude to that number, apart from special conditions and processes of standardisation which may supervene.

Thus we should conclude that distances are not only not equal in octaves, but rather about halved in size for any interval with each octave upwards[1] (cf. *infra*, p. 90 f., 162 ff.).

XLII. The impression of an increase of distance with a rise of octave must therefore be due to the increase in the number of discriminable steps that comes with rise of pitch. That would make the former apparent increase illusory. We need not hesitate to accept this conclusion, for all judgments of distance within the musical range are, as Stumpf admits, exceedingly difficult and doubtful. Theoretical leading might very well reverse them entirely.

---

[1] Cf. 111, 62; 113, 459 f., where Stumpf writes: "Experiences and ideas of other kinds, such as...especially the smaller (apparent and real) extension of higher tones and associations connected therewith, drive us further still: the tone realm seems to grow smaller and smaller upwards. A melody repeated in the octave higher, with retention of the distance relations, appears with regard to the absolute size of the steps like a reduced copy of the original. In real music, in the whole context of music, this illusion is in fact the dominating one," etc. The argument of our text would make it out to be no illusion, but reality. Cf. similar expression in 120, 23.

XLIII. But even if auditory distances do thus originally differ that would not preclude their being later standardised by means of interval. We find in the sense of touch great original differences between the distances given by stimulation of points objectively equally far apart on different parts of the skin, tongue, finger tips, palm of hand, etc. But these come to be standardised approximately to the proper amounts of real distance, although the tongue hardly acquires this correction. So too the original differences amongst the tonal distances of the octave and other intervals would become equivalent in the octave standard. Their original differences would not thereby be annulled. They could be recovered by suitable devices and brought before our observation as such. But this standardisation would at least soften for us the crude original differences of distance, and explain the unobtrusive nature of tonal distance over against interval. We should therefore conclude that the essence of interval is proportion of form; for the variations of distance would then make no difference, since all the elements of the form of any interval would change equally with any .raising or lowering of the interval. Nevertheless, as was noted above, the pitches that stand in an interval must not be lost from sight; the interval is referred to the pitches or rather to the 'tones' to which the pitches belong.

In a recent publication (120, 85) Stumpf notes that "Messrs Abraham and v. Hornbostel in the last few years have made long series of experiments upon distance judgments in tones...the familiarity with our intervals being as far as possible set aside or made harmless by the circumstances of the experiments. They found that it is really possible to equate small tonal distances with some certainty at different absolute pitches; and the distances thus judged equal showed the same relations of vibrations, not the same differences as one might think." It must be evident that Abraham and v. Hornbostel, in the face of the immense, if not insuperable, difficulty of uncovering the primary distances of pitches, have simply wandered unwittingly into mere interval, which is of course a matter of relations or proportions of volume. In fact their getting equal relations of vibrations is good indirect evidence that they did not judge on the basis of distance at all, really. For on any count the probability of pure distance judgments giving equal ratios is not great, surely. I have given what seems on my theory to be the proper method of dividing a true tonal distance into two equal parts above in a note on p. 67. The middle pitch between two c's is an f, between c and a an e, between c and g an $e\flat$ (cf. 14). But when we compare

two theoretically equal distances—e.g. *c–f* and *f–c′* or *c–g* and *g–g′*—
we do not readily detect amidst the sounds anything identical. It may
be there for all that. We must remember that we simply cannot strip
tones and tonal sequences of their volumes so as to reduce them to
mere points, between which distances might be traced. No matter
what we do, the basis of proportion, i.e. interval, and from habit the
attitude towards proportion, are both there; and they may well make
the proper abstraction of distances impossible. Perhaps somebody
will succeed with the abstraction some day.

XLIV. The octave and the other intervals are also of great importance in the naming of pitches. Relative nomenclature is obviously
based entirely upon these relationships. And so in fact is every absolute
nomenclature or absolute 'ear.' For absolute ear there is required,
besides, an absolute point of reference in auditory orders themselves.
In those who have a more or less perfect absolute ear, we may suppose
that every auditory order is an absolute individual, which can under
favourable circumstances be recognised as such apart from all names.
We can all do this with some accuracy, if we are allowed to find at once
the given tone on a musical instrument and to practise doing so in order
to overcome certain common sources of error, such as octave transposition, confusion of repeated trials without renewal of the given tone,
etc. We then get a tone in the instrument which lies within a fairly
small variable error of the given tone. The same result comes of a
similar test of our ability to localise a point touched on the skin. But
whereas we all learn to name the point touched on the skin with an
equal degree of correctness, only very few learn to name tones correctly,
without the help of some familiar instrument, voice or piano, etc.
It is difficult to explain this difference between the two senses.

Probably the chief source of the difference is the extraordinary
emphasis laid by music upon the relationships of pitches. Musical
instruments constantly vary in the absolute pitch to which they are
tuned. In fact a standardisation of pitch is only required for certain
special reasons; e.g. on the piano for the convenience of those who
have a very precise and rigid absolute ear, and who would be 'thrown
out' if they had to play a work a quarter or half tone lower than usual;
or for the convenience of those who are singing to piano accompaniment up to the limits of their voice range, and so on. Absolute ear
is a great help in musical practice, but it is quite dispensable. In fact
it seems to be rather difficult to acquire even when there is a certain

tendency towards it (cf. 43, 261 f.) and easily lost, if it is acquired with any difficulty. In some favoured persons it is acquired early and more or less unwittingly and never lost. Perhaps these persons have some special refinement of hearing, such as a much greater delicacy of volumic outline and especially of predominance, than have others. Or perhaps a highly favoured auditory disposition gives them the power to maintain their absoluteness of ear in spite of the universality of musical relativity. In that case we should all naturally possess absolute ear and then proceed to lose it or to lose the power to convert it into absolute nomenclature. In dealing with noises we all seem to retain a good deal of it, even the most unmusical of us, who recognise voices, noises, etc. But then noises are irregular sounds in which many orders emerge irregularly, rather than only one or a few all the time. And noises are not subject to the same relativity as music is. There is evidence also that young children may be brought to show absolute ear, if the snares of relational changes are avoided. And they can learn it the more easily, the less they have already had to do with music (32). They are taught tones in association with certain letters, and can reproduce the tones absolutely when given the letters[1]. Dogs perhaps also have a good measure of absolute ear. The whole problem is subtle and complicated. But it is not of any primary importance in the psychology of hearing.

We are now in a position to see how unimportant Stumpf's evidence in favour of octave qualities is. Errors of one or two octaves in absolute ear and the ease of octave transpositions are inevitable results of the relativity which the octave brings. They show that even absolute ear is in part subdued to musical relativity, seizing as of first importance only the placing of the pitch in its place in the octave, and of minor importance accuracy in specification of the exact octave. All these arguments, as well as the harmonic equivalence of the octave, are obvious consequences of the relativity of the octave and its importance for all music.

[1] Cf. D. Katz (38), and the tone-word method of training by Karl Eitz mentioned there, a method which uses names for tones very much like those of our tonic sol-fa system.

CHAPTER IV

THE ANALYSIS OF TONAL SEQUENCES

XLV. The chief differences between the study of tonal masses and sequences is that the latter is relieved of the problem of fusion. A gradual transition from mass to sequence is of course possible, if one of the two primary sounds is intoned and stopped a little before the other and the interval between the incidence of the two is gradually increased, until the second occurs distinctly after the first. It may be noted then that the phenomena of adventitious pitches and fusion become less and less readily noticeable. But they do not disappear as soon as the two sounds are heard as a succession. With strong tones of deeper pitch there is even then an instant of coincidence in the brief gap between the sounds[1]. But this rapidly disappears and the two sounds are then heard as a succession without any overlapping.

Each tone is then easily distinguishable from the other in every respect, intensity, pitch and volume. An exact comparison of intensities is not easy unless the tones are of closely neighbouring pitch; but some estimation of their relative intensities is possible in spite of considerable differences of pitch (111, 348). Various reasons account for this. In the first place it is difficult to measure the physical basis of the intensity of tones of rather different pitch and to equalise them. In the second place it is impossible to bring intensities to any sort of psychical over-lapping, especially as the pitches to which they are in this case attached are supposed to lie some way apart in order. Other reasons might be brought forward from physiological sources, but these do not concern us now.

Comparison of volumes is not affected at all by the succession of the sounds. Of course the same sort of judgments cannot be expected from successive sounds as from those that completely overlap. In the latter case the characteristic coincidences that constitute fusion emerge of themselves and hardly even require the help of attention for their observation. But it is evident that the same relations will exist in succession as in simultaneity. If the first tone is followed by its octave, the ordinal incidence of predominance of the former will be

---

[1] Cf. 112. 89; low tones are damped less easily.

coincident with that of the lower extreme of the latter. The transition
to the second tone will therefore be prepared by the first. In fact
a basis of transition passes from the first to the second. The only
change is the movement of pitch to the middle of the upper half of
the first tone and the cessation of the lower half. Similarly in the case
of the fifth the reception of the second tone is prepared by the first,
in so far as the characteristic points of the second lie at equal distances
on either side of the point of predominance of the first tone. But
the fifth cannot give the same degree of identity as the octave; for
none of the chief points of the first tone are identical with any of the
second, excepting of course the upper extreme point, which is common
to all tones.

It is clear then that relations exist between successive tones that
will inevitably standardise the range of successive pitches in exactly
the same way as the range of simultaneous pitches is standardised by
the volumic outline of tonal masses. Apart from the natural steps
given by such cases as octave and fifth, any step will give relations
that may be applied universally throughout the whole range of volumes
and so create an 'interval.' And that interval may be learnt and
remembered[1]. Experiments on the purity of intervals showed that
successive intervals can be adjusted as finely as and, especially in thirds
and octaves, much better than simultaneous intervals. For the third
70 cases of correct judgments were got for 2·18 and 5 vibrations respectively for succession and simultaneity. For the octave 90 correct
judgments for 0·46 and 3·1 vibrations respectively (146, 366 f.; 115, 55).
We shall consider the formation of scales later. So far we can see
that there is not the least problem or anomaly in the parallelism of the
relations established in tonal masses and sequences[2].

[1] Cf. M. Meyer (75, 207–214) on Quarter-tone music, where some experimental evidence
is brought to show that when intervals previously strange, grow familiar, they are expected
and anticipated, and then become more pleasing.

[2] Of course this is quite without prejudice to their difference. In sequences melodic
values (v. later) stand forth prominently. A major second is not a melodic discord; but
it is the same interval in sequence as it is in the mass; and in sequence it is as devoid of
balanced relationship to the tone preceding it as the two are in the mass; and so on.
There is no sense in running the statement of an aspect to death by generalising it in
opposition to all other statements of aspects. We must see the facts and their theoretical
basis in their fullest breadth; cf. 121, 329, where F. Krueger is quoted as having opined
correctly that no one listening to the scale would ever speak of it as a series of dissonances
(45, 246.). That is to encourage us to believe that successive tones get their relations
from common partials! Krueger himself believes that "the transference of the notion
of consonance to tonal sequences would never have taken place, or would be unintelligible
unless, chiefly from reasons drawn from physics and musical theory, we classed the mass

For Stumpf and others there is an insoluble problem in the parallelism, because, not having any psychological basis for the fusion of simultaneous tones, he can have none for the parallel relations of successive tones; and as the latter do not fuse, successive tones seem to call for another cause than the physiological one supposed to underlie fusion. Stumpf accepts as the most probable basis of the consonance of successive tones their relationship through common partials, a principle adopted from Helmholtz but disproved and rejected by Stumpf as an explanation of fusion. Stumpf's reasons in the latter case are: (1) consonance and dissonance can be got in absence of all partials; (2) any appeal to memory is illusory, fusion will not arise out of habit any more than the locomotive will run from custom, when the stoker forgets to coal up. These two reasons hold equally for successive tones. Stumpf's appeal on behalf of successive consonance seems rather inconsistent and helpless (115, 55 ff.; 112, 195; 121, 328 f.). His own feeling for this inconsistency leads him to give the relations of successive tones another name—"Verwandtschaft"—although it is clear from the facts and his discussion that something identical with consonance is implied thereby, in spite of Krueger's sage remark. There is an identical aspect, as I have pointed out, and also a difference, but it is not a case of all difference and no identity.

The only problem of these parallel relations is how they are brought into connexion in cognition. For in spite of the connexions just expounded, the two series are separated by obvious differences. The direction of observation in each is different. In the tonal mass the coincidence of volumes is actually present; it cannot but be felt. And it can be specially observed as soon as comparison of tonal masses favours its effect upon attention; it will then be more distinct, but not any more fused (i.e. any more like the perfectly balanced 'pure' tone) than before (cf. below, p. 99 ff.). The attention in this case does not establish the relation; it only favours its effectiveness. In the tonal sequence on the contrary, the relation is hardly actual until attention has been directed upon it. But that direction of the attention must be easily provoked even by the mere sequence of the tones, in the case of octaves at least; and with greater difficulty in the other cases. The transition from simultaneity to succession, which can easily be produced on many musical instruments, must help

of two tones and the sequence of the 'same' tones under one name (fifth, semitone, the same interval, etc.)" (*ibid.*). Inverted commas and extraneous reasons go well together, but they do not suit the good intrinsic sense of the 'transference' referred to.

to encourage the attention to see the identity of relations upon which successive and simultaneous intervals are founded, especially in persons highly disposed to auditory observation.

XLVI. But many are not so disposed. They feel the coincidence and balance in tonal masses, as we have seen in the study of fusion. But they do not readily learn to recognise and name the different forms of balance and still less the different volumic outlines that are devoid of much balance—the dissonances. The parallel relations of tonal sequences they find as hard to learn; and of course they do not spontaneously grasp the connexion between the two series; they have to learn each independently. Their incapacity to trace the connexion spontaneously is no evidence that masses and sequences are devoid of common relations; it proves only that the differences between the two are great enough to obstruct the view of these common relations for those who do not observe and learn sounds readily.

This incapacity of unmusical people has been proved experimentally by v. Maltzew (61, 192). There is even a difference in the memory dispositions for ascending and descending sequences. The judgment of descending intervals is found to be much harder, even by persons who have had considerable musical education and practice. Longer time is spent in·recognising a descending interval than an ascending one (*ibid.*). The peculiarity is probably based upon the habitual attitude towards tone masses already noticed whereby in a constant mass of sound the whole takes the pitch of the lowest component, even when that is not also the strongest (cf. 112, 384ff.). The point of observation is naturally central to the whole volume, unless it is drawn by special circumstances to one or other side or induced to spread itself over some extent. Stumpf pointed out other indications of this habitual standpoint. We judge of the tonal series from below upwards. Rising makes the impression of tonal recession, falling that of approach. We begin a scale involuntarily from below, not from above, and we end it below again[1]. When a major chord is given successively or simultaneously, we take the lowest, not the highest, tone as tonic; we consider the major, not the minor, third as the first interval (111, 149). Also, when an interval is mistaken for unison, the tone heard in the majority of cases is the lower of the two (117, 166). This habit is doubtless much strengthened by the octave standardisations of music.

[1] M. Meyer (75, 204 ff.), who shows some experimental evidence for the preference for a descending interval as the last of a series of intervals.

The octave standard is given not by the enunciation of a single tone, but of an octave along with one or more of its characteristic subordinate intervals, and that octave, seen from below, is of course implicit in the subsequent music in so far as all successive intervals are such as are compatible with it, or if not directly so, are introduced with sufficient preparation, or with little or no preparation for some artistic purpose or effect. The difficulty of identifying ascending and descending intervals might well be compared with the difficulty of identifying upright and inverted visual patterns. Towards visual pattern we also learn to adopt a standpoint. We must, of course, take as examples, figures that we are accustomed to see only in one position, e.g. figures and letters:

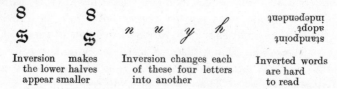

| Inversion makes the lower halves appear smaller | Inversion changes each of these four letters into another | Inverted words are hard to read |

v. Maltzew found no true evidence to show that the relations between successive and simultaneous intervals are established by our converting the sequence into a mass in representation, as Stumpf recently maintained (121, 328 f.). In cases of doubt or difficulty this procedure is hardly ever even attempted by observers and is of little use even then (61, 190 ff.). It is indeed difficult to see how an observer should proceed in order to sum the volumes of two successive tones in order to get the simultaneous volumic outline[1]. The coincidence of characteristic orders is enough for the tracing of identity when masses and sequences are given in sufficient proximity. But we could hardly expect two successive volumes to be summed or even identity to be readily traced through common points, if only the sequence was given and the mass had to be imagined therefrom. Distance is just as unable to explain the construction of intervals in the case of sequence as in that of masses. And it would show no difference between ascending and descending intervals.

v. Maltzew's own view (61, 196) is that interval is based not on any graded difference, but on something that is peculiar or typical for each interval. That is of course quite certain from the nature of the facts. And it is confirmed by the fact that when learners begin to take notice of this characteristic difference between intervals, they make great

[1] Cf. with this the difficulty of summing two sine curves at sight, e.g. the sine curves of sounds in ratio of 4: 5.

progress in learning them (61, 210). She proposes to call this peculiar 'content' of the experience 'step or passage experience.' But she is as unable to give this experience any definite psychological expression as Stumpf was in the case of his degrees of fusion. It is confusing to refer to the absolute way in which colours are named and recognised. That comparison and the use of the word 'qualitative' suggest that interval is a kind of psychological quality. But it would be absurd to look for qualities at this stage of the complications of hearing. Let us take other analogies. A word can be recognised and named without comparison with other words. So can a visual pattern or figure such as a circle, a cross, a square, etc. And these are after all the same thing psychically as words, which are only visual patterns. Not only that, but on our reading of it, interval is really and truly a matter of form, of volumic outline. And it is known now in the sense of vision that we have a very fine sense of proportion of forms (9, 138 ff.). This sense of proportion in sound would give proper expression to our ability to sing any interval or melody on any given pitch. The basis or scale of proportions is then given in the volume of the starting tone. And distance would in no way obstruct the proportions, for it would itself be proportional to the volume of the starting tone (cf. above, p. 82)[1]. But for that volume we could no more define the proportions of a melody or interval by giving the lower tone than we could define the proportions of a square by fixing a point as the beginning of an outline drawing of it. Such reflections lead us to see that there is no more difficulty in there being unequal distances in one and the same interval in different parts of the musical range than there is in differences of volumes in the tones of that interval. It is all a matter of proportion. So long as all the proportions are maintained, interval remains identical, if interval is a matter of proportions.

No doubt the basis of judgment in interval is the experience of 'passage.' That expression is quite compatible with the terms of our analysis. v. Maltzew's failure to get beyond this expression is

---

[1] Distance would then be of essential importance in the recognition of interval only when the intervals investigated were confined to a relatively small range of pitches. Then judgment on the basis of distance would lead to the confusion of neighbouring intervals, as happens so frequently when intervals are given in very short duration. Consonance (fusion) then loses its effect upon recognition; but distance seems to be less affected by reduction of duration. No doubt this is due to the fact that distance is only a part of a tonal mass, the part that stands in the more frequent 'focus' of the attention upon the ordinal field of tone, whereas the apprehension of fusion, as we have shown, requires the apprehension essentially of the whole of a tonal mass. Cf. 117, 169 ff.

due to the lack of any true psychological method of analysis. We cannot expect observers untrained in psychological method to push their direct analysis as far as it can be carried by theory. For theory is analysis guided by all available facts. And it must be able even in dealing with experiences to go further than any direct analysis could. Theory pierces in experience, as in any other realm of existence, into the real structure of experience. That structure cannot be said to be non-existent because it is not observed in all respects in ordinary analysis as it is properly held to be in theoretical analysis or 'in reality.' For experiences can only be described by being taken into cognition. And it is not evident that our highly practised direct methods of cognition should be sufficient for all aspects of experience. We may need for certain aspects all the indirect aids to cognition,—comparison, argument, inference. But as yet the theory of experience keeps very close to the results of direct cognition, in so far as a properly guided cognition can verify directly almost all the results of the theory of sounds. In the case of fusion and interval our theoretical expression, however, probably goes beyond the terms possible in direct description.

All the devices used by observers in the naming of difficult intervals go back ultimately to the recognition of intervals by formal proportion. Such are the inversion of intervals, the comparison of them with more familiar ones, their resolution (e.g. major seventh into octave) and musical reminiscences. In the last case the name of the interval is remembered with the help of the memory for melodies. But that again presupposes a keen sense of volumic proportions. Melodies are more interesting than are single intervals and so will be held in memory more readily by the less musical than will intervals. The only apparent evasion of interval is their naming by means of absolute ear for pitch. There the pitches are first named and the interval is inferred from them. But this evasion is only temporary; for as has already been shown the naming of tones by absolute ear is based upon the standardisation of the range of pitches on the basis of interval. It is only a handy device for those who have acquired stronger memory dispositions for the names of pitches than for intervals. Where the former survives the distraction of musical relativity, it should surely, being absolute, be a more powerful weapon than interval, which is purely proportional.

v. Maltzew's experiments show further that intervals may be distinguished according to the ease and certainty of their recognition. The seconds, the thirds, the octave, the fifth, and the fourth are much more frequently judged correctly than are the minor seventh, the

minor sixth, the tritone and the major seventh. Now if we count
the numbers of times that each interval occurs in our major and minor
(melodic) scales, both ascending and descending over the range of a
twelfth,—an interval that is seldom exceeded in melodies,—we get the
following (corrected) series of frequencies: major 2nd—32; 4th—30;
5th—26; minor 3rd—24; octave—20; major 3rd—17; major 6th
and minor 7th—16; minor 6th—13; minor 2nd—12; tritone—10;
major 7th—8 (61, 199, 239). The values for the octave give even a
better order (as indeed we should expect from the standardising
function of the octave): major 2nd—20; 4th—16; 5th—14; minor
3rd—13; major 3rd—11; minor 2nd and major 6th—8; and then,
tritone, minor 6th and minor 7th—5; octave—4; major 7th—3. The
octave comes second last in this series, but that is of no significance,
as the octave is of necessity the most familiar interval of all.
v. Maltzew proposes to infer from the former series of frequencies
that the more frequent in music and at the same time the shorter
an interval step is, the easier is it in general to remember.

v. Maltzew's experiments were made with the intervals of the third,
fourth, and fifth accented octaves. Frequent mistakes are made in
judging these intervals even by persons who can name every interval
correctly in the middle region. The height of the pitch of these octaves,
the decreased intensity and the unusual blend of the pitches of high
tones (v. 61, 213, 227; 112, 537) make recognition difficult. An analysis
of the mistakes yields interesting results showing that the operations
of memory affect the recognition of intervals. Three chief influences
(61, 239 f,) are apparently at work.

(1) *Similarity*. Thus seconds, thirds, sixths and sevenths are
interchanged, a minor third being given for a major third or *vice versâ*;
also thirds are interchanged with sixths, sevenths with the tritone, and
the fifth or the fourth with the octave. In the former group of cases
the similarity of proportions in the pairs of intervals is evident. There
is besides a tendency here to prefer narrower intervals to wider ones.
In the latter group the confusion rests ultimately upon those relations
that in tonal masses constitute degrees of fusion. The confusion must
therefore emerge after the given sequence has revived the memory
of the degree of fusion that is known to appear when the sequence
is a mass. We have already seen how the relations that bind sequent
and mass intervals are included in the volumic determinants of fusion.
The memory train would then be: given sequence—interval relations
uncertain—not enough to revive proper name directly—revive class

of *fusions* to which given interval relations belong—wrong member selected from this class.

(2) *Frequency.* In place of unfamiliar intervals there appear in consciousness, either at once or in the course of remembering, more familiar ones. Thus the major seventh is confused with the octave, the minor seventh with the major sixth, the tritone with the fourth and fifth. The basis of substitution is evidently the approximation of proportions, but the pull is towards the more familiar proportion. The errors of this class are less frequent than those of the former.

The statements of the last four paragraphs may be illustrated by Table IV, somewhat simplified from v. Maltzew (61, 164). The series of intervals is indicated horizontally and vertically from the diminished second (2), major second II up to the octave (0). The figures give the number of judgments. Thus of the 342 (only 331 are allocated in the table, the other 11 being scattered in an insignificant way) judgments on 2, 280 were said to be 2, 41 to be II and 10 to be 3 (minor third).

TABLE IV.

Judgments on 3rd, 4th, 5th, accented octaves

	2	II	3	III	4	T	5	6	VI	7	VII	0	% Errors
2	**280**	41	10	—	—	—	—	—	—	—	—	—	18
II	37	**275**	17	—	—	—	—	—	—	—	—	—	20
3	20	33	**240**	23	7	—	4	—	4	—	—	—	30
III	10	14	50	**230**	14	—	7	—	5	—	—	—	33
4	—	17	17	21	**235**	—	14	—	—	—	—	14	31
T	—	16	14	10	81	**166**	15	—	—	—	—	—	51
5	—	—	12	—	12	13	**240**	—	—	—	—	21	30
6	—	—	19	—	16	—	41	**192**	21	14	—	—	44
VI	—	—	19	—	16	—	—	31	**201**	13	—	18	41
7	—	—	—	—	—	—	12	10	41	**202**	13	24	41
VII	—	—	—	—	10	9	10	8	18	63	**157**	34	54
0	—	—	—	—	—	—	8	8	20	16	26	**231**	33

Note.—Distance errors, preference of smaller distances, consonance errors, % of errors, etc.

(3) The third influence deciding mistakes is perseveration. This is most frequent in the fifth accented octave, where mistakes are very frequent. Both pitches and intervals persist. The predominance of perseveration is a sign of the great difficulty of recognising intervals in this octave. Thus for one observer in a series of twelve judgments seven were said to be octaves.

These results for the naming of intervals in the highest regions of pitch are confirmed by similar experiments in the deep tones of the 'Contra octave' C_1–C_0.

XLVII. A special peculiarity of tones of very high (above g^4) and very low (C_1, D_1) pitches was revealed by v. Maltzew's experiments. Certain persons make more errors in the 4th accented octave than could be expected from their relative excellence of judgment in the octave below. And some intervals best judged in the 3rd, are worst judged in the 4th accented octave. These errors show moreover a confusion of the easiest and most familiar intervals with the neighbouring strangest and least familiar ones. This occurs finally oftenest when the upper tone of the given interval lies within the region g^4–d^5. Thus major third is confused with minor third, fourth with major third, fifth with tritone, minor sixth with fifth. Minor and major seventh and octave are almost exclusively confused with smaller steps as far as the major sixth; b^3–b^4 is said to be a major seventh, c^4–c^5 a minor seventh, d^4–d^5 a major sixth. Persons with absolute ear also declare these upper pitches to be too low: in the interval of f^4–b^4 the latter tone is said to be too low; d^5–d^4 is said to be $c\sharp$–d.

These facts lead v. Maltzew to the conclusion that "the perceived pitches in the second half of the fourth and in the fifth accented octave deviate from what we should expect from the physical rate of vibration" (61, 213 ff.). No obvious physical error was responsible for the facts, for tests showed no beats in the octaves and the proper difference pitches for each interval. Evidently the disturbance of pitch begins about g^4 and increases as the pitch rises: say at b^4 a minor second, at c^5 a major second, at d^5 a minor third, etc. The reproduction of the pitch of single tones by singing confirmed the conclusion stated. The displacement of nominal pitch begins at different points for different observers. Table V shows for the five observers at what pitch (according to rate of vibrations) the flattening (1) begins, (2) is not usually greater than a semitone, (3) is not usually greater than a tone, and (4) where its reproduction breaks down completely. In the latter case the tone indicated by the observer varies, but is often about the same; that most frequent pitch is also given in the last column. (All the trials went as far as a^5.) This last most frequent pitch cannot be identified with the last pitch given before the breakdown, although it lies somewhere in its neighbourhood. Only one observer carried approximate correctness any distance beyond c^5, viz. to f^5. One may therefore say that the appreciation of the pitch of tone becomes debased easily in the fourth accented octave and collapses in the fifth. The highest tone on the large concert grand pianos is c^5.

This distortion of pitch is not due to any difficulty in singing the given tones. The observers felt quite sure of their success until their judgment broke down. It is obvious that the 'illusory' pitch explains the frequent errors in judging intervals recounted above. In the regions where judgment regarding pitch lapses any correct estimations of interval are a matter of chance.

The minor displacements of pitch appear again in the lower regions of pitch (C_1, D_1) (61, 237 f.). Here the tone appears to be a little higher than it should be according to the rate of vibration. v. Maltzew's results hardly do more than detect the distortion here. A_2 is the lowest tone of the large concert grand piano.

TABLE V.

Observer	Flattening begins at:	is not usually $> \frac{1}{2}$ tone at:	is not usually $>$ tone at:	judgment breaks down at:
1.	d^4	e^4–b^4♭?	b^4	$c^5 = a$
2.	d^4	e^4–c^5	d^5	$e^5 = b\pm$
3.	f^4♯	a^4–c^5	—	$d^5 = b$
4.	f^4	f^4♯–f^5	—	f^5♯ $= e$
5.	a^4–d^5	—	—	$e^5 = b$♭ $+$

Modified from v. Maltzew (61, 218). In the last column $c^5 = a$ means that c^5 and tones above it up to a^5 were usually said to be of the pitch a.

When we seek an explanation of this peculiar phenomenon, we can expect no help from the theory of octave qualities, much as that seems to account for the existence of nominal pitches in general. On my showing, nominal pitches are the result of the standardisation of the whole range by the octave interval. Thus the judgments showing distortion of pitch revert to the same basis, whether the observer be endowed with absolute ear or not. For an explanation we must suppose that, in the extremes of the musical range, tonal volume (probably for some physiological reason) begins to be a little more extensive than it should be (cf. p. 63, note 2, above). This is doubtless due to the smallness of the volumes in that region and to the difficulty of getting the sensitive surface in the ear to respond in extents decreasing regularly according to the decrease in wave length of aerial vibration[1]. Thus the volume giving the octave, where the lower extreme of the upper tone would coincide with the predominance of the lower, would arrive a little too late, in relation to the usual ratios of vibrations.

In other words: the volume heard from a certain number of physical vibrations would be a little greater than it should be, were the relation between volume and rate of vibration still unaffected. So in order to get a higher volume whose lower limit should be at the point of predominance of a lower volume (the upper limits of the two volumes being necessarily identical, of course), we should have to use a rate of vibration more than double that required to evoke the lower tone; instead of $2x$ vibrations, it might be $2x + y$ vibrations per second. But $2x$ vibrations are physically, nominally, shall we say, of pitch c, whereas $2x + y$ vibrations are, similarly, of pitch d; but the latter, not the former, is heard as the octave of the c of x vibrations. My theory of interval, whether simultaneous or successive, shows that this process of standardisation does not involve any explicitly ratiocinative process. The observer 'sees' directly that the tone given by $2x$ vibrations does not touch off the points related to the points touched off by x vibrations in the regular proportion known as the octave; but that it touches off points more or less nearly related in the proportion known as the major or minor seventh. He therefore hears the new higher tone flat, or calls it b or $b\flat$.

In the same way, in the lower regions of tone, we may suppose that the ear ceases to offer sufficient room or a proper basis for the great volume required, and that the areas under stimulation are somewhat cramped. Thus the volume evoked by x vibrations per second would be too small; its centre of predominance would lie a little nearer the upper end of the tonal-pitch series than it otherwise would. So in order to get a volume whose central predominance should lie at the end of the volume evoked by a $2x$ rate of vibration, we should have to use

---

[1] Cf. Abraham and Brühl (1, 197), where it is shown that while two vibrations suffice for the production of tones whose pitch lies below g^4, tones are heard with three vibrations up to b^4, with four up to d^5, with five up to $f^5\sharp$, with ten up to a^5, and with twenty even beyond that. At the lower extremes there is some sign of a similar change, but it is much less distinct. The lowest limit for two vibrations is C_1, for four vibrations B_2. In v. Maltzew's case it is a matter of volumes, in Abraham and Brühl's of the definition of the predominant order in the volume as well. These values given by Abraham as observer are similar to the values given by observer 4 in the table from v. Maltzew's paper (p. 96).

a rate of vibration lower than x, say $x - y$. That is to say the $x - y$ rate would be called, say, c, while the x rate would be called, by simple inspection of the proportion of the ordinal position of the evoked volume to the ordinal position of the volume evoked by $2x$, say d. That is, very low tones would be heard a little sharp. But as the centre of predominance of the lowest tones lies still far away from, though of all tones nearest to, the low end of the pitch-order series (physically—the apex of the cochlea), we may well allow that much of such distortion of low pitches need hardly be expected.

It is possible, as Stumpf suggests (123, 320), that, within the range of smaller errors of a semitone or less, repeated work with these extreme pitches should lead to quite correct estimation of the pitch. The physiological process would then, as Stumpf says, gradually accommodate itself properly to the physical stimulus. But it is clear that this process of adaptation will only go a certain length and that we cannot expect it to appear where all judgment of pitch breaks down.

Thus we see that the musical range of pitch is the whole range within which the octave standard remains valid, while still (approximately) maintaining its consistency with the ratios of the aerial vibration. Beyond this range the volumes of tones evidently become quite inconsistent with the demands of the octave standardisation. They do not conform in any manner, not even if we seek out the required proportions of volumes without regard to the physical ratios of vibrations. No doubt the balance and symmetry of volumes then largely disappear. This need not, however, imply that in these extreme regions no differences of pitch-order are observable. These orders may well change without there being any proper basis for their standardisation to musical nominal pitches.

If we were to construct a diagram of the relation of change of volume to increase in the number of physical vibrations, we should have to reduce the relation somewhat for very low tones, to keep it constant throughout the definitely musical range, and to increase it gradually towards the upper limit of hearing, stopping it as indefinable soon after the musical range had been passed. The rest of the range of hearing is the range of mere audibility.

CHAPTER V

THE FURTHER STUDY OF TONAL MASSES

XLVIII. We are now in a position to consider criticisms, restrictions and extensions applied to Stumpf's treatment of fusion.

It is quite evident on my theory that fusion introduces into tonal masses a great deal of that regularity of system and balance which in its greatest perfection constitutes the pure tone. A fused mass approximates more or less to the unity of the single tone. This approach to unity may therefore legitimately be taken either as an index towards, or as a definition of, fusion (40, 143), if it is understood that all definitions of fusion are to avoid stating the exact basis and essence of fusion, as in fact all the definitions of Stumpf and others do.

At the same time Stumpf is quite right in looking upon fusion as an "unalterable peculiarity of sensory material" (112, 128). And it would follow therefrom, as Kemp says, that "every change that a degree of fusion suffers, is only apparent; it is only the apprehension of the fusion that changes" (40, 144). It is not apparent how by means of attention any change could possibly be produced in the volumic coincidence of two tones. Of course no one could deny in face of the great progress made since 1890 in our knowledge of the influence of attitudes upon observation[1], that by suitable instruction an observer may be more rapidly and singlemindedly directed upon the specific phenomena of fusion, the peculiarity of sensory material to use Stumpf's phrase. Similarly he can be led to abstract fusion from any other phenomena of tonal masses, e.g. from their pleasantness or from their harmonic affinities. That sort of abstraction was not impossible for Stumpf even in 1890. If we attend to the whole impression, it is more effective upon our observation; if we attend to the discriminable parts—the pitches—they determine our statements most. If we are practised we can discriminate parts sooner, if we are fatigued we cannot discriminate them so fast, because when special attitudes are opposed by fatigue, the habitual or natural attitude is the easiest (cf. above, p. 72).

[1] My *Beiträge zu einer Theorie des Denkens* (131) was the first decisive contribution to a study of the influence of the 'instruction' on a mental process Cf. my abstract of this book (132).

But it is hard to see by what right greater abstraction can be read as greater fusion. If it is, we should surely have to find some other instrument than abstraction if we are to get through to the original fusional differences of tonal masses. Our aim in the direct study of sensation is to bring our knowledge into conformity with sensation through the medium of observation. I fail to see that Kemp (40, 146) has shown any superiority in Külpe's method of dealing with fusion over Stumpf's.

Kemp says it is a fact that the impression of fusion is changed by many circumstances. But practice and fatigue, which have just been mentioned, clearly do not affect fusion, but only the analysis of pitches, or perhaps better the analysis of pitches as against the apprehension of the total impression, including the pitches, and without their discrimination. But neither of these things is really and properly fusion. It is no departure from actuality towards the 'ideal' to say that the phenomenon of fusion does not primarily include the discriminability of pitches, but is present in equal degrees whether the pitches be discriminated or not. That is just the sort of thing that is justified by our later knowledge of attitudes of observation. Only one group of facts might perhaps be brought under Kemp's statement, viz. the influence of intensity upon fusion (40, 159). Kemp accepts Stumpf's law of the independence of fusion from the intensity of the components only for absolute intensities within a middle region. For relative intensities he says it holds only for Stumpf's fusion, not for Külpe's, which is concerned only with "the impression, the experience of fusion."

According to Külpe the characteristic feature of fusion is the increased difficulty of analysis that is due merely to the simultaneity of the sensations (40, 145). The single components retire in fusion in favour of the mass impression. This conception of fusion would seem to give the analysis of pitches much more importance than they obtain in Stumpf's conception. Surely there is here a failure to appreciate the merit and justice of the abstractive analysis of fusion from the discrimination of pitches, claimed by Stumpf.

When the resonance box of one of two sounding forks is closed, the unitariness of the mass-effect and the imperfection of the analysis are both very much increased. Naturally; because the predominance and whole strength of one tone have grown very much less and it is notoriously more difficult to pick out a weak tone in a mass than a strong one especially if the higher is the weaker tone (40, 160). For the lower tone readily swamps the volume of the higher. The nearer we get to the intensive proportions of a single tone by great weakening of the upper tone of a pair, the nearer we get to the perfect unity of the 'tone.' But that does not mean that so long as the volumic coincidences characteristic of any one fusion suffice to give the mass a noticeable character, the fusion of the mass is changed by the weakening of the proportions due to one of the tones. Fusions do not all run into complete 'purity of tone' by continuous degrees proportional to the weakening of the intensity of one of the pair. It is the merit of Stumpf's second law of fusion that it abstracts fusion from the peculiar and different difficulties of analysis of pitches that accrue when in a tonal mass either the higher or the lower component is gradually weakened. Stumpf's point is: so long as the characteristic features of a fusion can be seized, so long that fusion is one and the same, no matter how different the relative intensities or the pitch-regions are. And my analysis bears out this position very nicely.

The matter may be summed up as follows: if we take fusion strictly as approximation to the regularity and balance of the 'pure' tone, then differences of intensity would produce slight differences in fusion; but these differences are very slight so long as both tones are readily audible; greater differences in approximation to the 'pure' tone are determined by the volumic coincidences of the fusing tones; so long as the two tones are distinguishable, these must provide a constant basis of departure from the pure tone; such differences are noticeable without any violence of abstraction and are far more important than are the minor differences of approximation to the pure tone produced by intensity; these minor differences would, however, gain in importance as the difference between grades of fusion decreases, i.e. below the grade of the fourth; here they come into competition with other influences, e.g. pitch-blends which also form a slight departure from the perfect tone[1].

And Kemp admits two things that bring his position very near to that of Stumpf. 1. "Two masses of different fusional degree differ

---

[1] On the influence of intensity cf. Faist (19, 125 f.). A slight difference towards indiscriminability is produced for his young unmusical subjects by pianissimo-strength except for the octave. His results show that the higher tone is more easily swamped by the lower than *vice versa*, as I have already deduced (above, p. 71). As Faist shows, it is difficult to say whether this influence of intensity upon *analysis* also holds validly for fusion. Faist's results are based only upon analysis (i.e. are there two tones—pitches— in the mass, or only one?). Cf. 114, 288 f. Of pitch-blends Faist finds that they increase the high fusions and decrease the low ones, i.e. they simply further the prevailing tendency as we should expect of them. Stumpf reports Faist wrongly (114, 292).

with respect to their fusion not only by the fact that in the one case analysis can be carried out more completely than in the other. The essential point is that in the two cases a qualitatively different fusion is experienced" (40, 149)[1]. This idea of qualitative difference is pushed still further by Meinong and Witasek (64, 199) to the impossibility of comparing grades of fusion at all. Obviously on my theory such an extreme view is tenable: the 'form' of any one fusion is as incomparable with that of another as are the forms of square and circle. But nevertheless grades of fusion are certainly comparable according to the degree to which they approximate to the perfect symmetry of the pure tone, i.e. according to their degree of fusion.

2. The differences of fusion produced by special attention to fusion are small, and if they are kept constant they need not swamp the differences given by different ratios of vibrations (40, 153). In view of the fact that it is difficult enough to get great constancy of order in the lowest degree of fusion among different observers[2], these minor differences must be so small as to be negligible. And if attention to fusion increases fusion as much as attention to a partial increases the subjective strength of that partial, we must remember that the latter is a very debatable matter and might be decided differently according as pitch is classified as quality or as order. When I attend to a visual point without moving to fixate it, it does not grow more intense. When I attend to an auditory order, need it therefore grow more intense? Do I not merely give it the same subjective benefit of attention as I give to the visual point? My attention passes over to its order, so to speak. With pitches as qualities there is no basis for any movement of the attention, so that the apparent effect of attention must be ascribed to change of intensity. For the pitch quality itself cannot be supposed to change or come into being with the attention. Nor is there any other variable character to explain the prominence given

---

[1] As Stumpf remarks (114, 298): "how is the octave recognised if not by its fusion? And don't we recognise the octave even when the one tone is weaker? Don't we recognise an octave with the same certainty as usual, so long as the weaker tone is still anything like clearly recognisable." This is true for the octave; it is primarily recognisable as *octave* only by its fusion; but it is clearly not true for intervals of the third grade of fusion (fourth and others); they are so individual and so easily recognisable because they are intervals, i.e. because of their volumic proportions not by their volumic coincidences or approximation to the balance of the pure tone. And then we must ask: are the fifth and octave not also intervals in this sense and recognisable as such? Cf. Stumpf's remarks on the fusion of the double octave (114, 294).

[2] Cf. Kemp's own results (40, 186 f.).

by attention. Hence it is supposed that the attention somehow brings about an increase of intensity[1].

The concept of fusion adopted by Kemp is that of "a phenomenon to be experienced in its peculiarity only by attentive observation of a mass impression" (40, 153). Unitariness and difficulty of analysis are only secondary marks of fusion. I cannot see any advance in this formulation beyond Stumpf's position. One might indeed see a trifling retreat, for whereas Stumpf does try to indicate his sense of the psychical presence of fusional grades, although he fails to express it, Kemp merely refers us to the phenomenon in experience itself. There is no empirical formulation here to contrast with Stumpf's ideal fusions; there is no formulation at all. It is for these reasons that it was said above that no essential advance had been made beyond Stumpf's results[2]. And no wonder! Neither Stumpf nor any of his successors found any psychological method of getting beyond a gesture towards the special phenomenon to a psychologically formulated concept of fusion, such as has been given in this work.

Kemp's experiments were carried out with certain improvements of method. The method of the comparison of pairs was used; by pair is understood in this case the mass sound consisting of two 'tones' of a certain interval. These pairs were given successively and compared in point of fusion without regard to the interval formed or the pitches of the tones or any other feature of the tonal masses. Thus the advantages of the incognitive method seem to be obtained. Its special service in this case is the avoidance of any witting transference of judgments

---

[1] I may say in this connexion that I think wanderings of the attention, in any proper sense of the word 'wandering,' are only possible within a sensory field, i.e. with the system which all the ordinal variations of a single sense create. The terms 'focal' and 'marginal' can also be properly applied only to the distribution of attention in such a field; these terms are generalised from a special case of sensory field, viz. the visual field with its specialisation of a most sensitive area. In the auditory field (i.e. of pitches) there is no 'focus' at all, but if the attention is directed upon one pitch, it is thereby diverted from another; and the diversion is in general the greater, the greater the distance between the two pitches. When differences of quality or, if it is possible, of intensity, occur apart from ordinal differences, we can speak of attending or not attending, but not of any wandering of the attention. Wanderings of the attention are probably possible in the temporal field, but not with any such ease and precision as in the systemic field.

[2] Cf. 40, 179, where Kemp supposes that there is really no difference between his method of observing fusion and Stumpf's—namely to face and judge the mass impression. Also p. 189 f., where he shows a willingness to suggest that any differences between the results of different observers on fusion is due to the variant observers not having observed fusion only, but something else as well. Is not that like an admission of the ideal constancy of fusion attributed to Stumpf? Cf. 114, 290.

from one experiment to another through the medium of the names of intervals. The use of the method presupposes such an indisposition to reproduce the names of intervals as persons devoid of absolute ear or special musical familiarity with intervals possess. But there is no reason to suppose that a comparison of the fusions of intervals is made any less objective by their recognition (40, 175). Stumpf's judgments were certainly given under full knowledge of the pitches of the tones used. For a person possessed of an ear like Stumpf's no incognitive method and no instruction could keep the intervals out of cognition. In any case fusion is not primarily, but only secondarily a matter of difficulty of analysis of pitches and an abstraction of volumic coincidences, i.e. fusion, is possible both with and without analysis of pitches. Thus, as Kemp says (40, 179), we may fairly conclude that there was no difference between Stumpf's method of judging fusion and Kemp's. Only the experimental methods differed.

And the agreement of results (cf. 40, 188 f.) confirms this view. If we take as an observer's minimum the placing of octave, fifth, and fourth in the first three grades of fusion (i.e. expecting their discrimination of fusion to reach at least one step into the group of minor grades) we find the following series from the papers of various experimenters:

TABLE VI.

Observers	No.	Intervals in order of fusion								
Faist (19, 104) ...	1	III	6	VI	3	*T*	7	II	2	VII
Kemp (*ibid.*) ...	1	III	II !	3	VI	*T*	6	7	VII	2
Meinong (64, 193, 198)	1	VI	III	3	6	*T*	7	II	VII=2	
Pear—Wa. (89, 66) ...	1	III	6	3=VI		—	II	7	VII	2
Pear—We. (*ibid.*) ...	1	6	III=VI		7 !	—	3	VII	II	2
Kemp (40, 186 f.) ...	5	III	3	VI	6	*T*	II	7	2	VII
Kemp exceptions (*ib.*)	⅕	VI	—	III	—	—	7	II	—	—
Most frequent of all 10	—	III	3	VI	6	*T*	II	7	2	VII
Stumpf (112, 135) ...	1	3rds and 6ths				All the others				

Of Pear's observers one was the most musical, the other the least so. Two of the other three observers did not even get the fifth into the second place. One of Pear's observers and Witasek put the fourth down from the third place to amongst or below the thirds and sixths. Meinong and Witasek doubt whether any definite order can be got out of the qualitative differences of fusion (64, 199).

In the face of the agreement between the results just shown such a conclusion is of course unjustifiably sceptical, but it is surely true, as I pointed out above (p. 58), that these grades of fusion are not nearly so distinct from one another as are the octave and fifth from one another and from the rest. There is undoubtedly in the fourth and those below it a greater departure from the unitariness and balance of the pure tone. The fourth may be supposed to be better balanced on the lower side of the upper predominance (v. Table III, p. 68), as that extent of volume is divided into two parts by the lower extreme of the upper tone. Of the next four intervals we might readily assent to the minor sixth's coming last as the proportions are there complicated by the introduction of halves (or 6—2 : 3—5). The other three might well be on a level; it is especially difficult to see what there is to choose between (III) 2—3 : 1—4 and (VI) 4—1 : 2—3.

The intervals of the last group give still more complicated proportions. But we need not follow out the parallel between conceptual and auditory proportions further. That parallel should certainly hold for the first few distinct degrees, but the differences perceived by the ear, subtle as these are[1] and visible only through considerable statistics, need not be evident in conception. Or in other words they are as evident there as we could well expect.

These proportions may also as Kemp's observations show present other features for hearing than their mere approach to the unity and balance of the pure tone. One of these Kemp calls the sensuous compatibility of the tones: an undisturbed concurrence, kinship, friendship, between the tones. This is said to be least for the major seventh, which was therefore used as a model for observation. Of this one observer says: "the two components strive with one another, I can't grasp them together; when I try to bring them together, one of them always eludes me." Another observer is brought to notice the phenomenon by being instructed to direct his attention more "upon the single components of the whole mass." When he had observed it, this observer said: "it seems to me to run parallel to the fusion, as if it were always the same thing that is observed, only from another standpoint." The

[1] Cf. Stumpf (114, 286 f.): "So much at any rate is certain, that intervals like II and VII fuse considerably less than III. That the sevens (4 : 7 and 5 : 7) lie between, and can in themselves as well be termed consonances as dissonances, does not prevent us from distinguishing at least the dissonance group from the thirds group, even if we go exclusively by the differentia of fusion. But a specific opposition, such as is intended in the distinction of dissonances and consonances, is never in this world to be deduced from fusion alone. Other differentiae must co-operate hereto" (p. 287).

phenomenon was detected by one observer, whereupon its study was undertaken by Kemp, another observed it "relatively easy," a third (the second quoted above) experienced considerable difficulty with it, three observers failed to carry on through their observations what was brought home to them with the model of the major seventh. This introspective uncertainty is borne out by the results of four observers, which only show two clear steps of difference: the fifth, major sixth and third as against the fourth, minor sixth and third. The proportions of the parts of the tonal volumes for these masses (v. Table III, p. 68) are: 2—1 : 1—2;   4—1 : 2—3;   2—3 : 1—4;   and 2—2 : 1—3; 6—2 : 3—5; 2—4 : 1—5.

It is possible that in these proportions, which in the first set are of opposite direction in the whole volume, a basis for a difference of harmony of proportions might be found as in pictorial art, where distances and proportions are often brought to balance round a centre. It is significant that in Kemp's results the series of grades for the pleasantness of intervals is almost identical with the series for sensuous compatibility (40, 202). But neither of the series is very distinct in any one observer or regular as between observers. It may therefore be supposed that sensuous compatibility means balance of proportions. That is much the same as basis for movement of interest, basis of pleasantness, as is the case in pictorial balance as well. The fifth and fourth are not very pleasing intervals and these are said by observers to be of 'empty fusion' while other intervals are of 'full fusion' (40, 190, 211). These terms point to the fullness and variety of a mass as against the formality and want of variety of a close approach to unity and balance. But where introspective observations furnish only indistinct series, we need hardly look for more than a probable basis in the conceptual statement of the volumic proportions of tones.

When we come to 'harmonic compatibility' (40, 201) we go beyond what is given in a mere isolated interval as such. Of course, something must be given in an interval that prompts its musical dissolution; but that may not be grounded in the interval merely as interval or mass, but in that interval as one of a special set, whereby each interval of the set has acquired special relations in virtue of being in that set, not in its own virtue as a mass or interval. That is confirmed by the word Kemp used as a lead in the instruction of his observers: "judge of the finality of the chord." It is absurd to suggest that a chord is more or less closed off or final, all by itself; not-being-closed-off points away to its completion, points through the paths of memory.

"Two tone masses of high fusion give the impression of greater fusion than three tone masses of high fusion (e.g. *cg* and *ceg*); similarly two tone masses of low fusion appear better fused than three tone masses of low fusion (e.g. *cb* and *cgb*); but two tone masses of quite low fusion appear less fused than three tone masses of high fusion" (e.g. *cb* and *ceg*) (40, 206). These rules follow directly from my theory of fusion as approximation to the balanced mass of a single tone. Other things being equal, a greater number of tones means less fusion; and yet some three tone masses can be much better balanced than some badly balanced two tone masses. It is also obvious that one badly fusing interval must make a whole tonal mass of low fusion (40, 209). If the qualitative differences of intervals disappear largely in three tone masses, these becoming much more similar (*ibid.*), that means that in three tone masses the essence of fusion—its approach to the unity and balance of the pure tone—becomes more apparent for most observers than the defining volumic points. But these are still quite obvious to those observers who have a very highly trained ear; they can recognise them at once apart from their fusional degree altogether.

Külpe's law (46, 298), according to which, if a three tone mass consists of intervals of equal fusion (e.g. *ceg* and $ce^{\flat}g$) the greater fusion of the lowest lying interval (*ce*) determines the greater fusion of the whole, is deducible from the fact that the usual region of observation of a tonal mass is its centre, i.e. its fundamental component (cf. above, p. 65). Parts near this centre will then be more effective on the whole, than more outlying parts. This law was verified by Pear (89, 59, 87) and Kemp (40, 207 f.).

Stumpf's third law of fusion (112, 136) maintains that, by the addition of a third or further tone, the fusional degree of two given tones is in no way affected; although the greater number of tones makes analysis more difficult. Kemp's examination of this law confirms it (40, 235) in so far as the two tone mass is abstracted from the three tone mass more or less completely. The abstraction is hardly possible, as we should expect, when the third tone lies between the two which are the object of abstraction. This fact confirms my classification of pitch as order; for if pitches were qualities, their mere resemblance would be no sufficient reason for any such hindrance to abstraction, especially as two such tonal qualities may be of closer 'resemblance' than either of them is to one which lies between them. Moreover the abstraction, again as we should expect, is easy when the third pitch lies far to one side of the other two. It is better when the third tone lies below than when it lies above them (40, 226). There is no reason to suppose that we cannot confine our attention to one part of a tonal mass. The volumic balance of that part must of course be to some extent adversely affected by any third tone, especially if any of the defining points of the latter enter into its main centre. But in so far as the main centre of comparison remains relatively free and retains at least approximately the volumic outline it would have if the third tone were absent, we may well speak of an equality of fusion of the two tone mass and of that mass abstracted out of the three tone mass.

But it must be clear that this abstraction is not the same sort of process as the suppression of the illusion in the Müller-Lyer figure by a special attitude of attention. When the process of abstraction does not succeed, the fusion of the three tone mass will, of course, be judged on the unity and balance of the whole mass, not on that of a part. Then Külpe's rules (46, 294) are said to hold: when to one interval others of lower or higher fusional degree are added, the impression of fusion (i.e. the total fusion) is lowered or raised. Thus for example when e is added to cg, two lower fusions—the thirds—are added to a high fusion—the fifth. When c is added to eg, the fifth and third should improve the minor third eg. When g is added to ce, the fifth should heighten, and the minor third lower, its fusion. These comparisons and results all seem justifiable on the basis of volumes, provided that in speaking of the fusion of the three tone mass we do not consider the number of predominances as detracting from the total fusion more than the relation of the parts in the whole creates a new balance or fusion. There is, perhaps, in this kind of balance a slight change from the balance that approximates to the perfect symmetry of a pure tone and that almost conceals the two predominances; it is a balance in spite of predominances[1]. That is so, however, only in so far as we consider the presence of distinguished predominances inconsistent with the notion of fusion. Stumpf does not think it is. He says: "what I call fusion can in itself be perceptible only when the fusing tones are distinguished from one another" (121, 330). If that is so, I fail like others to see why fusion cannot be present amidst three pitches as well as amidst two. Surely the sensory stuff of three or more tones can fuse more or less, as well as the sensory stuff of two. Stumpf's attitude to this (and to some other aspects of fusion) seems

---

[1] Cf. Stumpf (114, 290 f.): "Try it; we will only find that increase of unclearness that is produced by the addition of each new simultaneous tone, and that spreads itself equally over all the tones involved."

more obstinate than reasonable, so long as he offers no theory of the
real basis of fusion and of the real connexion it establishes between
the stuff of tones, without prejudice to the independence of their pitches.
Much can be said for Stumpf's view, as the preceding paragraph shows.
The question then is not one in which any once stated view can be
rigidly maintained against all others and forced through. We must
allow a little here, a little there, and a great deal according to the
attitude of observation taken towards a tonal mass. That is surely
one of the things most obviously required in the theoretical treatment
of music (cf. 121, 328). We need by no means hesitate to admit that
even fusions can apparently be affected by the momentary attitude
of apprehension, in so far as this leads the attention to take greater
or less note of a well balanced or ill balanced region of a tonal mass.

The theory of the volumic coincidences and proportions of tones
thus seems able to provide an adequate basis for all the chief phenomena
of fusion, whether that is taken with reference to the whole of a tonal
mass or to any special part of it, in so far as any part can exist in the
whole without being seriously affected by the third component and
can be considered separately. The doctrines of Stumpf and Külpe
are therefore supplementary, not contradictory, and are both compatible
with this theory of the basis of fusion.

Thus far we have considered fusion and interval only within the
limits of the octave. About the conditions beyond the octave there
is difference of opinion and uncertainty. Stumpf (112, 139 f.) asserts as
a law of fusion that beyond the octave the same degrees of fusion return;
the ninths have the same fusion as the seconds, the tenths as the thirds,
the double and triple octave as the octave. One must not be misled, he
says, by the greater ease of analysis. In Table III (above, p. 68) I
have shown that in the double octave the lower defining point of the
upper volume always falls exactly at the point where within the octave
the predominance of the upper tone fell. For the observing (musical)
mind that has already standardised intervals, this coincidence should
be enough to establish a very close connexion between an interval
and its extension beyond the octave. But it is clear that the approximation to unity of a tonal mass cannot be the same in the two cases. To
some extent the reduction of the upper volume will mean a greater
unity, for more of the whole lower tone is free of irregularity; but it
is clear that the predominance of the upper tone will stand out more
clearly, being farther from the other, while the upper volume does
not reach to the lower predominance. Apart from the relations between

intervals within and beyond the octave just referred to, the connexion between the two is just the one case where one might safely appeal to memory (or even to the relationships established by partial tones). For intervals, as we have shown, are standardised throughout the musical range and learnt as individuals.

It is to the relations established by memory and by habitual attitudes towards a familiar system of tones and their more familiar relations to one another that we must refer the basis of harmony, a basis that is certainly the result of a long analytic process, now become explicit in our music. This basis, that of the fundamental triads *ceg* and *ce♭g*, Stumpf finds so different from consonance, which rests upon fusion, that he invented a new name for it—concordance. But he seems wrong in relating the divergence of consonance and concordance to a supposed divergence between two tone masses and three tone masses. There is no such divergence, if we maintain the same attitude. As long as we retain our interest in the approximation of a tonal mass to the balance of the pure tone, so long can we talk of its fusion, whether it include within itself two or three or more pitches. But when we change our attitude and consider the capacity of a three tone mass to point through our memory to a definite system of tones (forming a scale or key), then we have left considerations of fusion out of account. At the same time, however, we have not thereby suppressed the existential basis of fusion. Both attitudes can be combined or brought to compromise and both undoubtedly do affect many of the tonal combinations we admit at any time. Moreover, it may hardly be possible for two tones to define any tonal system of ours, whether the attitude be turned upon it or not. But that is no extra reason why we should make a gulf between two tone masses and three tone masses *in the matter of fusion*. Stumpf, with his sharp distinction between consonance and concordance, seems to have pointed to a true cleavage of interests in the tonal basis of music, but he seems at the same time to have confused the issue and to have wrongly referred it to the difference between two tone masses and three tone masses in the matter of their fusion, whereas the issue really refers to the difference between that approximation to balance in a tonal mass (whether of two or three or more tones) which is called fusion, and that relation of the tones or intervals in a tonal mass which makes them capable of defining for us a large system of tones and tonal relationships and so of giving a specific set to our musical anticipations for a time. This latter relation is probably the more important for any explicit musical consciousness, but the former—fusion—undoubtedly maintains its force in a rather—shall we say, subconscious, affective, way; powerful and decisive in its effect upon the pleasantness of music, but yet less explicitly before the analytic eye of the musician than the systematic relations of tones (which, as we shall see, have developed out of these more primitive relations). Cf. 121.

TABLE VII.

Stumpf (112, 139)	0^2	5^2	4^2 etc.
Ellis (30, 191)	—	III	5^2
Faist (19, 104)	0^2	5^2	III^2
Kemp (*ibid.*)	5^2	0^2	III^2
Faist's scholars (19, 108) ...	5^2	0^2	III^2
Witasek (64, 191)	5^2	0^2	III^2
Meinong (final, 64, 198) ...	5^2	0^2	III^2
„ (preliminary, 64, 193)	0^2	5^2	III^2
Probable order	5^2	0^2	III^2

TABLE VIII.

Meinong's final series (64, 198)	Volumic proportions	Mean variation of all four	Mean variation of three
5^2	3:1—1—1	$\frac{3}{4}$	0
0^2	4:2—1—1	1	0·$\dot{4}$
III^2	5:1—2—2	$1\frac{1}{4}$	0·$\dot{4}$
VI^2	10:4—3—3	$2\frac{1}{2}$	0·$\dot{4}$
3^2	12:2—5—5	3	1·$\dot{3}$
6^2	16:6—5—5	4	0·$\dot{4}$
4^2	8:2—3—3	2	0·$\dot{4}$
T^2	45:13—16—16	11	1·$\dot{3}$
7^2	32:14—9—9	8	2·$\dot{2}$
VII^2	15:7—4—4	$3\frac{3}{4}$	1·$\dot{3}$
II^2	9:1—4—4	$4\frac{1}{2}$	1·$\dot{3}$
2^2	32:2—15—15	8	5·$\dot{7}$

In Table VII I have grouped together the observations of various writers on the highest grades of fusion beyond the octave. I have neglected the relation of these steps to the first grades within the octave. The most important fact to notice is the number of times that the twelfth (the fifth over the octave) is placed first and before the double octave. Meinong's preliminary determination must, of course, yield to his final result, got by better method. The change seen in Meinong weakens the strength of the case for Faist's observation. Thus we may oppose the majority of these observers to the law stated by Stumpf that the series of fusions beyond the octave simply repeats the series within the octave.

Now consider the volumic proportions shown in Table VIII. There the first figure in the second column gives the proportion from the lower limiting order of the lower (the whole) volume to its predominance (its middle point); the other three figures represent proportionately and respectively the stretch of volume separating the mid-predominance (the pitch of the lower tone) from the lower limiting order of the upper tone, the stretch from this latter point to the predominance of the upper tone, and then the other half of the upper tone. Is it not remarkable that the latter three stretches in the fifth should be all equal? It seems to me that that might fairly be read as a kind of regularity and balance, which as such exceeds the regularity shown by the double octave: $4 : 2—1—1$. I refer to the rest of the Table for what it is worth. As we concluded regarding the fusions within the octave, it is not easy to establish conceptually a series of degrees of balance which will clearly be parallel to those established by the ear, even if we accept Meinong's series as generally valid. But it would perhaps appear probable that Stumpf's law of the identity of fusions within and beyond the octave rests upon the musical relationships of the corresponding tones rather than upon their fusion strictly. These relationships would be established through the medium of the absolute-nesses of interval. At any rate, if my theoretical determinations regarding the volumic basis of fusions be accepted in general and in particular, that would seem to be the most probable explanation of the sweeping decisiveness of Stumpf's statement. At least, we may think so until Stumpf can show an acceptable full theoretical basis for the facts and his laws of fusion.

It is doubtless very difficult to apply to the intervals beyond the octave during their observation exactly the same concept of fusion as to the much less easily analysed intervals within the octave, except in the case of the fifth and octave. Meinong's series clearly approximates otherwise to Stumpf's law, except for the place of the fourth.

Meinong may also have been led chiefly by considerations derived from musical knowledge. But with these indications we may leave the matter for further advancement by observation (114, 293 ff.).

CHAPTER VI

MELODY

XLIX.   Melody is one of the most characteristic features of music, and the study of it follows naturally upon that of fusion and of interval. It might even be urged that the study of melody should come first, since it appears first in the development of music and its apprehension is earlier and easier in the individual. A common answer to this objection is that the tuning of the tones of the scales even of primitive music involves a reference to consonance, as scales are formed with the help of the chief fusions. In spite of the motive for this answer that lies in the prevailing inability to find any such basis for the consonances of successive tones as is found for those of simultaneous tones in the fusion of tonal masses, it seems likely that the plea is a valid one. Scales are no doubt largely moulded by the chief consonances. But the consonance of fusion need not be their only source. As we have seen the consonance of sequence is by no means lacking and must speedily become evident to an attentive observer, no matter whence the first call to consonances came. Besides the answer under discussion implies that some rudiment of a scale precedes all melody. This idea is natural enough; for all our melodies are completely subject to our scale systems. But, as we shall see, the implication is by no means necessary. It is good to take our notions from the facts before us; but, as we have repeatedly urged, in the study of hearing we may make great errors unless we find a proper method of approaching and analysing the facts. Whatever may be the case in any effort deserving the name of music, it is quite absurd to think that no series of tones of different pitch could be formed without reference to the consonances of tonal masses. All the birds must get on without this help, as probably do young children too. If it be asked in reply how we know that the tonal sequences of birds make melodies for them or for us, we can only answer with another question: how do you know they don't? Evidently again we must first seek for some ground on which to build a notion of melody, which we may then seek in the facts of tonal sequences.

I need offer no apology for seeking a method in our knowledge of the other senses; for every appeal thus far made to them has been confirmed. Whatever else they are, melodies are certainly series of tones of different pitch, whereby of course repetitions of the same pitch are not excluded. Pitch we have classified as order, so that we may read the former as the latter and ask what special features accrue to the experiences of the other senses when a series of sensations of different orders is presented. We come then upon motion. Or starting primarily from the other senses and knowing there that motion is a c'aracteristic feature of sensory series in which order varies, we may ask if the psychology of motion as we know it in the other senses can be confirmed in hearing.

Hearing itself also directly suggests the connexion between melody and motion. "All melodies," Helmholtz says, "are motions within extremes of pitch. The incorporeal material of tones is much more adapted for following the musician's intention in the most delicate and pliant manner for every species of motion than any corporeal material, however light. Graceful rapidity, grave procession, quiet advance, wild leaping, all these different characters of motion and a thousand others in the most varied combinations and degrees, can be represented by successions of tones[1]." Helmholtz had no theoretical reason to see motions in melodies, so that his words are quite sufficient evidence of the motional suggestiveness of melodies, if any such evidence is required. Any one can hear it for himself. Or rather it is so obvious that it cannot be overlooked.

Motion is very familiar in the sense of vision and less so in touch and articular sense. Apart from special experimental study it is in these senses readily defined as involving progressive differences in the two ordinal attributes, the systemic and the temporal. It is not so readily diagnosed as a distinct addition to experience over and above the progressive differences it involves. This diagnosis is very difficult in so far as the habitual attitude towards the simpler phenomena of sense is that of analytic cognition, such as we apply to the dynamic study of moving bodies or to the mathematics of 'moving' points. But it is evident to everyone from his own experience that we can notice motion without attending to the points through which the motion

---

[1] 29, 397; 30, 250. Cf. E. Gurney (28, 103): "If one thing is suggested by any other, physical movement is continually suggested by melody."

passes, and without knowing how long the motion takes to pass over
a given distance. We do not need to *know* the systemic and temporal
orders involved; they need only be there to constitute the motion,
and then we can compare the speeds of two motions, simultaneous or
successive, in different parts of the field of vision without any sort
of analysis of our experiences. The motions simply are different; that
is, they are experiences of one class, of different variety, and are compared
as we might compare two shades of a colour. Motions are prominent
only in those senses in which the attribute of order varies distinctly,
i.e. only in vision, touch, and articular sense (133, 157 ff.; 134, 26 ff.;
135, 251).

L. If with this much of motion in mind, we turn to the sense of
hearing for its confirmation, we cannot but feel rather disappointed.
We can make a tone glide up and down continuously over a tonal
distance. We can easily see the resemblance between this process
and motion; we call it a gliding, or a motion of tone; and we can easily
trace its speed; we now do so often in the tone of a motor, as its speed
of revolution varies. But this kind of motion plays practically no
part in music. Of course its absence may again be due to the systems
of intervals adopted in the various musical scales. But it would be
surprising if music went out of its way to avoid such an elementary
mode of sensory experience as motion—the only other one than distance
included in the single system of a single sense. Besides we should
then have got no whit nearer to an analysis of melody. If we hope
for a visual clue to melody, we must therefore look around in vision
again.

And for what? Why, for a parallel to a kind of connexion that
accrues when a series of sensations of fixed, but discrete, orders is given;
for a motion that comes without any real motion, but only from a
succession of orders. And a motion originating thus is familiar to
everyone in cinematographic projections. There each picture of the
series is shown at rest on the screen for an instant to be followed by the
next after an interval in which nothing falls on the screen. As everyone
knows the objects shown in the picture appear to move continuously.
Certain phenomena of the greatest interest for hearing appear when
the rate of succession of the pictures is gradually reduced. Let us
simplify the experiment and suppose that instead of an object only
a moving point is shown, for no object is required. In the old fashioned
'wheel of life,' the forerunner of the modern cinematograph, a picture

was sometimes given of a juggler throwing a *ball* up into the air and catching it again. Or in modern theatres we sometimes see a picture of an aeroplane arriving; nothing appears at first but a moving spot on the white background of the screen. Suppose five successive stages of such a picture; or a number of tiny electric lamps standing at variable distances and capable of being brought to glow at any desired rate of succession in otherwise complete darkness. Each little lamp is placed in a black box open towards the spectator, so that light cannot fall from one lamp upon the glass of another, and so by reflection simulate the continuity of motion (cf. 62, 60; 139, 179).

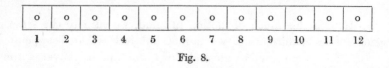

Fig. 8.

At a certain distance from one another and at a certain rate of succession, the illumination of the row of lamps gives the appearance of a single lamp appearing at point 1, and moving continuously onwards, as if a real lamp continuously glowing had been uncovered at point 1 and had actually been moved thence along the line 1, 2, 3, 4, 5, etc. When the rate of succession is lowered or the distance between the lamps increased, the motion first becomes jerky, as if one lamp moved quickly forward a space, then stopped an instant, moved forward again, and so on; with further decrease of rate little gaps appear in this continuity, as if the one lamp had passed behind a series of opaque pencils, perpendicular to the line of lamps, one between each two. As the distance increases or the rate of succession decreases, the breadth of these imaginary pencils seems to increase, until only a little tremor is seen where each lamp stands, when it glows, as if it were jolted once from left to right. If the rate of succession is slow enough, each lamp glows up where it stands and goes out again, while there seem to be as many lamps as there are positions or lamps in reality. This stage is preceded by one in which each lamp appears quite still, but is connected with its neighbour by a most evanescent and unobtrusive experience of motion, a sort of mere 'going-over' or 'passing' from one position to another[1].

---

[1] For the special study of this last phenomenon *v.* 139, 222 ff. esp. 226. For the sake of simplicity of statement I have appended Wertheimer's observations to Marbe's, as if Wertheimer's special observations had been observed with Marbe's row of lamps.

These phenomena are all to be regarded as motion, the same motion as we see in vision when any object moves before our sight. The only difference in the various rates of succession and distance is the obtrusiveness of the visual stuff or of the visual sensations which make up the motion. When there appears to be one moving lamp, the sensory stuff of the motion between the positions 1, 2, 3, etc. is as intense, full and intrusive as is that corresponding to each position, or that which is evoked directly from the retinal stimulation. As the rate or distance changes, this maximal intensity decreases, until it is so weak as to be no longer mistakable for the appearance of the lamp. The lamp then seems to move behind upright obstructions. These gaps increase till they correspond to the real distances between the positions, but even then there is still a motion to be observed between the positions, but it is borne on sensory stuff of minimal intensity or obtrusiveness and of very short duration (cf. 139, 247ff.). And motion is thus always continuous just as it is in our ordinary acquaintance with it.

If a cause is to be sought for the appearance of motion under these very peculiar circumstances of stimulation, it is clear that it must be sought in the physiological connexions that arise between the stimulations given by the lamps at these rates and distances (cf. 139, 247ff.). A psychological cause seems excluded. We need not follow out the subject along this line of interest. Our problem is to see whether the motional phenomena described can be found in hearing. And in fact we find there what must be held to be a very close parallel as far as it goes. The phenomena of hearing call for special research, which is not nearly so easy to carry out in an experimental form, as in vision. We must be satisfied with establishing a probable case for motional phenomena in hearing, remembering what a weight is added to any mere probability by the large extent of parallelism between hearing and the other senses already established.

The proper parallel to the series of lamps is a series of tones of different pitch, whose distance apart, or interval, and whose rate of succession can be controlled. The intervals we find in our musical scales are all too big to allow any tonal continuity to emerge. As far as I have been able to test the matter, continuity of rise of pitch is indistinguishable from a rise by discrete steps if these steps are very small and rapid enough. But the maximal step is probably considerably smaller than a semitone. When a chromatic passage is played rapidly, it gives a great impression of continuity, although it could never be mistaken for a gliding change of pitch. Its component points of pitch are easily

audible. The 'chromatic scale' may, of course, in spite of this discreteness, contain a less obtrusive gliding continuity that the ear cannot
readily detach from the rest for adequate description. As the rate
of succession of the steps becomes slower, the impression of continuity
decreases while the pauses on each pitch become more prominent.
At the rates at which tones follow one another in ordinary melodies,
there is no glide about the pitches at all, as far as they are concerned.
Each one is obviously a steady pitch, at least on instruments with fixed
tones; in singing, of course, there is probably often a considerable
amount of gliding just before and after the intonation of any one tone
and a fair amount of very brief and unobtrusive gliding between the
tones, in so far as intonation is maintained between them. This gliding
is reduced by training to the necessary minimum.

Nevertheless a melody is still a continuity. It is not a mere series
of tones of different pitch, but a series of connected tones. The ear
hears at once the punctuation of a melody, as it were, the points where
the connexion comes to an end momentarily, and where a new 'phrase'
begins. In our national anthem, for example, the first break occurs
after the first word 'King' is sung; the next tone begins afresh. It
hardly forms an interval with the preceding tone and there is little
continuity or passage between them. We can, if we will, hear some
of this continuity, but any considerable amount of it distorts the
melody. But it is probably not entirely absent in such a case. If it
is to be suppressed entirely, a longer pause must be made between
the two tones. This occurs in our national anthem at the end of the
third line, where the fresh beginning is most noticeable.

LI. This continuity of melody and the unity created by it are so
obvious that melody was chosen as the best example by those who
first drew attention to the additions to experience which accrue from
the collocation of a number of experiences of the same group (v. 13).
Melody was held to be a clear case of a figure-experience, a much more
obvious case than are the figures of vision, squares, triangles, etc.
A melody is recognisable even by those who can recognise neither
pitches nor intervals, It can be given high or low in the musical range,
and so is obviously something more than the tones that compose it,
since these can all be different, while it remains the same. No doubt
melody is a figure in this sense, just as a square is; and our ordinal
classification of pitch makes the parallel much better than could have
been expected by those who first saw the similarity between the two.

But melody is not only a figure in the static sense suggested by squares
and triangles; it is a motional figure as well; it is a unity because
of the *passage* that arises between the tones of each phrase or sentence.
In fact it seems highly probable that this motional unity must have
been the first melodic unity; the static unity can only have become
prominent when scales of definite intervals were formed by means of
which the motions of melody were restrained to certain figures and so
made more thoroughly subject to attention and expectation (29, 400;
30, 252). But it must not be supposed that the adoption of scales has
suppressed the motional figure; in fact this seems to be still the essential
ingredient in what we collectively call melody.

Melodic motion is thus easily distinguishable from the full gliding
motion of tones. But, as in the case of vision, it seems necessary to
suppose that the two are varieties of one and the same process, the
difference between them being one of fullness and obtrusiveness of
the sensory stuff which bears the motion in each case. The sensory
stuff in melodic motion is so unobtrusive that it is greatly influenced
by the direction of attention. One can often 'think' pause into and
out of melodic sequences, as we have already seen. The punctuation
of a melody which is produced by the conclusion of a phrase with tonic
or dominant also rests upon this influence of attention or attitude upon
the experience of 'passage.' This influence of the attention is found
also in the unobtrusive motions of vision (139, 218f.). If two visual
presentations are given successively, say an upright line and a horizontal
one, which if projected simultaneously would form a figure like an
inverted T, the motion resulting between the lines will take various
directions according both to objective conditions and to the direction
of attention. If the upright line slopes a little to the left, it will seem
to fall into the horizontal line to the left; if it slopes more to the right,
it will move down to the position of the horizontal line to the right.
If the slope of the upright line be made in successive trials more and
more from one side to the other, it will depend upon the habit of attention thus set up or upon voluntary direction of the attention in which
direction the upright line shall fall into the horizontal one.

In hearing, the influence of attention upon melodic motion extends
even to simultaneous tonal masses. If a chord is played, e.g. *e, g, c′, e′*,
the attention can pick out each component pitch in turn, and so the
melody can often be heard into the mass. Thus the above chord can
be heard as the beginning of Brahms's song "Ihr wunderschönen
Augenblicke." Stumpf calls this sort of analysis "singing by ear"

(112, 291). If it is practised and observed carefully, it may seem to be practically identical with the motion of really successive melodies. Such practice is of course easier with the fairly pure tones of tuning forks or bottles and with masses of only two pitches. The phenomenon then becomes very prominent, much more prominent than it is usually in ordinary melodies. One may surge down to the lower pitch, when the tone seems to swell out towards its pitch, as if it were actually growing louder and gliding at the same time. Accentuation of the upper tone in the movements of attention makes the upper tone seem to swell and glide into place. But one hardly gets the impression of a continuity between the pitches. The gliding is distinct only near the pitches, its extent on the side of the other tone being rather indefinite. A fast rate of oscillation of the attention seems more favourable for the development of the motion.

In vision this oscillation of attention in a stable presentation does not produce any such motional phenomena. Several reasons may account for this. The chief of these is undoubtedly the fact of the very subordinate part played by variations of visual intensity. We have reason to believe that the extremes of white and black are more intense than the intermediate grays, for a mixture of each with a positive colour shows that the extremes swamp the colour more than do the grays (81, 33). But between the extremes and the mean there is very much less variation of intensity than one might expect, apart altogether from the fact that we ordinarily think of black, not of the medium grays, as the minimum intensity of colourless vision. In sound, on the other hand, volumic outline, over which the attention has to wander to pass from one pitch to another, is essentially a variation of the intensity of the elements of different order which compose it. This reason might lead us to suppose that any semblance of motion derived from movement of the attention in a two pitch mass is really an illusion, due to the successive clearness which the movement of attention gives to the various parts of the whole mass. This may well be so, but the similarity of the changes thus produced to those produced by a gliding tone is important.

Another reason which might be advanced, asserts that the attention to any component of a tonal mass intensifies that component, so that a movement of the attention from one component to another would be the same as a slight and alternating increase of the intensity of the components. Thus oscillation of the attention would produce the same melodic phenomena as would be produced by the presentation of

successive tones of the intensity of the intensive increment due to
attention. But as already (above, p. 102) indicated, this intensive
effect of attention is by no means so certain as is usually allowed. It
is admitted to be a specially auditory phenomenon and I suggest that
its admission in hearing is due largely, if not solely, to the effect of the
qualitative classification of pitch, which excludes any other interpretation of the prominence given by attention to one pitch in a mass over
against any other pitch in the mass as a whole. If the volumic theory
of tones is admitted, the assumption of greater intensity becomes
unnecessary and therefore highly improbable. The whole effect of
attention can be got by a displacement of the attention from one part
of the whole tonal mass to another or from the whole tonal mass to
a part of it. In any case, even if attention in tonal masses does somewhat intensify the component attended to, it seems clear that it
cannot do so to anything like the extent we must suppose upon the
qualitative classification. We should thus bring the effects of attention
in hearing much more into line with their effects in other senses. And
similar behaviour in all senses is surely the more probable *à priori*.

In melodic sequences these two explanations would be of similar
validity. For even if the attention did intensify tones, it would have
to intensify successive tones equally, whereby their relative intensities
would hardly be affected. The melodic passage between tones would
therefore still have to be explained. On the other hand the succession
of the tones would play much the same part in calling the attention
away from the pitch just heard to the next, and so in making the
attention move towards that second pitch over its volumic outline
to its predominance. This would give the second tone that apparent
extension which, when the attention moved over it in one direction,
would appear as a gliding of the second pitch into its place. But melodic
motion is found even when successive tones are separated by a slight
pause. This would not, of course, exclude the movement of attention
over at least a part of the volume of the second tone to its predominance.
But in either case, succession or simultaneity, the latter hypothesis
would hardly suffice to explain the apparent passage that is characteristic
of melody from the pitch of one tone to the next. It must be admitted,
in short, that the whole problem is one calling for subtle observation
and experimentation before final judgment can be given. It is not
so much a matter of whether hearing offers a parallel to the motion
of the other senses or not. That parallel is undoubtedly present. It
is only a question as to how far melody contains an unobtrusive passage

phenomenon and how far this can be identified with the passage phenomenon of vision[1].

LII.   The identification favoured here is supported by certain
forms of early music. v. Hornbostel claims that the basis of melody
has been much affected by the one-sided development of tonality
and rhythm. The strong habits thus formed, he says, prevent us from
apprehending melody in a really melodic way. We tend now always
to think of it in terms of our own tonality and harmonic accompani-
ments. The music of non-European people is with few exceptions
purely melodic. The study of melody must therefore proceed from
this purely melodic music, and not from our harmonic music, as Th.
Lipps (57), Weinmann (138), and M. Meyer (73), attempted it. In a
melody we have more than tones and intervals; we hear 'motives' (32).

v. Hornbostel points to certain interesting facts in support of his
demand. In certain songs of unisonal music the intonation changes
in the course of a melody, but in quite regular ways: the pitch rises
continuously, the melody changes its *niveau* so to speak; or one tone
remains fixed, but the melodic steps from this tone grow bigger or
smaller at certain points of the melody; or changes are made that
for us would spoil the melody altogether, e.g. *gec* for *gebc*. These
melodic devices do seem from our point of view to show the pure motion
of pitch, free of all the usual restraints of tonal systems. A delight

---

[1] Max Meyer has propounded a very strange and revolutionary theory of melody,
which rests upon an alleged (melodic) relationship between tones, which is said to be
present in tones of the ratio 2 : 3, but absent entirely in tones of the relation 7 : 11, or
11 : 10. I am quite unable to observe this difference, which Meyer merely asserts without
any sort of record of observations from different persons and without adequate indication
of what difference is meant. A construction on such a basis does not seem entitled to
displace all previous efforts at theory of melody (*v.* 73). For a criticism of Meyer's theory
compare Th. Lipps (57). Lipps proceeds from a basis similar to that of Meyer, but more
mystical, if anything. These theories derive any merit they may have solely from their
attempt to explain either the dominance of the octave alone, or consonances in general.
They have no factual or logical validity and would never be looked at alongside a really
efficient theory of fusion and consonance. For an experimental test of Meyer's views
of relationship compare W. D. Bingham, (147, 22): "the characteristic feeling of 'relationship' was nearly always still present when the interval had been increased or diminished
32 cents (a third of an equally tempered semitone)." 48 cents destroyed it in 74 per cent.
of the judgments. Bingham thinks that the irregular results of his experiments upon the
preference for the second of two pitches as a close or resting point are due to the emergence,
now of one tonality, now of another, in the mind of the observers (p. 36). That seems
most likely and confirms the view obvious from comparative considerations, that the
study of melody should not be approached from a harmonic basis.

is taken in the mere variations of movement over greater or smaller distances, by different points through the same distance, or from different *niveaux*. The identity in variation is maintained by the direction of movement, which as an element of form is capable of providing a certain amount of guidance for attention. No doubt our elaborations of form much exceed this in complexity, but it is a mistake to suppose, as v. Hornbostel perhaps suggests, that our music contains no merely motional melody. It contains much of that but it is always under the restraint of our complexer forms of tonal systems—scales and tonality. Changes of *niveau*, whose amounts are, of course, made definitely conformable to the steps of our scales, occur very frequently in melodies, as in the second and fifth lines of our national anthem, as compared with the first and fourth; intervals are extended in many of these repetitions, and so on. But whatever the motional foundations of melody may be, they are always subordinated in our music to our static forms of tonality.

CHAPTER VII

THE FORMATION OF SCALES

LIII. The study of scale formation follows properly upon the study of melody. For the early scales were melodic, not harmonic, constructions. That is to say, they were certainly not formed by the analysis of the fundamental harmonies and the spreading of their component pitches into a series. It is a well known fact that there is hardly a trace of harmony to be found in any music but our own modern European music; and that harmonisation is a notion almost quite foreign to the primitive mind, if not more or less impossible without a reconstruction of their scales. Even polyphony is unknown amongst many tribes and peoples. Besides our own scales have been considerably affected by the development of harmony. The intervals of primitive music are not usually very precise; and the precision that attaches to our scales is undoubtedly a reflex of the harmonic processes which evolved out of polyphony.

At the same time we must not overlook the fact that relations similar to those of the harmony of simultaneity are established in melodic sequences. We have already considered this matter and have recognised the existence of a natural basis for similarity of relations, namely the positions of the defining points of the related tones in the series of elemental orders of hearing. The basis of the relations in simultaneous and consecutive tones is identical, then, but we do not therefore expect the relations which emerge to be the same in all respects—even if only because in the one case they hold for simultaneity, in the other for succession. A scale is not a sequence of dissonances, as Krueger aptly remarked. Nevertheless certain pairs of tones acquire a natural affinity in succession, just as they do in simultaneity. These pairs are the octave and the fifth or fourth.

The octave is the basis of standardisation of all scales whatever. No scale is known in which the octave is not the first division, as it were, unless it be some degenerate remnant of an earlier scale. A scale or a part of a scale may have passed from one place to another without the transference of any proper understanding of its nature and inventions[1]. Such a suggestion is, of course, no basis upon which to start the work of theoretical construction, but only a hypothesis to accommodate slight and improbable remnants.

The octave is not the outcome of parallel polyphony alone, as has been often suggested for want of a better explanation. For parallels are possible at any interval: third, sixth, seventh, ninth, or any irrational interval. Nor is it likely that women and men should naturally tend to sing exactly at the interval of an octave, unless that interval somehow exerts a strong attraction upon voices that naturally fall in its neighbourhood.

Helmholtz's explanation that in the octave we have again a part of what we hear in the fundamental, presupposes that the explanation given for the unity of partials in a pitch-blend is sufficient, which is not the case in Helmholtz's theory. His theory apparently succeeds so beautifully, because it pushes the explanation back into a region into which we can hardly follow it. Our full knowledge of the facts of partial tones was the gift of Helmholtz himself. So the primitive mind that knows nothing of them, could only be supposed to appreciate the greater or less coincidence of series of partials in some sort of 'subconscious' manner. And even if we concede the unity of pitch-blends, it is not clear that any of the same unity should attach to the objectively similar case of the octave parallel, in which the presence of two tones

[1] Cf. 120, 35. Many apparently primitive instruments are degenerate forms of earlier ones.

in parallel should *ex hypothesi* be perfectly obvious. For they are sung loudly and clearly, by different persons standing in different places in different 'timbres,' not always in exact coincidence, etc.

Moreover Helmholtz's theory suffers from the very assumption it made, that the tones of all scales coincide with any or many of the members of the series of partials. Of course the imperfections of tuning must be conceded to a theory which rests upon similarities whose basis remains unconscious or subconscious. But if we find numerous scales which, apart from the octave, show no contact with the series of partials at all, it then becomes more than possible that those scales which do cling to the series of partials do so, not directly, but indirectly, and that the universal prevalence of the octave is not due to the coincidence of series of partials. And even of those scales which seem to show a considerable amount of connexion with the series of partials, a number of cases do not really bear this interpretation. They have been identified with our notes which are indirectly related to partials only because the minds of those who observed or studied them for us, could only hear them in the manner of these notes of ours. Thus exotic notes get assimilated to our notes with which they may have no real relationship by derivation or intention.

LIV. Parallels, then, explain nothing, but presuppose an explanation upon which they rest. That explanation has been given above (pp. 63 ff., 90 ff.). And from it flows not only the natural predominance of the octave, but also that of the other almost universal interval—the fifth-fourth. The conjunction of these two seems required in fact, as well as being natural in itself. The fifth is a naturally predominant interval. And if it is given along with an octave, the fourth is thereby given as well. What we have to settle, is not that the fourth should be as prominent an interval as the fifth, but that it is preferred in practice and construction to the fifth, and why.

The preference in practice and construction seems indisputable. Ellis says: "all Greek music, and hence all modern European, as well as all old and medieval music, is founded on this interval. The Fifth seems to have been rather appreciated as the defect of the Fourth from the Octave, though modern tuners find the Fifth much easier to appreciate than the Fourth" (143, 525). In his translation of Helmholtz's work Ellis speaks of the "predominance of the Fourth, and mere evolution of the Fifth, in Greece, Arabia, India, and Japan" (143, 524). It is true that the Fourth seems to be used more in tuning,

but it seems to be altered as much as is the Fifth. Thus in 26 cases
of more or less 'observed' fourths and 28 cases of similar fifths in
Ellis's list (30, 514ff.), I find for the average value (in cents, *v.* p. 131 f.,
below) and the mean variation, respectively, 499 and 31 as against
690 and 18; the 'just' values of the fourth and fifth are 498 and
702 cents.

LV. While we admit the preference of the fourth in tuning, we
may, therefore, well doubt the assertion of disparity of age of the
two intervals. If the octave precedes and regulates all scale construction and the fifth is the only other naturally obvious interval,
then fifth and fourth are necessarily given together, although the
latter does not originate of its own impulse, so to speak, but only as
a consequence of the fifth. We are not called upon to find a special
source for the fourth or to evolve the fifth out of the octave and the
fourth, but only to show some reasonable ground for the preference
of the fourth in practice.

That the fourth could be retained as an interval with ease in spite
of its lack of an impulse towards self-realisation, so to speak, is quite
clear from our previous study of interval. Any interval can be retained
with precision, provided it is somehow given often enough. And the
fourth is given repeatedly, as we have just seen. Octave and fifth
can be found with precision quite apart from any power to remember
them as intervals with precision. The latter power, of course, does
exist, and will naturally join itself to the spontaneous impulse of these
intervals towards self-revelation. The use of the fourth on the basis
of the memory of its volumic proportions only presupposes sufficient
repetition of the fifth and attention to its consequence the fourth.
Helmholtz says: "the relationship of the fifth, and its inversion the
fourth, to the fundamental tone, is so close that it has been acknowledged
in all known systems of music. On the other hand, many variations
occur in the choice of the intermediate tones which have to be inserted
between the terminal tones of the tetrachord" (29, 405; 30, 255). If
we abstract from this statement its connexion with Helmholtz's theoretical basis in the series of partials, we can take it over as correct.

LVI. Its preferability in practice may have had several grounds.
Ellis says: "the quartering of the string may have had much to do
with its adoption." If a string is touched at half its length, it yields
the octave; if at a quarter of its length, it yields the fourth of the tone

given by the open string. Quartering is a much easier division than is tripartition which would yield the fifth; and in the descent from octave to fourth of the open tone, the successive fifth is given, as well as in the ascent from the open tone to the fifth above. In playing, it is more natural to proceed from the open tone to higher tones by shortening the string from the open tone than to proceed to lower tones by lengthening the string from the half-division of the octave.

Moreover, if the octave has been divided from one end into a fifth and a fourth, it is a fairly obvious idea to divide it so that the intervals are reversed, when a third interval—the whole tone (9 : 8) is obtained: c—f—g—c'. That is after all but a natural development of the first inevitable triad of intervals—the octave, fifth, and fourth. The intervals thus obtained, in their serial order from either end, would then be fourth, tone, fourth, whereby the fourth would acquire a greater prominence. The actual course of development in any particular case would depend very much upon the instrument in use. A stringed instrument might well lead to the construction of another fourth upon the first (from f) and so to the appearance of the whole tone as a defect from the octave. These are problems, however, for ethnological research. It is our interest here only to establish the natural basis upon which scales must develop. Much has surely been due to the caprice of tonal architecture, as Helmholtz said (29, 369; 30, 234ff.). But not all of the scale can have had that origin. Caprice is only possible within the limits left over by the natural proclivities that are grounded in the psychological nature of hearing itself[1].

LVII. These three intervals—octave, fifth, and fourth—then are the foundations of scale formation. Upon them scales are built up in detail by the action of a few principles of development.

(a) One of them is very familiar. It is the mere intercomplication of the foundations themselves. A series of alternate fifths up or fourths down from a given tone with the necessary displacement by an octave required to bring them all within one octave will give a series of tones which, allowing for the inevitable deficiencies of tuning and intonation, is a very close approach to our own diatonic scale. The many later forms of theory which grew upon this basis of reduplicated fifths or fourths created problems which could not readily occur to those who

[1] If the pure tonal *distance* between pitches or 'tones' as pitches has been of any effect at all, which is doubtful, the fourth may have derived some advantage from the fact that its pitch divides the octave distance exactly into two equal distances.

had not devised a mathematical basis for intervals. The primitive tuner might find considerable difficulty in carrying out his method of tuning to his complete satisfaction, but he would be urged thereby only to devise subsidiary methods of satisfying a desire for system or proportion in his scale construction. Even when theory has won free scope for itself, as in our own case, we find ourselves compelled in many circumstances to adopt a method of attaining system or proportion, viz. equal temperament.

LVIII.   For it is to be noted that the method by which a scale is obtained need not have the slightest relevance to the musical utility of that scale. There can be no question that any derivation of our diatonic scale by a series of fifths or fourths is entirely extraneous to that scale itself as apprehended by anyone in sequence or as the framework of a musical composition. In considering the relation of keys to one another the idea of a series of fifths may be a helpful guide. And the key of the fifth is an easy sequence to a given key, because the dominant is symmetrical to the tonic and comes to be closely associated with it, so that the change of key is favoured. But all that is of no significance for the scale actually adopted.

Nor is it of any significance for the scale of just temperament that it is actually derivable from the series of partials. For the series of partials can act as its source during musical activity only under exceptional circumstances; as e.g. the 'natural' trumpet (80) and the Swiss Alpine Horn (120, 38). It is not evident whether this origin would directly favour the construction of melodies in our scale. I should doubt it. The eleventh and thirteenth harmonics do not fit in well (80, 134). The series of partials could be for our music only the *de facto* source from which the exact relations of our scales have been derived. Once obtained, these relations are learnt and are then on an equal footing with any other scale of any other source.

Nor does it necessarily follow that the intervals of just temperament will fuse better than do those of other scales, apart, of course, from the natural intervals of the octave and fifth, about which there can be no doubt, as they precede and determine all scales. Of course in harmonic music the intervals of just temperament in combination will produce fewer beats amongst the upper partials than will the intervals of equal or various other temperaments. But harmony is not an essential ingredient of music, as all primitive music shows, and consonance is not primarily based upon coincidence of upper partials. Only in the octave can there be complete coincidence of partials; and in all other intervals the innocence of the non-coincident partials must rest upon their mutual fusional relations, so that here again any positive merit of just temperament reduces itself to the primary merit of the consonance of pure tones.

In short; in the consideration of scales we must rid ourselves entirely of all older 'regulating' notions regarding the theoretical origin or method of attainment of scales, and pin our attention to the scale itself and to its inherent merits. If we do not do so, we are certain to fall into the grossest misconceptions regarding the nature of all scales other than that which seems to us most 'natural,' and to try to explain all these from that favourite one.

LIX. A true notion of the inherent nature of a scale can be got from the theory of interval developed above. That theory so fits the facts as to persuade us to admit the facts straight as they are; and in the welter of conflicting notions about scales now prevalent, that alone is a considerable service. We saw above that an interval is a volumic outline, obtainable at any absolute pitch; it is a volumic figure whose essence is its proportions. Consequently a scale is a series of volumes whose proportions are constant, and from it can be built up a large number of more or less complex volumic figures of constant proportions. In the scale of just temperament, for example, the proportion between the volumes of c and d can be symbolised by x (cf. the ratio $8:9$); the others in succession by y, z, x, y, x, z (cf. the ratios, $9:10, 15:16, 8:9, 9:10, 8:9, 15:16$). This symbolisation, I may remind the reader, has been justified above on purely psychical grounds; it is not based upon the physical ratios given. Now in actual practice we bear that series of proportions in mind as the series x, y, z, x, y, x, z; and we can sing or play the scale on any absolute tone, because the volume of that tone and the series of proportions are enough to determine the whole series. Similarly for any other interval, thirds, fourths, etc.

LX. In the Greek and the ecclesiastical scales, on the other hand, the series of proportions was made mobile, as it were; it could be begun at any point and continued to an end in a cyclical order (if we admit for the moment that the proportions involved were primarily the same as those of just temperament, which is more than doubtful. We must make allowance for the imperfections of tuning and the perfecting and remodelling influences of theory. But the present argument holds for any series of intervals). Thus the starting point of a series may be any member of the symbolic series given above, followed by all the others in a cyclical sequence, the several scales differing, not in the cycle of proportions, but in that member of the cycle with which the cycle starts.

There is no more inherent psychical difficulty about remembering this psychical series and about beginning it at any point, than there is about remembering the series of digits and using them in addition as we do. For many people the process of rapid adding is very similar to moving along a series of lengths. Thus 7 and 4 immediately call up the idea of 11, because 4 'carries the mind forward' a definite length to 11. The addition of 8 carries it on another familiar length and there 19 is found. I do not, however, mean to imply that the Greeks or any others actually thought of the series of intervals of their scales cyclically. They may well have done so, but it is not necessary that they should, any more than it is necessary for every adder to think of numbers as lengths. He may add by mere mechanical association, so to speak. So the Greek may have had his scales in mind as a number of series of proportions, of which he knew otherwise that they could all be got from one instrument. Even that knowledge may not have been present to many, any more than those who can sing a number of modern melodies need be aware of the connexions and differences of their underlying scales. We cannot but go wrong if we try to force our recognised scales upon any or all of these, or try to see those that are strange through the more familiar. It may even be somewhat wrong to read exactly our scale feelings into objectively identical scales of other communities. For in spite of their objective identity, these scales may have had for their possessors a psychical atmosphere which was largely determined by interaction with their other scales. Or there may have been little or no interaction. It is dangerous to make any assumptions about the psychical aura of the musical constructions of any people until at least we know definitely the origin of what we ourselves experience, and can say whether a given aura would necessarily follow from a certain tonal construction or not.

(b) A second principle of development is familiar in our own practice, though not in general. That is the principle of equal temperament. It is obviously a secondary principle, applicable to proportions after they have already been supplied in forms so approximate to equality

as to be able to suggest equality as desirable. Our own equal temperament is a device for the reduction of a large system of keys involving
many different absolute pitches to one which involves only a small
number of notes, and so makes performances on a single instrument
possible in any key. We have so modified the series of proportions
which form our scales and the absolute pitches upon which we produce
them, that we can obtain these series of proportions no matter upon
which one of the absolute pitches or notes we begin. That is to say:
a series of proportions, that can be symbolised as x, y, z, x, y, x, z, or
(as x and y become identical in equal temperament) as x, x, z, x, x, x, z,
can be begun on any of the black or white digitals of the piano and
correspondingly on other instruments. We have here a system of
interaction between the scale as it is first produced by repetition of
fifths or fourths and the notes given by applying that scale to each
of its own notes and to the extra notes obtained by so doing. The
effort at systematic completeness induces a modification of the basis
of the system in order that the final system may be fully rounded off
and exhausted. Complete transposibility is thus attained.

The chromatic tempered scale represents a series of volumes, each
one of which differs from the preceding by one and the same proportion.
Thus on the whole of the musical range of tones a definite series of
points are determined. Any melody, whether harmonised or not,
that rests upon a definite sequence and grouping of these points will
also rest upon such points and only such points, even when its proportions are in each case modified by the proportion between the volume
of the tone it was first built upon and the volume of the tone it is now
to be built upon. As Stumpf says: every melody can be transferred
to any pitch "like a figure on a surface of constant curvature" (116,
89). That figure of speech is more applicable than Stumpf could have
supposed. We are all thoroughly practised in such transposition or
modification of volumes.

This principle of equal proportions is also found in exotic music.
The highest attainment in a systematic sense would, of course, be
when the intervals of all scales required no other notes than are required
by the intervals of any scale. That case is realised in the pentatonic
scale of Java and the heptatonic scale of Siam, first established and
described for us by Alexander Ellis. The proportions of the pentatonic
scale are defined by saying that the ratio of each successive interval is
as the fifth root of two to one; the heptatonic requires the seventh
root of two. Or in cents (of which there are 100 to each equal semitone,

the whole octave being divided up into 1200 equal—imaginary—intervals) 240 for the pentatonic and 171 for the heptatonic.

LXI. The progress of Ellis's discovery of these scales is of considerable interest. In his first paper "On the musical scales of various nations" (143, 510) only the Javese scale was given as one of equal temperament. The average values of the successive intervals observed were, in cents, 228, 256, 244, 232, 240, or in our scale c, $d+$, $f-$, $g+$, $b\flat-$, c'. This scale is so unlike any scale similar to our own and the average values of the cents are so nearly equal, that the notion of an equally tempered scale once conceived was not to be rejected. Moreover, Ellis pointed out that his interpretation was more conformable to the habits of tuning this scale.

But in his study of the heptatonic scale Ellis failed to seize the true relation in spite of the fact that he actually measured a number of fairly well-tuned instruments that might have suggested the idea of equal intervals, had that idea not been otherwise inhibited. Some of the instruments observed were indeed very much out of tune, owing to the loss of the lumps of wax by which they are tuned. In Table IX I have made a list of the measurements in cents of all the instruments, recorded by Ellis, whose scale was known to be heptatonic and equal or may now be supposed by us to have been so. In the first column is given the name of the instrument and the page in vol. 33 of the *Journal of the Society of Arts* where the records appear. In Table X Ellis's own interpretations of these observations are given. In Table XI will be found the average deviation (with mean variation) of the measured amounts (1) from the heptatonic interval of 171 cents and (2) from Ellis's suggestions. I do not mean to claim that all these instruments were really meant to give the heptatonic scale. But as there can be no doubt that nos. 9 and 10 were meant to give that scale, we can see at once that we might well assume from the measurements that all the others except perhaps nos. 5, 6, and 8 were meant to give it.

Soon after the publication of Ellis's paper giving all these figures, except those of instruments 9 and 10, a band of Siamese musicians appeared in London and Ellis proceeded to hear them play and to measure their instruments. While doing so, he was informed by the Siamese prince Prisdang that "the intention was to make all the intervals from note to note identically the same" (143, 1105). This information gave the key to the problem. In order to test its accuracy, Ellis made such a scale of seven equal intervals by calculation. This the native musicians pronounced to be good. Ellis then played them the scale of the Ranat Ek, no. 6 in Table IX, which was the specifically Siamese instrument measured for his leading paper. The musicians declared it to be out of tune. Thus the existence, both really and intentionally, of a heptatonic scale of equal intervals was assured. It has since been confirmed by Stumpf (116).

TABLE IX.

Ellis's Measurements. (143)

Cents calculated ...	171	171	171	171	171	171	171
1.　Balafong (p. 505) ...	187	169	170	147	183	129	237
,,　　2nd octave	180	167	181	189	160	159	—
2.　Tar (*ibid.*) ...　　...	175	179	158	208	176	166	175
,, 2nd octave　　...	205	173	150	195	221	160	—
3.　Balafong (*ibid.*)　...	169	181	193	166	185	146	165
4.　Patala (506)　　　...	176	174	183	174	192	154	193
5.　Balafong (*ibid.*)　...	114	236	200	137	151	194	164
,,　　2nd octave	—	—	—	147	154	208	181
6.　Ranat Ek (*ibid.*) ...	129	148	231	218	45	258	225
,,　　2nd octave	201	103	—	—	—	—	—
7.　Balafong (507)　　...	152	135	245	191	166	149	161
8.　　,,　　(*ibid.*)　...	148	141	178	—	—	—	—
,,　　2nd octave	195	94	224	173	110	212	201
9.　Ranat Ek (1105) ...	177	219	127	150	149	148	167
10.　　,,　　(*ibid.*) ...	185	165	160	200	159	178	174

Now, instrument no. 6 is the worst tuned of all, its average error being 59 cents ± 22 or a quarter-tone. We might, then, well assume that all the instruments of the list are really heptatonic. Probably they were. But to make any claim merely from these figures would be rash. We should have to be able to identify the actual instrument with a well-tuned one giving the heptatonic scale, before we could be sure. The identification, that is to say, would have to be by outward form and material substance, not by the musical functions of the instrument.

Two other scales given by Ellis suggest the heptatonic scale: the scales set by Rajah R. P. Singh, 1st and 4th (143, 504).

Cents observed:

183,   342,   533,   685,   871,   1074,   1230,
174,   350,   477,   697,   908,   1070,   1181.

Calculated (assuming 171+ as the equal interval):

171,   343,   514,   686,   857,   1028,   1200.

But it would be futile to pursue this similarity as it stands. Considerable uncertainty must attach to any results apart from the confirmation of the most efficient native musicians; and these latter should

TABLE X.

Ellis's Interpretations.

No. 2	200	150	150	200	200	150	150
3	150	200	200	150	200	150	150
4	150	200	200	150	200	150	150
5	100	250	200	150	150	200	150
6	150	100	250	200	100	200	200
7	150	150	250	150	200	150	150
8	200	100	200	200	100	200	200

TABLE XI.

	(1)	(2)
1	17 ± 12	—
2	17 ± 12	$19\pm\ 7$
3	$12\pm\ 7$	$15\pm\ 5$
4	$12\pm\ 7$	21 ± 10
5	29 ± 13	$9\pm\ 6$
6	59 ± 22	35 ± 16
7	26 ± 16	16 ± 16
8	34 ± 19	$12\pm\ 7$
9	24 ± 12	—
10	$12\pm\ 6$	—
Average	21 ± 14	—

be free of all the prejudice created so easily by 'improving' theories, especially those of a mathematical kind. The most we may take out of these comparisons is that probably the heptatonic scale is more widely distributed than Ellis supposed.

The course of Ellis's discovery is most instructive. It shows on the one hand how far out an interpretation may be that is made by a person who is accustomed to such a definite and special scale as ours is. On the other hand it emphasises the necessity, not only of actual observation of native music as played by native musicians, but also of the comparison of these records with the ideas of the best native musicians about their own music and instruments. These musicians must be such as can tune their own instruments in the very best way known in their community, not merely such as can play on them when tuned. Of course all understanding of the genesis of their own scale may be lost in a community. That is possible. But, so long as the scale is maintained in a fairly distinct form in the music of the community, it is not probable. Theorists who neglect to build solely upon the psychical apprehension of a scale by the native mind, may give us a very fine scheme, capable of great development, but they can give us no guarantee that their theory and interpretation applies to its alleged object. It may have substituted its own theoretical object. Treatises on scales show how their authors have wrestled to force various scales into the scheme of their theory. Remarks from listeners to exotic music show how that music inevitably tends to be interpreted in terms of the familiar scales and intervals. For a proper apprehension and understanding of exotic music we must put all our own habits out of mind, as far as we can. In theory we can do this perfectly, if we will[1].

LXII.   How were these scales obtained?   All that we need to do in answering this question is to show by what means a set of intervals could be got of so nearly equal proportions as to suggest the construction of a series of thoroughly equal proportions. We start out as before from the octave, fourth, and fifth: $c—f—g—c'$. Each of the extreme intervals is much larger than the middle one, so that there is in them room for subdivision. When that is done, and supposing it done perfectly, the larger intervals each being divided into two equal parts, we get a series of intervals in cents: 249 : 249 : 204 : 249 : 249. Four of these are the same, and that sameness could be appreciated. Of course, we must not suppose that a native tuner would get these intervals in such perfect division, but only approximately. But in so doing he would be liable to get an appreciation of their approximate equality. The middle interval being often a little out of tune and sometimes approximating more than usual to the size of the others, would only favour the idea of equality throughout. It remains then only for the tuner to conceive this idea of equality and to carry it out. And that can be done, without the use of logarithms, or abstruse physical knowledge, by ear alone, just as easily as we can sing up our diatonic scale from any pitch. Once the idea of equal intervals is established, the scale can be got at any time by tuning with fourths and by taking

[1] For a statement of the demands put upon the ethnological study of music with special emphasis upon the use of the phonograph for recording observations, see 120, 62 ff.

the fourth from either end[1] of the octave smaller than it should be (by 18 cents, less than a fifth of one of our semitones). That is, the fourth up from c is flattened a good deal. Then a fourth may be raised on this first one, and so on, by one or other method. Or the tuner might tune the whole scale by 'ear[2],' each interval between two notes being repeated over and over again, and rectified, if need be, by the revision of the whole scale. It would be foolish to attempt to decide by theory on the actual method. That is a question for ethnological discovery.

As for the heptatonic scale, the primary basis of its origin must be the same—the octave, fifth, and fourth. The interval between f and g is 204 cents. The other intervals are 498 cents. In the subdivision of the latter we need only suppose for this case that the interval between f and g had been sought in repetition between c and f. This would give three intervals: 204, 204, and 90; and a repetition of these between g and c'. Allowing, now, for the imperfections of tuning we can see good ground upon which the idea of equality of intervals might appear. That equality would presuppose the reduction of the f—g interval by a smaller amount than its deviation in the pentatonic scale (viz. 33 cents, or a third of our semitone as against 36 cents). Otherwise than by the idea of dividing the big intervals by taking the small one out of it repeatedly, the seven step scale may possibly have been suggested by the notion of perfection associated with that number (116, 90). Possibly it is merely to be laid to the account of a habit of tuning the fourth rather too large (by some 16 cents). In any case there is no improbability in its appearance amongst primitive people. For its psychological status as a case of equal temperament is part of the very essence of interval in any form—constancy of proportion. The occurrence of equal temperament is not confined to our intellectual race, that attained it only as the result of a long sustained and already highly elaborated effort to systematise thoroughly our musical constructions. We had begun by adopting a scale of unequal intervals, which has actually shown itself to be capable of higher evolution than the scales based primarily on equality of interval.

---

[1] Of the method of tuning Stumpf says: "First the octave is tuned and then intervals are taken from the two octave tones a fourth inwards and so on probably by fourths" (116, 96).

[2] As Mr Isawa said (v. 143, 522): a certain Japanese interval was got "not by consonance but by a certain melodic intuition."

There is in all this no contradiction with our own doings in the matter of scales. We need postulate no logarithmic inspirations or root extractions. Nor do we need any mysterious 'feelings' for equal intervals. That 'feeling' is given along with the consonance of fusion in any interval. The mistuning of the fourth and fifth required for the pentatonic scale is only 18 cents and for the heptatonic 16 cents; certainly not a large amount. It is only five vibrations for a tone of 500 vibrations, or about the high contralto tenor c, i.e. c^2. English tuners, as Ellis found (143, 489), make errors even of eleven cents.

LXIII. (*c*) The third principle of development is equal division of the playing string. "The principle is," says Ellis, "that equal divisions of the difference of two lengths of a string will give nearly equal intervals extending from one to the other" (143, 500). As examples of this Ellis cites "the mode in which the Persian and afterwards Zalzal's 'middle finger' was obtained, by halving the distance between the frets." On the Persian lute the middle finger had nothing to do. So a note was introduced for it between d and $e\flat$, a whole tone below the f got by stopping the string at three quarters of its length. There was a similar note introduced upon the second string. But these and other notes attempted did not please sufficiently. And it remained for Zalzal, a celebrated lutist, to make a stop half-way between one of those previously attempted and an earlier stop, thus getting a note of 355 cents (a neutral third, neither minor (300) nor major (400)) and dividing the fifth exactly into two halves ($702 \div 2 = 351$ cents). A similar operation on the second string gave what may similarly be called a neutral sixth. These notes of Zalzal's became of great importance in Arabic music, but they were finally ousted by notes derived by repetition of fourths (143, 493, 495). Ellis says that the repetition of the tones 0, 350, and 700 cents, i.e. c, neutral third, and fifth rapidly becomes pleasing to the ear (143, 498). The neutral sixth divides the upper fifth from f to c into two equal parts: 500, 850, 1200 cents. Zalzal's scale is still found on the Highland bagpipes: e.g. in cents:

    0,   197,   341,   495,   703,   853,   1009,   1200,

or a, b, $c + \frac{1}{4}$ tone, d, e, $f + \frac{1}{4}$ tone, g, a.

The approximation is so close that Ellis recommends the identification of the bagpipe scale with Zalzal's, either in a tempered form (1) or in a pure form (2):

    (1) 0,   200,   350,   500,   700,   850,   1000,   1200

    (2) 0,   204,   355,   498,   702,   853,   996,   1200.

Similarly the Indian scale is obtained by string division. "The *C* string is divided in half, giving the octave; the half nearest the nut is again halved, giving the Fourth *F*. The part between the nut and *F* is divided into 9 equal parts, each giving one degree; and the other part, from *F* to the octave, is divided into 13 equal parts, each giving a degree. From these indications it is possible to calculate the value of each degree and assign the notes (143, 502; 30, 523).

(*d*) Still another principle, although a rather vague one, has been advanced by Stumpf (120, 31)—the principle of *small* intervals. These, Stumpf thinks, could have been attained without the support or ground of consonant masses at all. "They just sang—perhaps at the instance of mere play impulse or by way of signalling-tones which were clearly enough different from one another, and acquired a certain amount of practice in the production of such steps, which could then be taken intentionally somewhat larger or smaller; so that songs thereby became possible which they could repeat from other starting tones." "Many songs of most primitive nature, e.g. amongst the Veddas of Ceylon, are of this kind and probably arose in this way." This principle is not, however, a new one, as Stumpf supposes, who refers it to the appreciation of tonal distances rather than intervals (120, 86). As I have already pointed out, that must be a mistake. These small intervals are just as much in essence intervals as are any larger ones. Of course, as Stumpf indicates, the fixation of definite larger intervals must be guided by other principles, which I have already stated.

LXIV. The earliest and all the primitive scales were melodic structures. Mere tonal motion is interesting; but it gains immensely in variety and interest by being brought at least close to the pattern of a series of definite movements of pitch. Besides, the listener is able to follow its movements better if they build up a set of familiar pitch relations. But primitive music need not follow these relations at all slavishly. It can still retain a good measure of the early melodic freedom, and increase or decrease intervals, by a small amount (143, 522), if any good effect can thereby be attained, just as modern singers often do (at least sharpening tones). Music travels a far journey before it comes to any harmonic development. The duration of that journey may often have been due to the inhibitory effect of scales which did not admit of harmonisation, and so did not encourage it when it occurred accidentally. It is true certain springs of harmony are found in primitive music[1]. But we know from the history of our own music how tentative were the beginnings of harmony, and how much of its ultimate development was due to the tenacity of life of the melodic interest. The observation and study of harmony then reacted upon scale structure and modified it so as to permit of the greater development of all musical interests. One of the last products of that development was our equal temperament, as we have seen. We do not need to suppose, by any means, that we have already reached the limits of the possible development of our basal musical structures. Development (120, 97) proceeds by a widening of the scope and applicability of the fundamental principles of musical practice, whereby something is sacrificed here to a gain there and *vice versa*. We have certainly discovered, developed, and satisfied, interests of which primitive music knows next to nothing. But there may be more to come. Only the fundamental elements of musical structure, the ideal of tonal balance and the endless interplay of the fusion that blends a manifold into characteristic unity and the analytic attention that can follow the manifold through the unity, will always remain. The attention is but a faint power that can do great work only when the application of its energy is made most economical by the protective guidance of habit. Without a wide basis of convention and familiarity the musical listener would only be confused and baffled. And music has its limits of development set at any time chiefly by the trend of habits of the listener and his powers. According to these powers the basal pleasantnesses of music may be spread through a greater and greater superstructure of detail.

CHAPTER VIII

PHYSIOLOGICAL THEORIES OF HEARING

LXV. The occurrence of auditory experiences is undoubtedly dependent upon the functioning of the organs of the ear. The physiological study of these organs is for this reason of great interest to those who are primarily engaged in psychological study. Not only do the two studies form neighbouring fields of work, but they play to a greater

---

[1] *v.* 120, 43 ff. Parallels of fifths and fourths, as well as of octaves of course, occur not infrequently. Cf. 145, 262 f.

or less extent into each other's hands. It is well to have a clear idea of what is involved in this reciprocity in each case.

Neither study is a mere appendage of the other. Both originate in a direct study of their objects, psychology in the direct study of experiences without reference to the body, and physiology in the direct study of the body without reference to experiences. This primacy of direct study has led in various quarters to the claim that the physiology of the receptors and the nervous system shall be constructed solely by direct methods of study to the exclusion of all others. Such a plea draws its justification both from the improved technique of direct methods and from the long continued failure of psychology to furnish highly reliable indirect foundations for physiological progress. But it is clearly untenable in any extreme form. Direct methods will surely be preferable as far as they go; but no science can afford to neglect to account for functions that are dependent upon its own direct objects of interest. And as the experiences of hearing are dependent upon the organs of the ear, it is for physiology as the basal science to explain them. In so far as it cannot deduce the phenomena of hearing from the results of its direct study, it must perforce extend these direct results by inference from the nature of the experiences of hearing so as to present a probable physiological basis for them. No new science of behaviour or any other subtleties of evasion will ever relieve physiology of this task.

But psychology is free of any reciprocal obligation. It is not called upon to supply experiences for all the receptory organs and functions of the ear. Its problems of study are limited by the facts and implications of experience and all that is dependent or founded upon them. The physiological functions of the receptors of the ear are in no positive sense of the term dependent upon the experiences of hearing. The dependence is valid only upwards, as it were, not downwards. Psychology is therefore not required to cross the limits of its elements into any 'lower' sphere of action. The physiology of hearing can set no imperative questions to psychology but only disjunctive ones. It cannot say: experience must be thus and thus, please find it to be so; but only: experiences may occur that are thus and thus, please say whether or not they do occur. Suggestions for psychological progress might thus be given by physiology. But psychology on the contrary sets imperative questions to physiology. The functions of the receptors of hearing, it says, must be so and so, please confirm.

This dictatorship of psychology, however, does not mean that the psychologist may at once proceed to convert his analysis into physiological theory by substituting for the terms of his analysis the most probable corresponding terms of physiology. The interests and objects of the physiological and psychological study of hearing are so different, that a concentration upon the one sphere is not likely to involve an equal concentration upon the other. Defects of familiarity and understanding of the other field may lead to serious mistakes in the translation from psychological to physiological. A translation of languages, we should all agree, is best done from a foreign tongue to the native speech. So we may agree that the answer to the psychologists' imperative questions had best come from the physiologist, who has by daily experience become intimately acquainted with all the facts and possibilities involved in the results of the direct study of the receptors of hearing, and can most readily reconstruct them according to demands. But once a physiological reconstruction has been made, the burden of work falls again upon the psychologist who will test the physiologist's translation by retranslating the version. The psychologist thus gains a certain right of criticism. He may not say whether a physiological theory is correct, but he may say whether it seems to him to be adequate to the experiences it subserves, and, with greater justice, whether it is inadequate to them. Such a method of co-operation should lead to a harmonious interplay of work and criticism without any mutual encroachment.

In considering the various physiological theories of hearing that have been offered, we may therefore avoid any discussion of the relation of each theory to a study of the organs of hearing by direct methods. Only two things concern us: (1) Does the theory provide an adequate parallel for all the observed facts of hearing, whether in their elementary or integrated forms? (2) Can the theory show, consistently with the main biological principles that psychology shares with all other biological sciences, how hearing could have developed psychically as well as physically, or psychophysically, from its lowest forms to the relatively advanced form in which we find it? These two points may be stated together: does the physiological theory satisfy the demands of the psychological question both for the present state of hearing and for the development of hearing? It must show both how hearing could have been evolved, and how it can now be evoked.

H. v. HELMHOLTZ, 1862 (29, 30).

LXVI. This theory satisfies the requirements of experience in so far as it admits for each heard pitch one relative maximum of resonance upon a longitudinal series of resonators, each of which vibrates transversely when in resonance. Helmholtz himself adhered to the traditional classification of pitch as quality of sensation, but it is obvious that his physiological theory is much more suitable for ordinal, than for qualitative pitches. The analogy of the visual colour theory of Young and himself, to which he referred in support of his own auditory theory, breaks down at the decisive point; for there is no arrangement of the specific receptors of colour in a retinal series parallel in some sort of manner say to the spectral series of colours or the like. The ordinal physiological series offers an adequate basis for such auditory phenomena as distance, interval, melody (which Helmholtz so decidedly envisaged as motion (29, 396ff.; 30, 250f.), the pitch analysis of tonal masses, and the auditory nature of noise.

Helmholtz's theory is inconsistent, in so far as it fails to show why experiences do not occur corresponding to the fibres (on either side of any relative maximum) that are simultaneously in sympathetic resonance. If these can give a sensation when very weakly stimulated, so long as they occupy a point of relatively maximal intensity, they should surely give the same experiences in conformity with the law of specific energies of sense referred to by Helmholtz (29, 232; 30, 148), when they are resonating in subordination to some other relative maximum. The tyranny of the qualitative classification of pitch (*ibid.*) doubtless prevented Helmholtz from making use of this extension of sympathetic resonance as the physical basis of the psychical volume of tones.

It is only on the basis of volumes and coincidence of volumes, as I have shown, that a satisfactory explanation of the psychical nature of tones as distinct from noises, of consonance and the standardisation of the pitch series into octaves, of intervals and of the psychophysical development of hearing can be given. Helmholtz's theory thus fails to satisfy all the requirements and so must be regarded as still admitting the insuperable mystery of the correlation of a series of qualities with a series of neural receptors. There is of course no fault in the correlation of the two series. The point is: how did the psychical series ever get linked up to the physical series? Not even the assumption made by Helmholtz that the psychical series has no features whatever other than its mere serial nature, could really dispel the mystery. The basis of explanation sought by Helmholtz for consonance and the like in the coincidence of upper partials was the best one left open to him, and perfectly consistent with his theory of the auditory elements. But it has been proved by Stumpf to be a complete failure and is utterly useless as a primary source of consonance. At most it can but add to, and amplify, consonance, once that has been established. For it is really only a fragment, as it were, of consonance by coincidence of volumes and of their characteristic points. The primary fault of Helmholtz's theory in this respect lies not so much in his failure to show how the coincidence of partials comes to be noticed, but in his failure to show how the presence of partials ever comes to be overlooked in a musical tone.

On my theory the psychophysical development of hearing from highest tones downwards (111, 339 ff.; 112, 218) is perfectly evident and in accord with the greater biological probabilities. The whole line of progress from a single vibrating hair to a perfect cochlea can then be seen at a glance. For its realisation we need only invoke the aid of well-known biological principles—the 'chance' reduplication of organs and the advantage resulting therefrom. With these two devices we start a line of advance which will carry us over the whole journey. For the cochlea is only a large number of vibrating hairs with all the adjuncts that the advantage of each accidental accretion would serve to bring about. Such a work as Gray's *The Labyrinth of Animals* shows with the greatest possible clearness the chief stages of this development that have survived. And it is a short way therefrom to the construction of the whole development in abstraction from the special conditions of each animal's phylogenetic history.

The present standing of Helmholtz's theory may be well indicated by a quotation from K. L. Schaefer (102, 5 ff.): "I take my stand outright upon the ground of Helmholtz's theory. It has indeed been subjected in the last decades to sharp attacks, especially in a sphere not completely exhausted by Helmholtz himself—that of the secondary clang phenomena, whereby I understand beats, combination tones, variation tones and interruption tones. But one may confidently maintain that it has victoriously resisted these attacks and at present stands faster than ever before. Besides, of the many other theories of hearing that in the course of time have been published, none is equal to it in respect of comprehensive and often most detailed agreement with the facts." That is true; but it does not remove the difficulties of Helmholtz's theory to which I have referred.

A useful extension of Helmholtz's theory was offered by A. A. Gray (25, 26). Gray goes back to the objection made against Helmholtz's theory by Rutherford that no single transverse fibre of the basilar membrane could vibrate alone, but would drag the portion of the membrane on each side along with it. Gray observed microscopically that the ligamentum spirale increases in size and becomes more distinctly fibrous as it passes from the apex of the cochlea to the base. This seems to be true of all mammals. But the basilar membrane itself diminishes in breadth from apex to base, while the rods of Corti, the hair-cells, and the hairs themselves, all become smaller. Now, since the ligamentum spirale consists either of unstriped muscular fibre or, more probably, of fibrous connective tissue, it must produce tension on the basilar membrane, a tension which will increase towards the base of the cochlea. A fibre b, therefore, that lies beyond a fibre a, will be subject to a slightly less tension and will vibrate in sympathy with the note proper to fibre a, though not with so great an amplitude. Thus a stretch of the basilar membrane will vibrate to each tone. This, of course, Helmholtz himself deduced from the principle of resonance[1].

But Gray developed this result interestingly by comparing the psychical results with those obtained by analogous physical processes in the sense of touch. Two neighbouring points are not distinguishable, but sum their excitations to a resultant point. Gray believed, however, that of the whole excitation we hear, as in touch we seem to feel, only the point of maximal stimulation. He did not extend the psychical parallel by ascribing volume to tone. "The mind pays attention only to the maximum point of stimulation of the nerve terminations" (25, 336). At the same time, there can be several maxima in the total stimulation of the basilar membrane. A maximum for Gray is always a relative maximum. A noise he compares with a line of stimulation in touch. In so far as the basilar line lies higher or lower in the cochlea, a noise has a more or less indefinite pitch; that is, it will be vaguely higher or lower; and so on. Gray's paper shows how Helmholtz's theory can be extended (without examination of the principle of resonance adopted by Helmholtz) towards what I shall later suggest as a suitable basis for the psychological analysis of this work.

This aspect of Helmholtz's theory has naturally drawn a good deal

---

[1] v. 29, 223; 30, 144: "An elastic body, set into sympathetic vibration by any tone, vibrates sympathetically in the pitch number of the exciting tone; but as soon as the exciting tone stops, it goes on sounding in the pitch number of its own proper tone."

of attention.   Thus Wien has maintained that the amplitude of vibration of fibres a considerable distance from a certain fibre may (on Helmholtz's principle of resonance) still be so great (if the tone proper to the latter fibre is given in great intensity) as to be far beyond what is required to produce these 'false' tones.   But these 'false' tones are never audible along with the 'right' tone.   This result is so inconsistent that Wien thinks the resonance theory would have to be dropped, if it could not be overcome[1].   O. Fischer gets over this difficulty by appeal to the small space (v. Retzius) separating the membrana tectoria (Corti) from the hairs of the hair-cells.   He points out that the smaller amplitudes of the 'wrong' resonances could find play-room in this space without the hairs being brought into contact with the membrana tectoria and so stimulating the hair-cells.   But ter Kuile holds (his actual words, 48, 147, are: "we now know") that the hairs are permanently embedded in the tectoria and stimulate by their pull on the hair-cells when the basilar membrane is bulged downwards (cf. 154). Besides Fischer's solution would only hold for the further reaches of the waste amplitude.

A. Lehmann (50) attempted to correct the difficulty by an experimental study of vibrating membranes.   He admits that extension is a true property of tone sensations, directly experienced, not based upon associations.   And he compares it with the extension that is given in other senses by the size of the stimulated surface, e.g. in the sense of pressure[2].   This, he says, should lead us to expect that the greater extension of deep tones is due to the excitation of a greater number of nerve-fibres.   Helmholtz's theory could be readily modified to cover this property of extension in tones, except, as Lehmann points out, in so far as the modification would require the abandonment of the doctrine of specific energy of the several nerve fibres peculiar to Helmholtz's theory.   It is doubtless this doctrine which has so far prevented Helmholtz's theory from developing to include a real extension in sounds[3].

C. S. Myers also points out that "sensations of tone (and to a less extent, sensations of noise) appear to contain a certain spatial quality, a character of voluminousness, which is dependent on pitch.   Such tone character is perhaps analogous to the extensity of visual and tactual sensations.   Conjecture may relate it either to the length of

---

[1] I take this from 20, 132.   I have not seen Wien's original (140).

[2] Similarly W. McDougall as quoted on p. 45 above.

[3] Cf. 112, 111; and a theory by Hostinsky quoted by Stumpf (112, 272).

the sound-wave or to the number of simultaneously excited hair-cells[1] within the cochlea" (82, 33, 49).   At the same time Myers accepts Helmholtz's view that the pitch of a tone is determined by the position of the apex of the vibrating wave or bulge on the basilar membrane.   It is true Myers does not explain any more than does Helmholtz[2], why we should hear only according to the apex of the wave; or if the suggestion regarding voluminousness is to cover this point, he does not expound it sufficiently or point out or develop its implications.

Thus we see how Helmholtz's theory, which is still the chief favourite, calls for relief from the same difficulty both on the physiological and on the psychological side.

W. RUTHERFORD, 1886 (97, 98) AND TH. LIPPS, 1883 (56, 57).

A group of theories of which W. Rutherford and Th. Lipps are the two chief exponents refers the proximal ground of the special nature of auditory experiences to central, rather than peripheral, receptive processes.

Rutherford's rejection of Helmholtz's theory rested on at least one valid objection—Helmholtz's failure to give a satisfactory account of the blending of consonant or harmonious tones.   Rutherford says (97, 18): "If the motions in the (three) sensory nerve cells are eventually to be blended, it seems unnecessary that the already blended sound vibrations should have been analysed in the cochlea."   So he supposed that the hairs of all the auditory cells of the cochlea vibrate to every tone, just as the drum of the ear does.   The hair cells transform sound vibrations into nerve vibrations similar in frequency and amplitude to the sound vibrations.   Simple and complex vibrations of nerve molecules then arrive in the sensory cells of the brain, and there produce, not sound again, of course, but the sensations of sound, the nature of which depends not upon the stimulation of different sensory cells, but on the frequency, amplitude and form of the vibrations coming into the cells through all the fibres of the auditory nerve[3].   For the transmission of high frequencies along nerves Rutherford adduced some direct experimental evidence—tetanus tone of 352 vibrations got

---

[1] Cf. 130, 24 ff.   [2] But cf. Stumpf's efforts, 112, 111 f.

[3] With this theory compare that of Ayers, who admits the general principle of reso-nance, but "gives preponderance" to the supposition that all the hairs of the hair-cells yield to all the varying stresses like a wheat-field in a gusty wind (154, 295).   The infer-ences which follow are naturally far from lucid.   Ayers can hardly be considered to have put forward a new type of theory.

from rabbits' muscle by nerve stimulation of 352 shocks—and mistaken inferences towards higher frequencies from the tones of insects' wings.

Rutherford's theory would be good work, if it had really proved that the peripheral organ of hearing could not possibly account for the peculiarities of auditory sensation. It would then have taken rank logically beside Stumpf's work on fusion, which has proved definitely that fusion is inexplicable by reference to any of the psychological adjuncts of the primary tones involved in the fusion (cf. above, p. 59 f.). It is necessary to point this out in view of occasional misunderstanding of the logical status of such work. Of course neither theorist derives any support for the conclusion he propounds from the fact that he is utterly unable to explain any of the phenomena of his special field and so seems weaker than the weakest of his rival theorists. But no strength is needed to hold the field if all the foes are slain.

The same cannot be said for the other type of theory held by Th. Lipps. That advances to its goal, not by logic, but by a process of elegant and clear diction which Lipps was wont with olympian vigour and scorn to recall to the minds of sceptical earth-bound critics as *thinking*. But as in many other teutonic fathers it is really fiction which mistook itself for thought.

Th. Lipps, 1883 (56, 238 ff.).

Lipps's theory may be taken from a short summary of his own (57, 228 ff.):

(1) The effective and receptive in psychical life is in all cases not the contents of consciousness, but the psychical or, if you like, 'central' processes which underlie them. The interaction between tones must therefore be considered as an interaction of the psychical processes which underlie the contents of consciousness called tones.

(2) These processes are really processes, not permanent states.

(3) We must assume that to the rhythm of the physical vibrations that evoke a tone there corresponds in the parallel tone-sensation-processes, or in the parallel change of psychical or central processes, an analogous rhythm; that the psychical or central process of the tone sensation divides into a sequence of psychical processes.

(4) Take for example a *G* of 300 vbs. and a *C* of 200 vbs. The physical rhythms of these two (tones) series of vibrations have in common a ground rhythm of 100 vbs. This rhythm we must transfer to the rhythms of the sequences of elementary part-processes of the tone-sensation-processes, or in short to the 'tone-rhythms.'

(5) When two such tones meet in the Psyche, they form a whole, that has this common ground-rhythm as its point of unity. This unity is a case of the aesthetic unity of a manifold, etc.

Lipps says in concluding this lightning summary: "The view thus shortly indicated is not an hypothesis invented by me *ad hoc*, but it is the application of most general psychological ground notions to the particular case. These ground notions, besides, find application to all possible spheres of psychical life." That is true: there is such a thing as rhythm in our experience; and, no doubt, there are also central processes or elementary psychical processes, not immediately identifiable with the observable aspects of our experiences (their 'contents'). Lipps's explanatory notions are not sheer inventions. But their application is obviously quite arbitrary, not due to an error of logic like the harmony of the spheres, but innocent of all logic whatever. If we *must* assume these psychical rhythms, we should at least be offered some trace of proof of their existence.

C. H. HURST, 1895 (33).

The basilar membrane is considered to be strongly elastic transversely, but hardly at all elastic longitudinally. When the stapes thrusts forwards, "the inertia of the whole column of fluid in both canals prevents their sudden movement and only the basal portion is moved first, the rest being only subsequently set in motion by the elasticity of the membrane called into action by its displacement" (33, 330). Thus a wave-like disturbance arises and travels along the basilar membrane, the conditions at a more proximal point being exactly those found later at a more distal point. When the stapes has just completed one period, the part of the basilar membrane affected falls into two halves: the forward half is bulged downwards towards the scala tympani, the basal part is bulged up towards the scala vestibuli. And the elasticity of the basilar membrane is pulling the latter down, and the former up towards the level of rest. And the whole wave therefore moves forwards towards the apex. When it gets there, it runs "round the wall of the lagena and down by the Reissnerian membrane to the base of the cochlea" (33, 333). "The smaller waves will probably be almost lost before reaching the base, and the larger ones will, apparently, die out at the base in the form of small vortices or eddies of the perilymph." The effects of the spiral coiling of the cochlear canals will be to concentrate the disturbance on the outer part of each turn of the spiral. Effective stimulation of the auditory receptors is caused, not by the passage of one wave over the basilar membrane, but by the meeting of an upgoing second wave and a returning first. When these meet, as they must somewhere, in opposition of phase, "the ends of the stiff hairs of the hair-cells of the organ of Corti are suddenly thrust down upon the nerve ends of the auditory nerve fibres" (33, 340). This explains why two vibrations are required for the occurrence of a tone sensation.

Pitch depends on the point of the basilar membrane where the opposition occurs. For high tones it is near the apex, for low tones near the base. Hurst gives an ingenious explanation for the loss of low tones on destruction of the apex of the cochlea.

Hurst is forced into difficulties by the reflection that for any one rate of vibration waves would pass in opposition of phase at numerous points of the basilar membrane. This difficulty even induces him to believe that if an intense tone is listened to for say five minutes, the chief point of stimulation becomes fatigued and the next comes into predominance of function, so that we then hear the octave lower (33, 344).

The theory reaches some sort of explanation for the first difference tone and for consonance and dissonance. But these aspects of the theory are not worked out fully enough to be clear.

The interest of Hurst's theory lies, as he himself indicates, not in any explanation it may give of the sensations of sound, but in the foundations for such explanations given by the analysis of the physical processes in the inner ear. As we shall see later, it is possible that by a slight modification in the primary physical analysis a theory might be made to give consequences consistent with the demands of auditory experiences that in its first form gave absurdly inconsistent results. A theory that is very incongruous on its subjective side, may be much nearer the physical truth than one that is subjectively much more plausible. Hurst's theory is the first of a series, each of which sought for a new ground of construction which might avoid the difficulties created by Helmholtz's theory. None of these theories can compare with Helmholtz's for general success; but they may well be on the better road to final success for all that.

P. Bonnier (1901) also adopted as the basis of his theory of hearing the assumption of a longitudinally extensive bulging of the cochlear band. "Every detail of the curve is sensed at every moment by an element of the papilla, and during the continuance of the longitudinal extension of the bulge all points of the curve are successively felt by all points of the papilla." The vibration form is spread out over a large sensitive surface, which is traversed in its whole length by the vibration. There is thus a magnification, as it were, of the vibratory form (*L'audition*, p. 134, quoted from 151, 371). Bonnier does not seem to have formulated his idea in detail.

Nor does A. D. Waller (152, 474) whose whole statement is as follows: "We may regard the basilar membrane as a long narrow drumhead, repeating the complex vibrations of the membrana tympani, and vibrating in its entire area to all sounds—although more or less in some parts than in others,—giving what we may designate as acoustic pressure patterns between the membrana tectoria and the subjacent field of hair-cells. In place of any analysis by consonation of particular radial fibres, it may be imagined that varying combinations of sound give varying pressure-patterns, comparable to the varying retinal images of external objects."

M. MEYER, 1896 (65, 66, 68, 70, 71, 72, 74, 76, 77, 151; cf. 44, 282 ff.).

The only significant aspect of air-curves is the perpendicular value of each positive or negative movement. (The form of the curve round these perpendiculars is irrelevant.) The length of thrust of the stapes is proportional to these values and upon that length depends the quantity of fluid displaced by the thrust. This fluid must find place for itself in the cochlea and does so by bulging out the basilar membrane to the required extent. That bulge is only possible to a limited depth and there is no wave-motion in the cochlea. Hence the extent of the bulge towards the apex of the cochlea depends strictly on the quantity of fluid displaced and is proportional to it; allowance must, however, be made for the greater breadth of the basilar membrane towards the apex. Every negative movement of the stapes acts from the basis of the basilar membrane forwards, pulling back the quantity of fluid determined by the negative amplitude and so reducing the bulge of the membrane up to a definite point towards the apex; a forward portion may remain over unreduced for a part of a tonal period, as the elasticity of the basilar membrane is negligible. The next positive movement of the stapes again bulges out a portion beginning from the basis of the membrane, a negative movement reduces all or part of this or also the part left over from the first movement. And so on. Thus each receptor on the basilar membrane is stimulated so many times a second, these rates being different at different parts of the membrane.

All parts of the basilar membrane then become functionally equivalent. The pitch of a tone depends upon the number of times in any period that the stimulation of any particular receptor passes from negative to positive. The intensity of a tone depends upon the extent of the receiving series which is being affected by any such rate. Pitch-blends and chords are given by the different rates that occur in different parts of the length of receiving membranes.

Meyer does not explain how the auditory receptor comes to respond to (or to 'receive') rates of change of stimulation. In this respect his theory is, of course, no worse and no better than Helmholtz's, Rutherford's, Lipps's, or Tominaga's (127). Nor is the correlation of psychical intensity and length of receiving series affected made probable by any physiological parallel or analogy. I know of no such parallel as would make either of these hypotheses acceptable. Meyer points out (151, 379) that the latter hypothesis regarding the intensity of tone—that it depends upon the number of nerve-endings stimulated, —was held by Johannes Müller.

Moreover the main basis of the theory requires certain subsidiary hypotheses. (1) The rates of stimulation included in a period may be irregular, but this irregularity has limits which are still unknown (66, 29). (2) Sometimes two pairs of transitions from negative to positive collapse into one transition each, whereby a rate (very distinct in the main analysis) of 5 becomes one of 3 (as required to meet what is actually heard (66, 31). (3) Sometimes one rate may be interpreted according to the rate in the adjoining parts of the receiving membranes. This Meyer calls the ambiguity of the stimulus (*ibid.*).

Whatever may be the motives urging to these hypotheses, they certainly make a big draft upon our credulity. We are so wont to think of pitch as a very fine and subtle index of differences in vibratory rate, that we cannot readily admit into its physiological basis such arbitrary modifying influences as these. It would surely be difficult to delimit the scope of the three from one another. Regarding the first, Meyer does not think it is an arbitrary assumption, or a subsidiary hypothesis. It is "an assumption to which observed facts force us," and he appeals to the results of experiments with the siren of holes; one hole missed in a few does not change the pitch given by these, which depends on the rate at which the holes left open follow one another. The plea is obvious, but not so the logic of it within Meyer's theory. The experiments with the siren might just as well have forced Meyer to suppose that his main theory was wrong, had he been inclined to consider such a possibility. For it is not the irregularity of the pauses that is the distinctive feature of the experiment, but the regularity of rate of succession of the holes that are left open apart from the pauses altogether. Besides, the periodic pause causes the appearance of a new tone, having the pitch of the frequency of the pause, which Meyer cannot explain owing to a certain theoretical use he has made of the siren to prove the utter impossibility of ter Kuile's theory of hearing (72, 70ff.; cf. p. 158 note, below).

An observation alleged in support of (3) must be corrected. When two tones making a major third (4 : 5) are sounded together, a second difference tone (ratio 3) is heard; but there is no necessary oscillation between the tones 3 and 4, each being louder alternately; if one attends to them alternately, each will appear to be alternately louder and the attention will oscillate for the same reason as it does in a geometrical optical illusion, e.g. the stair figure; but it is not necessary to attend *separately* to either pitch; one may listen steadily to the whole mass, hearing both at once. The very special hypothesis (2), fitting so well into the needs of Meyer's diagram (66, 26), and the peculiar limitation of the above observation to the lower primary and the second difference tone make one think the observation has been influenced too much by the diagram. The same oscillation is to be noticed between any two simultaneous pitches. And, besides, the ambiguity Meyer postulates should hold for any rate of transition from negative to positive, so long as there are at least two rates on the receiving membrane. That would, of course, be too much of a good thing! But how limit the process to those cases required by Meyer's diagrams? Subsidiary hypotheses are dangerous pets, apt to go wild unexpectedly.

The apparent success of Meyer's theory is due to the way in which it seems to meet the needs of difference tones. Take a simple case for example. In the mass created by tones of the ratio 2 : 3 each wave interferes with the other once in a period, first adding together, then coming to maximal opposition (never complete) and then returning to summation again. There is bound to be a minimal resultant in the middle of the period; and the upper primary will always determine the total number of turns apparent in the whole period, if it is intense enough. Now the smallest wave can be subtracted from all the waves. Thus we get at once a wave of the frequency proper to the upper primary.

But the basis Meyer uses for calculating its intensity is half its amplitude. And it follows, as a matter of course, from the nature of interference of curves, that the nearer the ratio of the two primaries approximates to identity, the smaller in Meyer's way of calculation will the intensity of the upper primary be. Thus though each primary is supposed to be sounded with equal force (20 units), the upper primary yields only: in the interval $3 : 8$ ten units, in $4 : 9$ ten, in $5 : 8$ seven, in $2 : 3$ four, in $20 : 23$ two. In the chord $5 : 8 : 10$, 10 obtains only two units, while 5 gets none at all. Similarly in the chord $4 : 20 : 23$, 23 has an intensity of only one, while 4 has none!

Having subtracted the smallest wave, Meyer then subtracts the smallest of those left. Now the number of maximal interferences in a period is equal to the difference in the ratio numbers of the two tones. These minima are all equal, although their curves must be all of different form, or else the period would recur before its due time. Hence the elimination of the smallest wave will eliminate as many turns of the curve as will reduce the total number to the frequency of the lower primary. The intensity of this tone necessarily turns out to be much larger than that of the upper primary, because the former is at some distance from the points of maximal interference. We are getting gradually towards the region of maximal summation. But with the subtraction of this wave we take off all the more from the residues due to periods of greater summation.

These residues then serve Meyer as the ground of discovery of the difference tones. But as the smallest of the curves of the number of the lower primary is of considerable size, the subtraction of that size from all will leave only a small remainder. Thus only small numbers of turns are left for the difference tones. With the help of Meyer's subsidiary hypotheses—or, as he prefers to think them, necessary conclusions,—the required difference tones can be got out of these. In the curve $2 : 3$ only one piece can remain over after the second subtraction in each half period, namely at the extremes where the greatest summation is. Its amplitude is almost as great as that ascribed to the lower primary, because the displacement towards maximal summation is about as great from the first subtraction to the second as from the maximal interference to the first subtraction. We really ought to hear the interval $2 : 3$ as the interval $1 : 2$ with an upper partial 3 in the tone 1.

Of this analysis of the air-curves Meyer properly says that "in spite of all agreement with actual facts it would hardly be more than a geometrical amusement, could we not also prove the physical possibility of such an analysis" (65, 225). It seems open to question whether Meyer has done aught but write down the results of his geometrical amusement in the most plausible physical terms without any regard to the physiological or psychological probability or even possibility of the translation.

Meyer's attitude towards problems may be judged from the following case. It is a consequence of his theory, which he admits, that no tone should be audible in conjunction with a lower tone which does not produce new turns in the curve of the latter—e.g. the octave interval. For the curve of 2 added to that of 1 only produces slight changes of form in the latter. Upper partials, one would then naturally conclude, should be inaudible; which is absurd, for very faint partials can be heard; hence Meyer's theory is wrong. Not so; Meyer proceeds (68, 2 ff.) to calculate how strong an upper partial must be to be audible, i.e. to produce new turns in the curve of the fundamental.

In a later publication (77) Meyer improves upon this attitude by allowing for a certain elasticity of the basilar membrane, thus taking the form of the superposition curves into account. Thereby, however, he sacrifices that assumption which determines the special nature of all his results. But he does not go on to revise his whole theory in terms of this new assumption; he limits his consideration to the special case which in his results obviously needs amendment, namely the case of partials and such like. Meyer gives an analysis of the interval 24 : 25, which makes it all come out as required: 25, 24, mid-tone and beats and difference tone! But if the first principles of his analysis were followed, as they are for all the usual intervals, there should be many other difference tones, besides 1, probably all from 1 up to 24 (100, 515) —but for the help of the siren inference. Meyer's theory admits the influence of differences of phase (77, 44).

In speaking of the efforts of others, Meyer says that, whereas they (ter Kuile and others) proceeded without regard to the facts of hearing to formulate a mechanical theory of hearing and only subsequently indicated its applicability to the "physiological-psychological facts" of hearing, his own procedure was to start from the facts of hearing, and to inquire what mechanical processes would agree with them (72, 63 ff.). The perpendicular values of compound sine waves do not seem to be facts of hearing in the sense implied.

The title of the University of Missouri publication is given more properly as an introduction to the mechanics of the inner ear. Meyer wishes this exposition to be considered the standard account of his work (151, 375), the validity of which he still maintains in spite of all criticisms (*ibid*. 373). But, nevertheless, as Meyer himself has said, the source of the whole theory is the geometrical amusement with the superposition curves. It can hardly be said that Meyer's primary concern regarding the mechanical assumptions he made was their agreement with the facts of hearing; because they do not agree with these facts, and much of his later publication on the matter consists of a tinkering at the mechanical assumptions in order to attain this agreement. If a judgment on the matter is of interest, I should say that the only virtue of Meyer's procedure over that of others is a tactical one; its absurd consequences have been hidden over with the various subsidiary hypotheses, which are so far beyond control that they are undebatable. Thus criticism is in a sense disarmed. And Meyer even protests against their being held to be subsidiary hypotheses.

J. R. EWALD, 1899 (15, 16, 71; 50, 121; 44, 288 ff.).

This receives its characteristic form from the result of its author's attempt to construct an artificial membrane (16, 489 f.) capable of responding to a large range of tones and of dimensions approximating to those of the basilar membrane. Ewald showed that so small a membrane could respond effectually to a range of tones from 20 to 32,000 vibrations per second. But in his construction it did so always as a whole, no matter to what rate of vibration it was submitted. Standing waves arose in the membrane of a length proportional to the rate of vibration given. For greater rates of vibration, of course, these waves were reduplicated so as to fill up the whole length of the membrane.

The merits of a theory of hearing analogous to the outcome of this reconstruction of the basilar membrane are reducible entirely to the basis it offers for the volume of sounds. This corresponds to the length of the standing wave. Ewald pointed out that these waves use up the superfluous resonance of Helmholtz's theory and account for consonance and dissonance, and for our arrangement of tones as higher and lower. The psychical nature of noise is due to the restlessness of the waves evoked by noise. It is obvious that in these respects the theory comes closer to the demands of experience than does Helmholtz's theory.

But in other radical ways Ewald's theory is inconsistent with experience. The whole mass of the auditory receptors cannot possibly be involved in the hearing of every tone. For if they were, all tones would have one very obvious feature in common, which would necessarily be one of volume. Experience offers no verification of this. Besides the arrangement of tones as higher and lower is only apparently explained by Ewald's theory. For who is to determine which point of the receiving membrane shall be the standard of reference? This point for Ewald must obviously be one of the end points of the membrane. For any other points would be on one side of a short series of higher tones and on the other side of the next higher tones than these, if their relations are determined by the place of the nodal points or of the middle of the waves on the membrane. If this is not the basis of higher and lower, that basis can only be the length of the standing waves. This would suffice to give the terms higher and lower in so far as these are mere volumes; but it is to be noted that the corresponding pitches would possess no inherent order at all, or at most a very irregular order. Besides and worst of all, we should have to hear, if Ewald's theory held, a whole set of tones inside a volume constant for all tones, namely as many tones of the same height as there were standing waves of one size on the receiving membrane. That is belied by experience altogether.

Ewald further claimed that his theory explains the phylogenetic development of hearing. It does so indeed—partially. What it cannot explain is how the neural attachments of the repetitions of a standing wave come to be brought together so as to give only *one* tone. Ewald attempted an explanation by saying that "not equal stretches of the membrane, but always an equal number of standing waves are connected with a central point in the brain" (15, 183 f.). But he does not explain how these brain connexions come about. And in fact they are as mysterious as are the connexions postulated by Helmholtz to which Ewald so strongly objected. Obviously this part of his theory must be abandoned[1]. The receiving membrane may be very small and its excitation may be extensive, as he suggests. But the whole extent of the membrane cannot be involved in the excitation of each tone and there can be no repetition of extents of stimulation.

Ewald's work shows how a physical experiment may demonstrate the possibility of much that is demanded by the relations of experiences to one another and to the cochlea in general. But it also exemplifies

---

[1] Cf. 71, for an exposition of the hopeless difficulties that arise at this point.

the very real danger inherent in the construction of a theory of hearing on the basis of such an experiment. The theory of hearing can be constructed on the basis of such experiments only to the extent that it then fulfils the demands made by the purely psychological analysis of auditory experiences.

According to A. Lehmann (50, 121) who has done experimental work similar to that of Ewald, the latter's regular sound pictures do not really occur; they are merely visual illusions, whose regularity depends only upon the restriction of the point of observation.

E. TER KUILE, 1900 (47, 48, 72).

The thrust of the stapes displaces a certain quantity of fluid which finds room for itself by displacing the basilar membrane lying in the path of its advance. The depth of bulge of the basilar membrane is variable, depending on the amplitude of thrust of the stapes. There is a wave motion over the basilar membrane towards its apex. All wave motions in the cochlea advance along the scala at the same linear rate. The bulge is complete when the stapes has reached the limit of its thrust; but in the succeeding instants the stapes is in recession; this leads to the gradual eating up of the bulge at its end nearer the stapes, as the bulge moves forward over the basilar membrane; so that when the bulge has travelled its own original length along, it has just ceased to be. This wave motion over a definite length of the basilar membrane happens once in each sine period. A greater amplitude of vibration means a deeper bulge wave, not a longer one; but these amplitudes are always very small, and can change only a little for a fixed simple tone; this little suffices for the slight lowering of pitch that follows the intensification of tone[1].

The pitch of a tone thus depends upon the point of the basilar membrane at which a bulge passing along it just expires. ter Kuile does well to point out that his theory explains why we arrange tones in a series (48, 508). The intensity of a tone depends on the stress put upon the hair-cells by the greater amplitude of bulge of the basilar membrane. There is only one specific energy (quality) of sound. Noises are irregular excitations of the receiving membranes.

Although ter Kuile thus establishes the objective order of the tonal series, he does not thereby establish its ordinal nature in experience.

[1] Cf. 112, 242 f.; also 18 for a survey and experiments. The lowering of a tone of 100 vibrations can be as much as one-eighth of a tone.

In fact he says: "that spatial differences in the excitation lead only in the eye, and not in the cochlea, to spatial differences in the sensation is obvious." Only the association with the keyboard gives a sort of spatial difference to the sensation. We cannot hear or imagine a melody without adding the fixed points of the keyboard in thought. ter Kuile thus falls into the constant trap of the spatial preconception to which I have frequently referred. Besides it seems very difficult to believe that a just expiring stimulation could effectively determine a thing so clear and decisive as pitch. And there ought to be in experience some effect corresponding to the movement of the bulge along the receiving structures. The theory seems in this respect unable to offer a proper parallel to the full psychological analysis of tone, as given in the present work.

Nevertheless ter Kuile's results for pitch are exceedingly suggestive. Especially valuable is his conclusion that the distance at which the bulge of a tone expires, reckoned from the basis of the cochlea, is proportionate to the vibratory frequency of the tone. If only we could get the bulges of simultaneous tones to *overlap* in that way, then we should have a much more hopeful basis for our psychological analysis.

"For the analysis of chords," says ter Kuile (48, 509), "it is sufficient to find lymph quantities that change in the period of the components. I shall speak of this only in a couple of words, firstly because I see that Herr Max Meyer, of whose theory I have only just learnt the principle, has apportioned the curves otherwise; and secondly because I am convinced that we may not simply transfer the superposition curves of the particles of air to the stirrup plate. Consider...a curve of two tones in the relation of the fifth. If O is the surface of the stirrup plate, there is then a quantity $ab \times O$ that changes once in the whole period (difference tone); a quantity $bc \times O$ that changes thrice (upper primary); and a quantity $cd \times O$ that changes twice (lower primary). Because there is always still a little lymph there during the whole total period, the lymph quantities will apportion themselves evenly and each assume the period proper to itself."

It seems clear that analysis in these terms is very much akin to the methods of analysis pursued by Meyer. Meyer himself has shown[1]

[1] 72, 67. Meyer adds (p. 70 ff.) a second proof of the impossibility of ter Kuile's theory which would surely render any theory of hearing impossible, except, of course, Meyer's own. It would have been helpful if Meyer had referred to, or given, the proof of the basis on which this proof itself rests: that the siren of holes can easily produce such vibrations as are represented in his Fig. 4, either at the siren hole or from there at the ear.

that on ter Kuile's physical principles the two primaries gd' should yield together the pitches G, f', g', instead of G, g, d'.

While ter Kuile's theory is thus in its own way quite unable to give an adequate basis for the analysis of hearing expounded in this work, it offers in certain respects a basis which is much more appropriate than that offered by any other theory. The relative lengths of membrane traversed by the waves of simple sine curves are just such as are here required. Only we should need to have the basilar process maintained for each, both when alone and when in conjunction with other tones, right from the basis of the membrane on to the point of expiry with a point of maximum bulge in the middle. We shall inquire later what physical processes must be presupposed in the cochlea in order to obtain this. If our psychological analysis is correct, a corresponding physiological process must occur; so that we have here an important guide to the discovery of the physical processes between the external meatus and the basilar membrane. This is really a method of constructing a physical theory to fit the facts of hearing.

A. Lehmann, 1910 (50).

Lehmann's theory has been mentioned above, but it deserves separate treatment. The author inclines to place it as a modification of Helmholtz's resonance theory, but it has in experimental basis and in its consequences great similarity with Ewald's. Lehmann produced waves in a large piece of rubber membrane in contact with a vibrating fork and showed that in a membrane narrow at one end and broad at the other, as the basilar membrane is, the vibration set up by any tone stimulus is limited to the part of the membrane of the appropriate length. Such a membrane can take up two rates of vibration at once without their mutual interference. In this sense Lehmann obviously improves upon Ewald.

But Lehmann's sound pictures are not by any means yet reduced to one vibratory part for each tone. There are two or three of these at least. Lehmann supposes that these superfluous effects are damped out partly by the arches of Corti, partly by the surrounding fluid, so that we do not hear supernumerary noises and tones. No essential objections can then be brought, thinks Lehmann, against the assumption that the vibrations of the basilar membrane correspond to the vibrations of his membranes, stretched transversely, but free longitudinally, as the basilar membrane is. Thus the vibrations of the basilar membrane are like those assumed by Helmholtz; the breadth, tension, and stiffness of the basilar membrane suffice to give the membrane the range of octaves covered by our hearing; and the vibrations are such as make room for a certain mass of fluid. The means by which the basilar membrane falls into these vibrations is also akin to the principle of resonance. Only that part of the basilar membrane which has the period of the oscillations of the oval window will regularly make room for the fluid displaced by the latter. Parts nearer will be bulged out first, but they will clash with the period of the stirrup at once and so the fluid displaced will be pushed onwards till it gets to the part in tune with the motions of the stirrup. Then the oval window, this part of the basilar membrane, the round window and the columns of fluid between these windows and the basilar membrane will pendulate synchronously, and any vibrations of other parts will be damped out. The hearing of the unmusical would be accounted for, if their basilar membrane were lax instead of tense, transversely.

Lehmann's theory does indeed unite a number of the merits of Helmholtz's and Ewald's constructions while avoiding their greatest difficulties. Pitch varies with place on the basilar membrane, volume with the length of the vibrating part. But, as we have seen, much more is required than this, both on the psychological and on the physical side. Lehmann's scheme offers no basis for the consonance and dissonance of normal hearing, but only for the failure of analysis of extremely bad ears, such as he himself seems to possess (e.g. a twelfth, he thinks, for himself reduces to a between-tone-fusion). But most important of all, in supposing the organs of Corti and the fluids surrounding the basilar membrane to do so much and so perfect damping, Lehmann has practically assumed everything left unproved by his experiments. And that is enough to make a process that approximately fits the requirements of hearing quite useless for their actual attainment. As a physical theory Lehmann's, like Ewald's, can only be a step on the way to a knowledge of what is required of a physical theory. And that requirement, as I have shown, can be got far more easily without any physics from a purely psychological study of hearing.

O. Göbel, 1911 (22, 23, 24).

Göbel calls the part of the + phase from equilibrium to maximum condensation + I, from the latter back to equilibrium + II; the other half is called the − phase, from equilibrium to maximal rarefaction − I and the remainder back to equilibrium − II.

Göbel believes that tone sensation arises at the end of the $+$ I phase owing to the pressure of the membrana tectoria upon the hairs. High tones stimulate the basis, low ones the apex of the cochlea. No matter how sound enters the cochlea, by the stapes or by bone conduction, the $+$ I phase displaces the cochlear partition more energetically than do the other phases. For this reason and because of the slow return of the cochlear partition to its position of rest, the partition does not reach this position at the end of the whole period. Thus there is a certain amount of summation of $+$ I phases in respect of their action on the cochlear partition. The sensation of a simple tone depends upon the stimulation of a fairly large part of the partition. The differentiation of neighbouring tones is due to the difference in the strength of stimulation of the series of receptors affected, which are largely coincident.

When two tones occur together, the effect therefore depends greatly upon how their $+$ phases are related to one another. If they are coincident, the shorter $+$ phase (of the higher tone) cannot stimulate the ear, but only the longer one. The two tones thus affect one another's pitch and constancy. Thus when c and c^4 sound together, c^4 shows a light, fast vibration, not to be confused with beats. This is the interruption of its continuity by the simultaneous lower tone. Two forks an octave apart are each heard lower when sounded simultaneously than when singly (22, 141). When $g'e^2$ is played, and e^2 observed, it seems to have a pitch between d sharp and d; when $c'e$ is played, the pitch of e seems to be between d and d sharp, etc. For these observations comparison was made between the memory of the tone observed and the actual sound of single tones played afterwards. When two tones b and c' are played together, Göbel hears a slightly discontinuous weaker higher tone and a very strongly discontinuous, much louder and deeper tone. The higher tone lies in pitch between b and c'. The difference in pitch of the two tones is considerable. The deeper one is not so much a tone, as a discontinuous sensation of blows or knocks that belong to a certain pitch region and have something whirring about them (22, 145 f.). The continuous oscillation between the high and low pitch (the tones being discontinuous) and this whirring constitute dissonance. The sensations of dissonance and of subjective combination tones rest on one principle: the simultaneous excitation of other parts of the receiving series than are excited by each tone alone.

Whatever may be the merits of Göbel's views in so far as they rest upon direct physical and physiological observation, it must be

evident that his psychological deductions and observations depart
very much from the results of what we must consider to be the best
and surest psychological observations, upon which our main exposition
rests.   The illusions of continuity and simultaneity asserted are untenable; and tones do not affect one another's pitches in the way
alleged.   Anyone who claims to observe such things nowadays, must
be written down as an incapable, or at least, highly suggestible, observer.
The same holds of other 'observations' of Göbel, e.g. those upon which
he bases his theory of the fusion of the octave: that when a c^2 fork
is struck gently, only a c^2 pitch is heard, but when it is struck strongly,
a c' pitch is heard as well.

My Own Suggestions.

LXVII.   I have pointed out in the introduction to this account
of the physiological theories of hearing that it is not the duty of the
psychologist to propound a physiological theory of hearing to suit
his facts.   The psychological analysis of hearing has a standing and
validity of its own.   But this very primacy suggests that the great
confusion of opinion displayed in our review of physiological theories
may be resolved by approaching the physiological problem from the
psychological side and by asking what sort of physical processes in
the cochlea would form a suitable counterpart for the system of psychological facts expounded in this work.   We should then have to inquire
only whether that group of physical processes is consistent in itself
and with the other physical processes that lead up to it.   If this consistency were established, the group of physical processes proposed
would at once acquire a probability of a high degree.   The psychological
system would thus be, as it were, the key to the puzzle of physical
possibilities.   It is in this sense that I offer the following considerations,
which seem to me at the same time to lie in the line of convergence
of what is most acceptable in the physiological theories we have reviewed.

LXVIII.   I would adhere to the rejection of the resonance hypothesis common to Hurst, Meyer and ter Kuile.   I should, however,
suppose that the stapes follows the variations of pressure displayed
in compound sine curves, both in their positive and negative parts.
For although the stapes is not pulled back by the negative pressures
before the tympanum (as ter Kuile holds), it is allowed to recede under
the force of the pressure exerted upon it from within the cochlea only

by the progress of increasing rarefaction before the tympanum. Further, I should adopt the main principles of action expounded by ter Kuile: the basilar membrane[1] is so elastic as to make possible many different depths of bulge upon it, and there is wave-motion over the basilar membrane, at a constant linear rate for all tones, so that the distance traversed before the expiry of a wave is proportionate to the vibratory frequency of the tone. And the greater amplitude of the air motion finds expression in the greater amplitude of bulge of the basilar membrane over the constant extent bulged. Thus far I am in perfect agreement with ter Kuile.

LXIX. The essential point of difference is this. If, as ter Kuile supposes, the basilar membrane is a very elastic structure, will it not react upon any pressure exerted upon it at any point of its length so as to make that pressure return and, if possible, dissipate itself *in all directions*? Of course the thrust of the stapes will create a wave that moves along the basilar membrane at a steady rate in spite of its increasing breadth, just as the wave from a dropped stone moves in ever widening circles over the surface of a sheet of water. The successive parts of the head of the wave will properly represent the successive pressures of the stapes in the first quarter period, because the progression of the wave is unhindered and unaffected by return pressures only in the forward direction.

We may not start the air curve at the point of its equilibrium; we must start it at the maximal rarefaction. A sort of *real* negativity of phase—from equilibrium *down* to maximal rarefaction and back— must somehow be eliminated by the action of the ossicles, or the like. We must reckon all movements—from 0 to maximum,—and their disappearance—from maximum to 0 again,—as positive pressures.

Let A, B, C, D, E (Fig. 9) be the moments respectively of maximal rarefaction, of equilibrium (maximal acceleration of stapes), of maximal condensation, of equilibrium again, and of maximal rarefaction, ending the whole period; let a and e be respectively the basis, and utmost limit affected in the whole period, of the basilar membrane; and let b, c and d be respectively the points defining the quarters of the length a, e. ter Kuile supposes that the bulging is completed by moment C, and occupies the length ac, and moves on, ever diminishing at the

---

[1] Or the membrana tectoria, if that is the elastic receptory membrane (cf. 154, 157, 158). There is something to be said for it, but the arguments are not compelling, and could be opposed by others. I prefer to think of the basilar membrane as the essential structure.

proximal end, towards the apex, till it expires at *e*. As far as the basilar membrane is concerned, nothing happens behind the stapes after moment *C*.

But if the basilar membrane reacts elastically to the pressures exerted upon it, it will not let the pressures behind the stapes reduce from moment *B* to moment *C* to nothing, parallel to the accompanying reduction of the rate of movement of the stapes from maximum to nothing. It will return or maintain the pressures upon it outwards in all directions from itself and thus the pressures exerted upon the basilar membrane by the stapes will be returned to the stapes at the same constant rate as pertains to the motion of the wave advancing along the basilar membrane. Thus although the stapes enters upon its return movement

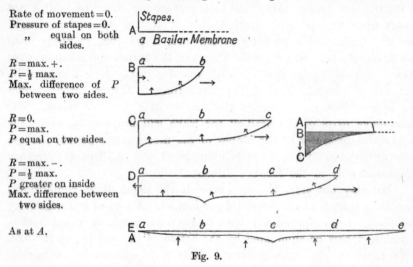

Fig. 9.

after the moment *C*, the pressure on the cochlear side of it will not then begin to be lower than the normal pressure within the vestibule; it will be much higher—in fact just below the previous maximum, if anything—because the basilar membrane will have returned that maximum, with some slight loss no doubt, against the plate of the stapes, whose primary pressure is then less than its own.

This analysis may be established in another way (*v.* Fig. 9). It is clear that there can at no time be a very great difference between the pressure exerted on the stapes by the incus and that on the other side of the plate of the stapes just within the labyrinth. This difference is doubtless the greater, the greater the rate of movement of the stapes or the steeper the air curve at the moment. For the difference is just what regulates the rate of movement of the stapes. The pressures therefore in the vestibule will rise steadily from A to B, and at moment B the difference between the two sides will be maximal. From B to C the difference of pressures will decrease to nothing; but the stapes is still advancing and at the moment C the pressure on the stapes from the tympanum is at its maximum and about to decrease; hence the pressure on the vestibular side must be also maximal; and it is certainly a good deal greater than it was at B, or the rate of motion of the stapes would not have diminished so much from B to C. So we must suppose that, although the stapes from B to C has only advanced and displaced as much lymph as from A to B, yet the return pressure from B, which would have just reached the stapes from B in the time allowed at all moments from B to C, has added to what was given by the stapes enough to bank up a maximum against the stapes.

From C to D the rate of movement of the stapes increases to maximum again, while the pressure on the tympanal side of the stapes reduces to half. But the pressure within must be somewhat greater, more especially if the stapes is not so much pulled out by the tympanum as pushed back from within (48, 497). All this must however be done at the expense of the pressure within the cochlea, not only from b towards a, but also from c towards b, and from parts between c and d backwards; in fact homogeneously throughout.

In the final quarter the rate of movement of the stapes reduces to nothing, and the pressures become equal again on both sides. Then all the pressures within the bulge, which will have just reached e, are also equal and there is no more any forward push in the whole.

Still another analysis may be offered (cf. Fig. 9).

From A^1 to B. Suppose at a moment soon after A, the basis of the basilar membrane were bulged out to a depth x. Owing to the elasticity of the membrane the extent of membrane bulged would return the pressure upon it, but would find no place for the fluid before it (as the pressure on the stapes is increasing), except forwards towards the apex. So the membrane in that direction would be bulged out and the depth of the bulge x would reduce itself in proportion to the length

---

[1] In a detailed study of the behaviour of the part a of the basilar membrane, the facts and theory of pp. 95 ff. above, would have to be considered. This consideration might lead to modification of the graphs of Figs. 9 and 10 at their a ends. But I have thought it best to ignore this subtlety for the present.

of the extra membrane bulged out. But as the stapes is advancing at a greater rate than before, the depth x is not only not reduced but further extended. And so on.

The rate of progression of the forward movement of the wave on the basilar membrane thus depends on the elasticity of the basilar membrane. For the less the depth to which any excursion of the stapes will bulge out a point near the basis of the membrane, i.e. the greater the tension in the membrane for any given depth of bulge, the longer a stretch of the basilar membrane must be bulged out to accommodate the fluid displaced by that excursion of the stapes. Thus the length of the basilar membrane required for the reception of sounds is entirely within the command of the interadjustment of tissues within the cochlea and is only relatively dependent on the length of the aerial waves of sound.

The constancy of the length of the basilar membrane (i.e. the pitch) affected for different intensities is due to the fact that the excursion of the stapes varies with the intensity of sound, and that the depth of bulge of the basilar membrane varies with the amount of fluid displaced by the stapes in a given time. When the intensity of a tone gets very high, so that the elasticity limits of the bulge are reached, the rate of flow of wave in the cochlea will increase considerably; and there may seem to be some slight increase (i.e. lowering of pitch) for moderate increases of intensity, i.e. the bulge of the basilar membrane is not under all circumstances, but only within a normal range, quite proportionate to the excursion of the stapes (above, p. 157, note).

From B to C. Consider first a moment soon after B, namely B'. Let the distance from b to b' be y. The stapes at B' is not receding. Hence the pressure of the moment B will have spread itself equally over the whole distance y. For although this pressure as a whole is moving forward, it has for any distance of progress only half the distance of regress to make; so that the regress will never lag behind the progress. But during this time B—B' the stapes has moved forward at a rate only little less than the maximum. Hence the bulge next the stapes will still be the greatest.

If the stapes did not move any more till C, this increase next the stapes would spread itself evenly over the whole distance a—b with the exception of a space y next to b. But the stapes does move at continually decreasing rates. Hence layers of less and less depth will add themselves to this first imaginary even level from a—b, each layer beginning at a next the stapes, being increasingly shorter and thinner, to correspond to the decreasing rates of the movement of the stapes. Hence the bulge at moment C will be as in the figure. The level of bulge due to moment B has decreased far below its depth at moment B. But the other layers coming on the top make it up. And the decreasing rates of movement of the stapes, and the decreasing amounts of fluid displaced by it are properly represented by the lengths and thinnesses of the layers. It is obvious that the extra pressure due to the last movement of the stapes before C, has time to spread itself over only a very little distance from the basis of the basilar membrane.

For the periods from C to D, and D to E, the reasoning is exactly similar to the above, only the process is now reversed.

C to D. Let the bulge have moved along for a very short distance y. If the stapes were motionless during this period, the pressure over the distance y from the basis of the basilar membrane would be homogeneous. But to produce this, a reduction would have to be made in the depth of bulge of the basilar membrane all over, each part losing and adding to the parts next it. But the stapes was not motionless, it receded a little, owing to the return pressure from the basilar membrane and to the increasing rarefaction on the tympanal side, and made a little more space than the elasticity of the basilar membrane would have made for itself by the forward movement of the whole wave. Hence the bulge of the basilar membrane will be reduced a little more than it otherwise would next to the stapes, because the undue reduction of pressure has only time to cover that part. And so on.

LXX. Now the elasticity of the basilar membrane is not perfect. Therefore it must not be supposed that the pressure on the vestibular side of the stapes is exactly equal to that on the tympanal side precisely at the moment E. Nor will the pressures over the length a—e be entirely normal, although they will by that time have been equalised, so that the progress of the motion will be at an end. They will have also been equalised on the other side of the basilar membrane in the scala tympani (of course without any use having been made of the helicotrema). The basilar membrane, in short, will not regain its normal position precisely at the end of the period. With each succeeding period this remnant effect will therefore increase, till a position of equilibrium is attained, after which the periodic movement of the stapes will produce a certain periodic increase and decrease of the amplitude of the whole bulge over the extent of the basilar membrane affected (a—e), whereby any effect upon experience of the progression along the basilar membrane of the successive moments of the period would be largely obliterated. Thus we should have a proper basis for the initiatory increase of the auditory excitation (1, 202), and for the brief after-effect of tonal stimulation, till the excitation has again died down (2, 411). The time of expiration of tone seems to be some thirty thousandths of a second.

LXXI. The increase of breadth of the basilar membrane towards the apex need not be due to any merely receptive necessity, as the resonance theories suppose[1]. It is a peculiar fact that this increase of breadth is concurrent with a decrease of diameter of the scalae that must be quite as great. This suggests that the increase of breadth of the basilar membrane is a device to attain greater sensitivity. Both changes (basilar membrane and diameter of scalae) could then be expressed as an increase of the relative proportions of basilar membrane and the rest of the wall of the scalae. The relatively bigger surface would be much more easily bulged by the probably small changes of pressures that survive passage far along the scala[2]. Are not low tones less intensive for the same physical force than high ones? The increasing difficulty of getting trills in the bass would then be a mere reflex of the slight change of pressure thus far along the basilar membrane and the consequently slow recovery of the basilar membrane left unaffected by a momentary rise of pitch.

Hearing by bone conduction should probably be possible for the same reason as accounts for the passage of the wave bulge along the basilar membrane. This is the only direction within the cochlea in which the molecular movement could change into the adequate stimulus. Molecular movements may, of course, at the same time cross the contents of the cochlea in all other directions[3]. That

---

[1] On this point cf. Hurst (33, 332) who was perhaps the first to depart from the Helmholtzian view. The increase of breadth from base to apex—some twelve times—could be made compatible with Helmholtz's theory, but does not exactly encourage it. Denker (10) points out that in the parrot—which has a range of hearing wide enough for the perception of our speech and of many tones,—the broadening of the basilar membrane is much less than in our ears, for the greater part of the membrane not more than twofold.

[2] Cf. above (p. 144) where reference is made to Gray's reminder that the ligamentum spirale increases in size and becomes more fibrous towards the base of the cochlea, thus putting greater tension on the basilar membrane at the base than at the apex of the cochlea.

[3] Cf. F. Bezold (6): "While the waves which impinge upon the labyrinth directly remain inaudible, probably only those of the waves of sound arriving by air or bone conduction are heard which on their way to the labyrinth have traversed the apparatus for sound conduction; and of these again only those which have set the latter apparatus along with

such a conversion from molecular movement into push is possible, seems as likely as that air waves should push the tympanum inwards, apart from the intensifying power of this special mechanism. The evolution of the cochlea presupposes that the mere molecular movement is not incapable of this conversion even without the special transforming mechanism.

My physical analysis gives no indication of any cause for combination tones and such secondary pitch phenomena, other than beats, the basis of which is as obvious here as it is in the superposition curves of the air. The secondary pitch phenomena probably have their ground in processes of physical interference outside the forces upon which my analysis builds altogether; so that they would be carried from their point of origin to the basilar membrane by the processes I assume for my analysis in the same way as any objective tones. Peterson says: "We seem to be at a juncture where physiological theories of hearing have to do, so far as the existence of all perceived tones is concerned, principally with the primary phenomena of tonal analysis" (90, 317. Cf. above, p. 55).

The above analysis might be true independently of the question as to how the auditory stimulus enters the cochlea, whether by the stapes and oval window, as is commonly supposed, or by the promontorium (142), or by the round window (59). These various ways would no doubt make differences in the intensity of the experiences; but such differences do occur, as between air and bone conduction. And bone conduction does seem to imply the existence of alternate routes of entry. My analysis would show a correlation between changes of air pressure and changes in bulge of the basilar membrane without prejudice to the route by which the correlation is determined.

LXXII. The analysis of tonal masses by the ear may be illustrated by a simple example—the octave. I take again as basis of analysis a period from one maximal rarefaction to another (v. Fig. 10).

It is clear that from the moments A to B there will be a summation of the pressures of the two tones, just as in the superposition curve

the column of labyrinth water resting upon it as a whole into transverse vibrations, i.e. incursions and excursions." "The work of the sound conducting apparatus," says Bezold, "consists in converting the longitudinal sound waves of the air as well as the longitudinal sound waves directly traversing the skull into transverse vibrations, which are alone able to set the neural end apparatus of the ear into perceptible sympathetic vibration." According to Bezold the sound conducting apparatus is required for all sounds up to the once accented octave.

for the air. But from B to C the pressure will proceed to a maximum in respect of the lower tone, but to a minimum in respect of the higher tone. Thus far (i.e. in respect of the higher tone) the whole block of pressures set up from A to B will be greater than the sequence of pressures set up from B to C and there will be room in the latter for some retroactive dissipation of the former: just as much room relatively, in fact, as there would be, were no lower tone present at the time. Thus while the maximum of the whole volume (i.e. the volume of the lower tone) comes at C, a relative predominance will occur at the basilar

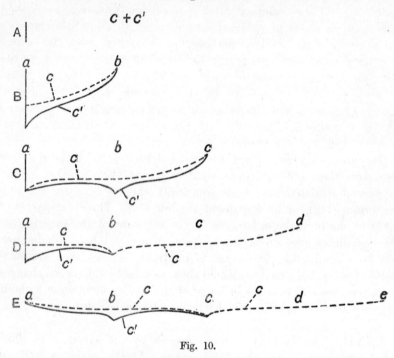

Fig. 10.

point b. Similarly on the down grade of the lower tone, this relative maximum will recur. The basilar point b lies half-way between the basis of the membrane and the point c, which gives the pitch of the lower tone, i.e.: it is an octave higher.

The relations for any other interval can be studied after this pattern. I find it easiest to conceive the matter by introducing the second tone in minimal amplitude and by then supposing the amplitude to increase. What holds for a small amplitude will hold for any amplitude, apart from the special lowering effect of intensity. No new principle is introduced for these tonal masses. The processes of equilibrisation which go on as the tone advances, cannot distort one another, the higher disfiguring the lower tone, as it were. For the reach of these processes, as we have seen above, is limited by the constant rate of propagation of pressure difference over the basilar membrane owing to the average and constant elasticity of the basilar membrane. So the debit made retroactively on the lower volume can only proceed as far as the previous credit has been given by the higher volume. Here we encounter again the regularity, balance, or symmetry peculiar to the tone as such. This account, however, be it noted, ignores for the sake of simplicity of analysis any relative obliterating effect that may well be exerted by a lower tone upon any higher tone as a whole (cf. above, p. 70 f.).

And it is evident herefrom that the processes of bulge of the basilar membrane are essentially independent of any phase relations. It makes no difference to the equilibrisation whether the higher tone sets in at the moment A or at B or at any intervening period; it will still affect exactly the same part of the basilar membrane. All periodic waves, no matter how irregular, will therefore be resolved into their pendular components, i.e. into such components as result from the law of the uniform spreading of pressures over the basilar membrane in virtue of its elasticity. The spread will always be balanced and symmetrical round points of relative maximum, i.e. the analysis will result in tones, balanced volumes. Any vibration, whether periodic or not, will produce a sound; but only periodic vibrations will produce tone or tonal mass. Tone, thus, has long had a physical definition, although in this work it has been shown for the first time what distinguishes a tone psychically from other sounds.

LXXIII. As regards the minute localisation of pitches and volumes upon the basilar membrane, the physiological evidence seems to be hardly sufficient as yet. It seems, however, fairly certain that the higher the pitch of a tone, the nearer its receptors lie towards the basal end of the basilar membrane. That was Helmholtz's inference from the variation of breadth shown by the transverse fibres. And the recent work on the experimental injury of the cochlea by very loud tones has confirmed it (cf. 141). Pitches are found in a series also centrally (cf. 49, 618). But the fact does not necessarily presuppose that the variation of breadth of the transverse fibres is the essential variant of the tonal receptors. It is quite compatible with the theory just propounded.

The results of experimental injury do not seem to indicate with all desirable precision the exact position on the cochlea of particular tones. For the injuries that have been found cover considerable lengths of the basilar membrane, much greater lengths than could be accommodated by Helmholtz's theory[1] (cf. 17, 192). An attempt should be made to produce *minimal* injuries for tones of different pitch, so that the point of incidence of the pitch of these tones may be determined. But probably the cochlea is not adjusted for stimuli of injurious intensity, so that an exact correspondence between the place of incidence of injury and that of the normal excitation could not be guaranteed. There would naturally be some sort of correspondence between series of either; but it might well be that excessive stimuli would produce their injurious effects too far along the basilar membrane towards the apex. This is strongly supported by the dependence of pitch upon intensity within the normal variations of the latter (cf. 157, note, above). Measurement of the point of incidence of injuries should certainly not be given in terms of the whorls of the cochlea, but in terms of distance from the base of the basilar membrane and in relation to its whole length. The cochlea is differently coiled in different animals and the first coil always includes a much greater length of basilar membrane than do the others.

The existence of tone islands and tone gaps, as described by F. Bezold, whose work I have not been able to see, obviously calls for no particular justification or explanation within my theory. The only point to notice is that a tonal gap would not necessarily involve complete deafness, or auditory insensitivity of every sort, to the tones whose *pitches* fell within the range of the gap.

In the following table (No. XII) I have made an attempt to show the implications and the possibility of my theory with reference to the cochlea. According to Retzius (93, vol. ii. 346) the number of transverse fibres in the human basilar membrane is 24,000. Hensen's number, 16,400 (149, 114f.) refers to the number of hair-cells or neural receptors. As the basilar membrane is the basis of reception, the limits of receptivity must be closely determined by its subdivision.

But the hair-cells, in which the receptive terminals are embedded, do not lie in parallel rows, but in alternate rows, like the cells of a honeycomb or like the bricks in a wall, each member of an upper row lying on the line between two members of the lower row (cf. 93, ii. 350; 48, 507).

---

[1] I have not been able to see the original work in experimental injury, the most o which has appeared in the *Ztsch. f. Ohrenheilkunde.*

The receptive capacity of the neural terminals might therefore be greater than that of the transverse fibres. Twice as great a capacity has been allowed, and even a greater amount is conceivable, so that we may treat the total number of hair-cells approximately as if it were a single series[1].

The further assumption is made that the number of transverse fibres to the unit of length is constant along the basilar membrane. But it might well be smaller towards the apex where the fibres are longer. That would leave a larger number for the reception of higher tones. The number for each octave would increase as we go upwards

TABLE XII.

No. of transverse fibres (Retzius)	No. of neural terminals (Hensen)	Pitch. Vibrations per sec.	Limits of correct naming	j.n.d. in vbs.	No. of j.n.d. in octave	No. of fibres per j.n.d.
24,000	16,400	A_2 27	Lower			
12,000	8,200	A_1 55				
6,000	4,100	A 110		0·4	137	22
3,000	2,050	a 220		0·3	370	4
1,500	1,025	a' 440	(The musical range of pitch)	0·3	730	1
750	512	a^2 880		0·3	1460	·25
375	256	a^3 1,760		1·0	880	·2
187	128	a^4 3,520		4·0	440	·2
93	64	a^5 7,040	Upper	16·0	220	·2
46	32	a^6 14,080	Cf. above, Table V, p. 96 ff.	Cf. above, p. 81	—	—
23	—	—		—	—	—

in pitch, without prejudice to the reduction of the volume by one half for each octave upwards.

In the last column of the table the number of transverse fibres available for each just noticeable difference is given. Allowing a just noticeable difference (j.n.d.) in the octave between a' and a^2 of 0·3 vibration per second, we should then have in the whole octave 1460 distinguishable sensations. For these there are available some 375 fibres, which would give about 0·25 of a fibre to each distinguishable

[1] Cf. 154, 118: "In place of these fibres of the basilar membrane I would substitute the 385,000 percipient capillary processes floating freely in the endolymph and connected directly with the sensory cell transmission apparatus...as the parts of Corti's organ which are sympathetically affected by sonorous waves entering the ear." A reassuring number!

difference. That allowance would hardly be exceeded for the higher octave, if we suppose the threshold of discrimination of pitch to increase as indicated in the third column from the right. In the octaves lower than a' the number of fibres to the just noticeable difference increases. There, as we have already assumed (above, p. 81 f.), discrimination does not depend directly upon the number of transverse fibres, but upon the distinct displacement of the point of predominant volume. As the predominance in low tones is probably rather blunt, a considerable shift would be required to produce a distinct impression of change of pitch.

It would therefore seem that the dimensions and structure of the cochlea are at least approximately compatible with the various facts brought together in the table.

LXXIV. But further concessions may be made without abandoning any of the principles upon which my psychological analysis is based. It might, for example, be urged that the theory of this work involves much too special an hypothesis—that the rate of propagation of a wave upon the basilar membrane is constant and the distance traversed exactly proportional to the time allowed, i.e. to the rate of physical vibration. No objection can be made on that ground to the psychological analysis from which the physiological demand was deduced. For the fusions of the octave and the fifths must be special volumic coincidences, as shown above by purely psychological means. And yet a little freedom and licence might be desirable on the physical side. A small deviation would make no appreciable difference to the balanced and symmetrical nature of tones.

One of the results that flowed from our psychological analysis seems to offer this desirable scope for individual variation—the absolutely thoroughgoing proportionality of all intervals, that has been so striking. What if this proportionality has so seized hold upon the whole of hearing that it has moulded even the basis of the great consonances—the octave and the fifth—to itself? Suppose the elasticity of the basilar membrane is not constant throughout, but decreases towards the apex. That might be the function of the increase of the length of the transverse fibres; not only a greater sensitivity, but a slowing down of the wave progression would result. But the effects would be, as nearly as possible, proportional throughout, otherwise the ear would be a bad instrument, unsuitable at least for musical appreciation.

The result for the octave (cf. Fig. 4, p. 70) would be that the point of predominance (the pitch) of a tone an octave lower would always be by a definite proportion (less than one-one) further along the basilar membrane: but the lower limiting point of the upper volume would still always fall exactly on the point of predominance of the lower tone. For the fifth (Fig. 5, p. 70) the two determining points of the upper volume would no longer lie at exactly equal distances on either side of the point of predominance of the lower volume; but the distance from the latter point on the lower side (physiologically— towards the apex of the cochlea) would be smaller than the distance on the upper side (basis of cochlea) by a definite proportion. No difference would, then, result throughout our whole scheme of volumes; only, as proportion would now be the essential matter, not only for intervals, in respect of the whole volumes that compose them, but also in respect of the parts of the volumes marked out within them, all the relations above considered important on the basis of a one-one proportion would still be important on any other proportion. The availability and utility of tones for their special purposes would thus be greatly widened, and it would be easier for nature to conform to the psychical ideal set for her. The expense incurred by her in accommo-dating low tones would not be so disproportionate to the number housed.

For the probable existence, and effects, of minor deviations from the uniformity of elasticity of the basilar membrane compare p. 180 ff., below.

CHAPTER IX

BINAURAL HEARING

LXXV. Modern research has established the fact that the two ears serve to localise sounds. For those who deny the presence in sensations of sound of any spatial attribute, that fact is itself the strongest confirmation of their view that could be desired. And for those who are so minded it affords ground for the belief that hearing is originally devoid of spatiality altogether, getting it only by associa-tion or conjunction with other senses. Almost all theories of the spatial powers of hearing have followed these lines up to the present time. That is only natural, for they are but the consistent pursuance of those laid down for the elements of hearing, which we have already discussed and rejected. If localisation is present in the double ear and absent in the single, it can obviously get there only from some other source than hearing. So the argument would run; and any theory would naturally turn to seek the likely source.

A likely source may readily be found, but trouble arises when the means has to be indicated by which spatiality comes to be borrowed and lent. It is easy to postulate the transference, but very difficult to establish it validly and irrefutably. In fact it cannot be done. The transference of sensory modes is as much a castle in the air as the transmission of acquired characteristics. When it is really justified, it is found to be untrue. It is therefore a quicker means to the good end to reverse the whole argument. Thus: whether hearing seems to have borrowed its spatiality or not, it has it in the double ear; therefore it must have had something in the single ear from which spatiality might have emerged. Localisation is a kind of order; a single ear will therefore possess a kind of order; pitch differences are a kind of order. So pitch differences will be the basis upon which localisation rests. This conclusion is confirmed by the fact that the localisations of binocular vision are products of those of uniocular vision, and these are primarily matters of order.

This inverse deduction will seem to many to give just the absurd sort of conclusion they expected. For if no one has argued quite in this way, the attempt has been made to fasten localisation on to pitch in one way or another, e.g. by Mach, and has necessitated subsidiary hypotheses so far beyond verification or proof that no one could hope thereby to bring the psychology of hearing to a successful conclusion.

But the deduction regarding the connexion between pitch and localisation is valid for all that. The fault lies not in it, but in the hypotheses by which it had to be buttressed, when it was not built out according to the natural plan of its parts. It is the finest structures which are most dependent upon the harmonious presence and co-operation of all parts. I have already shown why the true theory of hearing was never found by those various thinkers who fell upon one or other of the foundations of that theory that are so obvious when they are once seen. The chief obstruction was the ever recurrent problem of space. The inability to think the space of experience as one of a class of ordinal systems, a want of faith in the systematic nature of sensory experience, the prejudice of physiological investigation and theory, and the failure to think out principles to the end, no matter how absurd and impossible much of the work might seem in the doing of it.

The aim of this part of my work then, is to show that the ordinal differences of the elements of hearing are the basis of the binaural localisation of hearing. I hope to show to the conviction of the reader that all the main phenomena of hearing can be deduced from the theory of the elements I have propounded; and that whatever remains over is doubtful or problematical for no want or weakness in my theory as far as it goes. The presumption must rather be that these outstanding fields will yield on further knowledge to my theory.

The problems of binaural hearing find a parallel in the problems of binocular vision. Each ear, like each eye, is a vast system of elementary sense-organs, or a vast system of elementary ordinal differences. The problems of binaural and of binocular processes may therefore be grouped together as the problems of bi-systemic integration. It is important that these problems should be kept in mind together; for the problems and results that stand out clearly in the one sense may be obscure and unobtrusive in the other sense. And great advantage may accrue from transferring to the one sense the results of labour spent upon the analogous problem of the other sense. I have elsewhere dealt with the problems of binocular vision at considerable length (148). I may be permitted, therefore, to treat some of the problems of binaural hearing a little less *ab initio* than was necessary in the first assault upon a specific level of integrative action.

LXXVI. One of the less obtrusive problems of binaural hearing is how we come to hear the same with both ears. This problem of sameness is quite obvious in vision, at least as far as the sameness of form is concerned. For we do sometimes get double visual images from one and the same object; and so we naturally wonder why we ever fail to distinguish the two images we always receive. The only reason that can be adduced for our ignoring the problem in hearing is the qualitative classification of pitch. That classification begins by postulating the whole series of pitches in the single ear without explaining how it comes to be there. And later theories that reject Helmholtz's theory of consonance by identity of partials have to postulate also all the peculiar properties of the series. So much being taken for granted, a little more may seem to be of no importance. The pitch series is surely as identical in the two ears as is the spectral series in the two eyes. And if it be recalled in protest that we can easily reduplicate the spectral series in the two eyes by letting it fall upon disparate points of either eye, the answer would be: in hearing there are no disparate points; there is only one point for each quality of the series, and so, of course, the two series are identical. We need only make "the simple assumption that corresponding points of the two cochleas are such as are stimulated by the same tone" (55, 252). That assumption is so simple merely because in a few words it assumes everything. If every pair of ears is thus assumed to be attuned to each other, so to speak, it is a mere trifle to assume further for the purpose of explaining certain unusual facts, that certain pairs of ears are tuned differently (55, 236).

It is a merit of my theory that at this point it can bear a new burden of service in the general cause of biology. We have already seen how the origin of the tonal series and its special features are to be explained. Now, this explanation offers a ready basis for the identification of the series as given in either ear. Each series is, of course, constituted by a primarily different series of orders. Any assumption of identity would be as arbitrary as is the assumption of the original correspondence of the two retinae (148, 146 f.). How could two organs be in conformity with one another from the very start, unless some miracle of pre-established harmony were admitted? And if they were really identical, the duplication of the ears would be useless. It is obviously a sort of all-or-nothing case. Either the two ears were originally identical, which is absurd; or they were two and totally independent. The only conceivable original relation between the two is that given by their differences of orders; the two would form one larger system including all their orders. As a fact we find that the two ears can be distinguished auditorily. We can tell with fair ease whether an objective or, perhaps better still, a subjective sound is of the left or right 'system' (ear) (41, 204f.). This can be done, as Baley (3, 347ff.) has shown, even with ten simultaneous tones, separated from one another by an interval of not less than a fourth, and distributed between the two ears, as soon as the single tones emerge clearly out of the whole mass. The tones are, of course, usually identified and localised at the proper ear successively, although two tones can be heard and ascribed to opposite ears at once. In such a large grouping of tones, however, an error of localisation, as between one ear and the other, can occur (3, 371).

But as we find them the two auditory systems or fields seem to be not simple parts of a greater system, but coordinate parts of a complex system. It is not immediately evident how great this complexity is. Perhaps it is not nearly so great as it seems to be. But on the basis of the analysis of this work, it is at least easy to see how the tonal coordination of the two fields has arisen. The medium can only have been the identity or great similarity of the volumic forms which would appear in each ear through their relations to the common stimuli. Every tonal complex heard by one ear would repeat itself in highly similar, if not in identical, form in the other system. And this high grade of similarity would necessarily bring the experiences of either system to a common centre of interest. In fact all the integrations of the one system would be equally present in the other in so far as they were founded upon the experiences of a single auditory system. And all attentional and practical processes directly based upon the one would inevitably find equal application to the other. This equality would arise, if only because the deviation to the other system from the one first chosen as the object of attention would be irrelevant for the issue. Thus attention would come by mere probability to be equally divided between both. Such a division, however, is no division.

And this equal division of attention would find its chief justification and maintenance in its result—the localisation of sounds. In the general analysis of the hearing of a single system we leave out of account altogether the development of binaural localisation that has accompanied the development of uniaural hearing (or intra-systemic hearing). In the study of binaural hearing it is not possible to leave the identification of the intra-systemic aspects out of account until we have justified their identification. But in the treatment of binaural localisation we can then abstract from the intra-systemic aspects or treat them as if the two so complex systems had shrivelled into mere points. This punctate basis of localisation seems in fact to be realised in the auditory processes of certain insects (*v.* below, p. 191 f.).

The two auditory systems then are identified because of their similarity. Or, if the passive voice of the verb suggests cognitive activity, we might rather say: they are not identical to start with or in respect of the elements out of which they are composed; but they become identical, in so far as their integrative products are identical or very similar. The identification is a 'natural' process, so to speak, not a process of cognition in the logical sense.

LXXVII. Moreover traces of the identification can be discovered by special examination. It is a well known fact that in many persons there is a difference of pitch between the two ears. One and the same stimulus appears higher to one ear than to the other. G. Révész has made a special study of this subject in the interests of his theory of octave qualities in pitch. He found that in the neighbourhood of the second accented *b* (ca. 1000 vbs. per sec.) most persons of normal hearing show a difference between their ears, often amounting to a semitone. If one and the same tonal stimulus is presented successively to either ear, the observer notices a difference of pitch; but if the stimulus acts on both ears simultaneously, a new third intermediate pitch arises. Suitable variation of intensity of the stimulus as it affects either ear, makes the pitch deviate towards the stronger pitch from the one pitch to the other. Usually the binaural pitch lies quite close to the pitch of the more intensely affected ear. Moreover the binaural tone shows a summation of the intensities of either ear (96, 91f.). These relations were confirmed in the abnormal case of Dr P. v. Liebermann (55).

Révész thinks that these facts prove the occurrence of a mixture of tonal qualities similar to the mixture of the visual qualities, e.g. red and yellow, whereby a colour intermediary in the series between the two components results. But it must be evident that not a proof, but only a confirmation, could thus be given. The facts allow of other interpretations and could only be definitely interpreted in the sense of qualitative mixture, if it were already definitely proved that pitches are qualities. Baley (4, 334), who has studied the 'mixture' of slightly different pitches presented to either ear separately, and has thereby found considerable agreement with the observations of Révész, believes that the mixture can be explained with the help of the spread of resonance on the basilar membrane round the point of maximum resonance, as that was deduced by Helmholtz. And this explanation is very much in line with the explanation which inevitably follows from the analysis of tones propounded in this work. The two different pitches presented to either ear represent two maxima of volumic intensity which are slightly displaced against one another, and would then presumably add themselves together centrally so as to form a new volumic outline with a maximum usually lying between the two original maxima, according to the relative magnitudes of these.

But why the two auditory systems should contain such differences of pitch as Révész worked upon, we are not required to decide here. Their probable basis is physiological and at the best only vague indications of their nature could be given. The point of greatest interest for the problem of the identification of the two ears is that such differences do occur. The ordinal arrangements of the two systems are not necessarily identical in all details, although they have in the long course of time naturally been brought for the most part into co-ordination with one another. Indeed so far as the basilar membrane is of a texture to receive the auditory stimulus, a large degree of similarity must necessarily result in the two systems, at least as far as volume is concerned. But minor deviations might still be possible at any time. The point of predominance of the uniaural volume may be affected by other factors than merely the intensity of the stimulus, e.g. the sensitivity of the receptors, the irregularities of form or texture or elasticity of the receiving membrane, etc. Thus pitches might vary without any variation of volume.

These are the factors which in one way or another doubtless account for the peculiar phenomena observed by Dr v. Liebermann in his own hearing and used by Révész as the basis of the distinction he advocates between octave qualities and height or brightness of tone (137, 13ff.). Phenomenologically the findings of these two authors carry us beyond the phenomena of ordinary hearing only in that they show that the point of predominance of a tonal volume is not under all conditions the usual central one.

In persons whose ears show considerable pitch differences, the standardisation of the musical range in terms of octaves would not necessarily be upset. It is in fact conceivable that this standardisation should hold first for either ear separately and then for binaural hearing, and yet show different results when the pitch of a stimulus presented to one ear is compared with the pitch of the same stimulus in the other ear. This would happen if all volumic coincidences were main-tained in either ear in spite of the displacement of one or more of them relatively to the corresponding coincidences of the other ear. Thus if we suppose the whole volume of a tone divided into two hundred equal parts, the predominance of the octave tone might fall at 48 in the one ear and at 50 in the other. And yet the lower limiting order of the next higher octave in the former ear might still fall at 48, thus producing the regular volumic coincidence of the octave at that point. When the two uniaural tones were sounded together, we should then get a tone of an intermediate value, say 49. That order, however, would be the one usually designated the octave pitch, so that the pitch of the one ear would seem to be lower and the pitch of the other ear higher, and yet each ear would hear the double stimulus as the octave fusion. No disturbance, as e.g. of musical nomenclature, of fusion, of interval, etc., would be apparent in hearing apart from specially arranged observations. This case may be supposed to be the most frequent, being produced probably only by more or less normal physical variations in the texture of the basilar membrane, which would affect all tones equally in so far as they involved the affected part.

In other cases the standardisation might hold only for binaural hearing. This might happen in those cases where in the one system a false predominance was created by some special sensitivity of one ear, to be corrected by the combined use of both ears—a sort of ortho-symphony, to use Révész's term. In other cases again a slight disturbance or lapse of standardisation may occur. It is conceivable that errors of this kind are responsible for much of the musical incapacity of many persons[1].

LXXVIII. Let us now consider what exactly is involved in the notion of two curves of excitation each containing a central maximum, adding themselves together. That is a kind of overlapping, like what is presupposed in the superposition of two sine curves or in Bernstein's theory of single touch from double contact. But, if it were a complete overlapping, such as is presupposed when two equal straight lines are superposed on one another, all possibility of binaural functions would disappear. The tonal excitations would sum themselves all along the line, and their distinction would thereby become as impossible as is the introspective separation of two very close touches on the skin. Obviously the overlapping must have, not only a longitudinal aspect—along the pitch length of the tonal volumes,—but also a transverse aspect—across the volumes,—and the overlapping in the latter case must always be only partial. For if there were no transverse overlapping, there could be no summation of intensities. In the dilemma between the impossibility of binaural function and denial of the fact of summation of intensities, we must choose the hypothesis of partial transverse overlapping of volumes.

LXXIX. This hypothesis is at least not commonly adopted, even if it may have been advanced before. I am not acquainted with any such suggestion. But certain facts give it considerable support. Those of a physiological nature are most familiar. The receptors of the basilar membrane are supplied with three to five parallel lines of neural terminals (93, ɪɪ. 350; 48, 507). After the destruction of the cortex of

---

[1] Cf. 121, 325. Stumpf had not the first possibility suggested in the text in mind. The binaural case is not quite on the same footing as uniaural fusion.

a whole temporal field hearing is much reduced on the opposite side and little reduced on the corresponding side. That indicates the incomplete decussation of the auditory fibres (49, 619; cf. 7).

But this physiological evidence is not by itself sufficient. We must first establish the presence of a transverse aspect psychologically; then these physiological facts will gain voice. But it must be admitted that a transverse aspect is not psychically very obvious, unless it be inferred from the persistent use of the notion of volume in reference to the extensity of sounds. Volume implies two dimensions. This unobtrusiveness of the transverse aspect might, however, be put down to the fact that it is probably invariable for all tones, no matter what their pitch is. But, if it appears at all, it should appear where its variation is possible, i.e. in the comparison of uniaural and binaural tones.

And, in fact, Baley's observers spoke of such a difference between uniaural and binaural tones. In his experiments tones of different pitch were led separately to either ear; this method of hearing he calls, after Stumpf, dichotic, as against the usual action of the same tones on both ears at once, or diotic hearing. One of Baley's observers, Dr v. Hornbostel, observed something peculiar in the dichotic tone, as against the uniaural tone, that he called its 'breadth' (4, 340); other observers spoke of the 'fulness' of the dichotic impression.

Now, if the binaural tone consists of two strips of tone which overlap partially transversely, the whole binaural mass should be distinguishable into three parts—one in the centre and binaural, and one on each side of that and uniaural. This is confirmed at some length by Baley's observers. "So long as the tone is still qualitatively unitary, it seems to this observer in respect of its spatial nature still to be an undifferentiated mass that stretches from one ear to the other partly within, partly outside, the head. With increasing difference of pitch of the primary tones this mass falls into three parts, of which the one lies medially, while the two others appear to the right and to the left of that, in the neighbourhood of the ears, and become the source of two different pitches contained in the impression." As the pitches come to differ more and more, the median part of the whole seems to shrink in favour of the two outside parts. At the same time the maxima of the uniaural components, when they differ, will lie severally above and below the resulting binaural maximum. "Thus the observer sometimes does not in the first moment succeed in hearing in the impression two tones of different pitch"; but if he passes with his attention from one ear to the other, he notices "that it sounds at the one ear somewhat higher, at the other somewhat lower." Even when the tones of either ear lie far apart in pitch, they appear broader than a uniaural tone; for if one of the tones is stopped, the other seems to shrink and grow small, withdrawing into its ear (4, 343).

We shall see later on that the binaural function of localisation presupposes this partial transverse overlapping also. We may then consider it to be well established.

LXXX. A similar process of identification by means of similarity of forms presented in the two systems is found in vision. In that case a new set of orders arises that is different from those of either integrating system. It is easy to convince oneself of this new system for any relations of points other than that of exact 'correspondence'; but correspondence in vision is itself clearly only a special case of stereoscopy, since true stereoscopic differences integrated from disparate forms are found both 'nearer' and 'farther' than the orders produced by correspondence. The question thus arises for hearing whether we must think the pitches of binaural tones as a new system of orders, not identical with that of either ear singly, but created by their integration. It is clear that there is in binaural hearing no such obviously new system of orders as in binocular vision. If there is any new system, it is so like the uniaural systems as to be hardly distinguishable from them. Nor does theory indicate in hearing any need for a new system in a distinctive sense. It seems possible to satisfy all the demands of theory with such a transverse overlapping of system as has been assumed above. We could talk of a really new system of integration in this case as little as we can in the case of Bernstein's overlapping touch circles. In both cases we have only a displacement of the distribution of intensities owing to the summation consequent on overlapping.

In judging this question we must not think of the original differences of orders which make up the two uniaural systems as if they were necessarily as different as the two ears are far apart. The distance of the peripheral receptors of hearing is no better evidence of the degree of difference of order of the sensations they evoke than it is of the distance of their central projections. The peripheral receptors are placed where they are in order that the stimulations they receive may be as different in intensity as possible. But that requirement presupposes nothing regarding the difference of order of their sensations.

The positions of the peripheral receptors in the head require only some degree of difference of order in the corresponding sensations, as does the psychical integration based upon the latter. And the psychical overlapping we have detected requires partial identity and partial neighbourhood or difference in the transverse orders of the two sets of uniaural sensations.

In vision there is no summation of intensities and consequently no overlapping or identity of the uniocular fields. The correspondence of the two eyes is a purely functional identity of forms or rather an integration of bisystemic areal forms to produce a new direction of form, a third dimension of form. The integration of forms in vision is favoured to a high degree by the similar changes of distinctness and acuity of vision in each system from the point or area of clearest vision to the periphery. This ensures a parallel movement of the attention over any similar forms that may appear in the two fields. In hearing there is no point of clearest sensitivity, nor is there need for any. All the requirements of binaural hearing are satisfied by the assimilations of identical or similar forms and by the transverse overlapping of volumes.

LXXXI.   Let us now consider the relation of transverse overlapping to the binaural function of localisation.

The maximum of transverse intensity would probably lie about the middle of the whole transverse volume, if the intensity of either uniaural component was the same. If either of the latter exceeded the other in intensity, the point of maximum intensity would pass to the side of the greater intensity, just as it does in cases of longitudinal overlapping shown by Révész's results. So an oscillation might be produced from one side to the other, from a preponderance of the right uniaural component with the maximum at the right side to a preponderance of the left component with the maximum at the left side. We should thus obtain a line or series of orders peculiar to binaural hearing, not of course a new system in the sense in which the third visual dimension of orders is new, but new over against the probably complete invariability of the transverse outline in either ear. The new series is, as it were, merely the mobilising of the transverse uniaural volumes in their own plane, not in any new direction.

This summation and consequent oscillation is the basis of the binaural localisation of sounds. Hearing has nothing more to offer than this as a correlative within experience to the placement of a source of sound at any point of the surface of any sphere concentric with the head. The ordinal differences of the uniaural system are unavailable for the determination of localisation; or they suffer practically no displacement in consequence of the displacement of their physical source. (Near sounds are a little lower because they are more intense.) At most their existence is sometimes dependent upon the position of that source, and in this way the latter does affect pitch-blend to some extent and so provide a basis for correlation with the varying position of the source. I shall consider this case later on. We need notice at present only that the basis for correlations thus provided is not a true direct basis, as is the interaural oscillation. The latter is composed of two relative predominances of an ordinal kind and yields a compound predominance of an ordinal kind, which oscillates over its own volume. Being ordinal, this is a proper basis for correlation with those ordinal displacements of other senses that underlie the differences of localisation attributed to their experiences; in other words it is a proper basis for localisations. Or—to think in the reverse direction—auditory localisation calls for a primary ordinal basis, since localisation is itself a kind of order, namely that system of orders which binds all the senses together and falls into cognitive correlation with the spatial orders of material things. (We cannot go into the nature and origin of spatial localisation here.) This primary ordinal basis must be binaural and the demands put upon it by our actual powers of localisation in hearing seem to be satisfactorily met by the oscillations offered by the binaural series we have deduced.

LXXXII. Intensity is not, as has often been supposed, the direct basis of auditory localisations, but only the indirect basis. It is required secondarily to provide a means whereby the predominance of one order over others may be attained. It is the only such means available in hearing. But the essential or direct basis, which carries the psychical integration, is the order thus made predominant. Stumpf attributed a difference pq to the auditory sensations of the right and left ears. This difference is not itself a reference to the ear as an object; for that requires association with the experiences of other senses, especially touch and sight, and such like. But it is the basis for these associations. Stumpf, however, thought we had no reason to designate p and q as themselves 'right' and 'left,' as 'places' in the usual psychical sense. We might only say they corresponded to right and left[1]. This

[1] 112, 53 f.; cf. above, p. 28, note 2, and J. Sully, 124, 129, who speaks of a 'quasi-local difference' between the ears.

account agrees perfectly with that above presented, if we remember that Stumpf did not see localisation as a kind of order and so had no method for discovering what the primary basis of the pq difference was. But it is clear that his intention goes exactly in the direction of our theory. He set up the problem in this case correctly for analysis, although neither he nor any of his successors ever solved it.

LXXXIII. Let us now examine the actual capacities of binaural localisation and see whether the basis we have above provided for localisation can adequately meet the facts.

A circle round the head at the level of the ears and nostrils defines the horizontal plane. A circle from ear to ear over the top of the head gives the frontal plane, and one from the nose over the head to the back of the neck the sagittal or median plane. The discrimination of the direction in which a source of sound lies in the horizontal plane is finest in front and behind. The threshold—the angular distance through which a source of sound must be displaced so that a sound coming from the original position as compared with a sound coming from the position reached after displacement, shall be judged to come from a different direction—is variously given as 2·5° (91, 56), 0·9° (18,000 measurements 104, 60f.), 1·7° (109, cited from 41, 182) in front, and 3·3°, 1°, and 1·7° respectively behind. Opposite the ears the threshold reaches its maximum; the values are 8·5° (91), 4·5° (104), 7° (109). That the point of least sensitivity to change of position is opposite the ears and the maximum at the median plane is to be attributed to the operation of Weber's law. Between the front and back minima there are five relative maxima, but, of these, that opposite the ear on each side is the greatest. These relative maxima are doubtless due chiefly to the shape of the external ear and to the position of the meatus in relation to the position of the ears in the head, and they vary very much from one person to another (91, 60) when the sounds used originate within a few feet of the head, as must be the case in most experimental tests of localisation. We seem justified in assuming from the results that if the head were in any plane a perfect sphere and the organs of hearing equally accessible apart from their position on that sphere, then between the two minima, front and back, and the two maxima opposite the ears there would be a gradual increase of the threshold value (cf. 41, 210f.; 91, 118f.).

For the frontal plane the same general scheme of relations holds. In the median plane the threshold of localisation is lower in front than behind, which is no doubt due to the position of the external ears behind the meatus.   Myers has shown (84, 159; cf. 41, 185) that the distinction of positions in the median plane is got from slight differences in pitch-blend and loudness of sounds as they come from these positions. This is noticed introspectively; and when the pitch-blend and loudness of a sound are changed from time to time, the numbers of erroneous localisations become distinctly greater.   The median plane is thus eliminated, as far as true localisation is concerned.   And as the four cardinal points of the median plane are included in the other two planes, it would follow that these are also distinguishable, at least towards their sections with the median plane, by the same means of pitch-blend and loudness.   Rayleigh (92) showed that the directions in front and behind outside the median plane are regularly confused with one another.   But the right and left hemispheres are never confused.

The three planes thus reduce themselves to one series of directions proceeding outwards from the centre of the head, as it were, and ranging from the direction 'opposite the left ear' to 'opposite the right ear.' We must think of the sphere of directions first collapsing into a circle of directions with the elimination of the median plane, and then collapsing into a line of directions with the established confusion of 'behind' and 'in front.'   It then becomes doubtful whether we can speak of directions at all.   The term directions would itself seem to be a cognitive and not a true primary feature of auditory localisation.   As certain we can claim only a continuous ordinal oscillation from a maximal left to a maximal right capable of acting as a basis for the cognition of directions.   Of course, as Stumpf pointed out, the terms right and left are also really cognitive.   In the stuff of auditory sensation we have only 'extreme order at one end of a series' and 'extreme order at the other end of same series.'

This is no more than we could claim above.   The differences noted in the threshold of direction present no real difficulty, but rather provide a basis for determinations regarding the spread of intensity in the uniaural volume and in the binaural volume, or, if these must be supposed to be regular, in the ratios of the uniaural intensities as determined by the various positions between the extremes of the series.

All these results are in perfect accord with the physical theory of the relations of the uniaural intensities in their dependence upon positions round the head.   As the ears are equidistant from all points of the median plane, a source of sound produces equally intense impressions on either ear from any point of that plane.   Similarly, for any one point of the front horizontal semicircle of positions, a point can be found in the back horizontal sector at which a source of sound would act upon each separate ear equally intensely. It is, of course, true that for any point r with a rightwards angle of incidence to the line joining the ears a point l can be found with an equal left-wards angle of incidence to that line, from which a source of sound will affect the two ears with the same absolute (and relative) intensities. There is, however, no confusion of the directions of these two points in our hearing because the distribution of the two intensities between the ears is distinguished by the ordinal differences of the uniaural systems. The localisation is based neither upon intensities nor upon ratios of intensities, but upon the predominance of orders within the transverse binaural volume which results from the distribution of the intensities (cf. 134). This is the sole basis upon which we can explain the psychological fact that in auditory localisation we are directly aware of the localisation so far as the ordinal series above described is concerned, but that we are seldom normally aware of the difference of the intensities of the right and left impressions.

Sewall (105) has shown by experimental test that an intensive predominance of one ear over the other is only noticed when the electrical vibrations which evoke the differences of intensity are double the strength in the one ear of what they are in the other. This stands in marked contradiction with the great accuracy of binaural localisation, and confirms the view that binaural localisation is not a matter of differences of intensity, but of ordinal predominance. For a similar reason Hocart and McDougall (31, 404) infer that it "seems necessary to postulate some local difference of the tone sensations determined by the unperceived differences of intensities of the stimulations of the two ears."

LXXXIV. If the number of distinguishable angular directions on the aural axis seems too great to be given by the transverse displace-ment of predominance in the binaural volume, which (in view of the number of parallel rows of receptors in each ear) might consist of hardly more than eight or ten different ordinal steps, we must remember that those differences of pitch-blend and loudness which can give occasion for a judgment regarding localisation in the median plane, where all intensive ratios are identical, can also enter to refine the localising judgment in the transverse line itself (cf. 159). These differences of pitch-blend and loudness in the transverse line emerge for introspection, when auditory localisation is carried out uniaurally. If changes of intensity are introduced during the course of a series of binaural localisations, the distinction of directions of localisation becomes more uncertain. And uniaural localisation can be carried out on the basis of observed differences in pitch, even if intensity has been eliminated (41, 230f.). If the intensity of a sound is so reduced that it could no longer be conducted to the auditory receptors through the bones of the skull, but only through the meatus and attached organs, all localisations become very uncertain and even left and right may be alone distinguishable (41, 184, 229).

It has been found by all observers that complex masses of sound are better localised than are simple ones. With pure tones localisation is reduced perhaps to its lowest limits of differentiation, but even then there is never a confusion of right and left (41, 183). Hocart and McDougall (31, 392) found as values for the threshold of direction for noises and tones: in front circa 3° and 20°, opposite the ears circa 15° and 35°, between circa 7° and 20°. But "a very slight and unappreciated impurity of tone suffices to reduce the threshold of discrimination to, or very nearly to, the same value as that of noises" (31, 393).

It is not by any means clear why noises and complex sounds are better localised than simple tones. There are several probabilities. (1) As a complex sound contains many points of pitch predominance it will therefore also contain many points where the position of transverse predominance will be of outstanding clearness. For we may properly presume that where the intensity is low for both ears, the point of transverse predominance will not be so well marked as where it is higher. And even if the opposite presumption seem more acceptable, one or other of them will hold; and thus irregular variations in the clearness of transverse predominance will be produced throughout the length of the sound's volume, as against the even gradation in the simple tone. Thus the observer will have many points at which he may fix his observation, which will then be keener and more rapid. In the case of very high tones, whose partials lie beyond the range of our hearing, localisation is bad (cf. 37, 146; 41, 235). (2) As the complex sound contains many pitch predominances, these will be subject to modification in intensity and, it may be, to obliteration by the position of the source of sound relatively to the head; the resultant differences between the uniaural impressions would provide a basis for cognitive correlation with differences of position of the source of sound. This second reason is not so good nor so preferable as the first, because it

does not like the first provide any improvement in the direct basis
of localisation, i.e. in localisation itself, but only a new, different,
secondary basis of localisation by means of cognitive correlations.
That this second ground of advantage for complex sounds is not the
only one seems to be supported by the fact that the advantage remains
even when both ears are closed with the fingers (31, 395 f.; cf. 41, 210 f.).

As the object of this chapter on binaural hearing is to show that
the theoretical groundwork of hearing provided in the earlier chapters
forms a proper basis upon which a purely psychological function of
binaural order can be built and that that function corresponds, approximately at least, to the scope of the direct processes of binaural localisation and so confirms and justifies these, it is unnecessary to proceed
here to expand or discuss the processes of purely uniaural localisation
or the judgment of the distance of sounds from the observer, and such
like. The greatest weight of evidence goes to show that these processes
are not, as it were, the direct presentation of differences of localisation
or distance in hearing, as binaural localisations primarily are; they
are secondary processes of cognitive correlations between minor differences in pitch-blend and loudness, due to positions relative to the
head, and these positions themselves, as known through other senses
than hearing. However interesting and important, then, the theory of
these secondary processes of localisation may be, they do not affect
the theory propounded in this work. As regards the peculiarities of
localisation within the head, it is to be noted that the differences provided
by it do not exceed the primary rudiment of normal localisation, i.e.
an ordinal series 'from ear to ear.' Special conditions doubtless
decide whether a sound shall be located within or without the head.
These conditions form an interesting topic for study. But it is evident
that the primary differences underlying these subjective localisations
are identical with those of normal objective hearing. The reader may
be referred to Klemm's excellent summary.

LXXXV. While observing a mosquito under the microscope,
A. Mayer noticed that the sound of a tuning fork set the numerous
elastic fibrils of its antennae into sympathetic vibration in varying
strength (63, 95); "the mosquito," he says, "turns his body in the
direction of that antenna whose fibrils are most affected, and thus
gives greater intensity to the vibrations of the fibrils of the other
antenna. When he has thus brought the vibrations of the antennae
to equality of intensity, he has placed his body in the direction of the

radiation of the sound, and he directs his flight accordingly; and from my experiments it would appear that he can thus guide himself to within 5° of the direction of the female" (63, 98). Klemm (41, 222) asks whether this arrangement of the mosquito's does not approximately embody what is demanded by many theories of spatial experience as the condition of any true localisation, viz. stimulation of the receiving organ at some of its elements, or, if all its elements are stimulated together, at its different elements with different strength, according to the position of the source of sound. This question must be answered affirmatively. But we do not need to seek our instance in the mosquito; our own process of auditory localisation exemplifies the same thing exactly. The only difference between the two is that our fibrils are not on the surface, and are in each uniaural system brought into a state of enormous complication whereby a fine response to differences of vibratory rate is attained.

There is no primary difference either physiologically or psychically between the binaural basis of localisation and the uniaural basis of pitch. The two are distinguished only by their differences of function, which are excited physically by different variations in the stimulus, and psychically integrate into different complexes. But these psychical complexes remain always akin to the primary atoms of their substance; both in pitch-volumes and in localisations they begin as orders and end as orders. Pitch-volumes never come in experience into cognitive correlation with objective places, but remain as they are; binaural orders, on the contrary, integrate with those ordinal differences of other senses that are dependent upon the physical positions of their stimuli, and so become localisations. For localisation is our cognitive name for the ordinal system of a certain level of integration.

The minimal requirements of the mosquito's act would be met by two auditory 'spots' of sensation, of neighbouring order, capable of variation of intensity. Greater excitation of one receptor giving predominance of the corresponding order, would create a basis for the direction of turning; equality of excitation a basis for direction of flight. Of course a greater refinement of direction would be given by a slight increase in the transverse mass of the 'spot,' as we have supposed above in accordance with the indications of intensive summation.

CHAPTER X

SUMMARY

Note. The Roman numerals below correspond with the same numerals appearing throughout the preceding text. They indicate where the subject of each paragraph is expounded in the text, but a complete correspondence is not guaranteed.

I. The study of hearing is primarily a purely psychological effort, based upon a direct examination of the facts of auditory experience in conjunction with a study of allied groups of facts, namely the experiences of the other senses, p. 1.

II. If every obstruction and difficulty could be overcome by frontal attack, the direct examination of auditory experience would doubtless yield results perfectly conformable to the results of direct examination of the experiences of other senses. But the failure of this condition raises the conjunction of the study of the different senses into a method. Outstanding difficulties in any one sense may be expected to be solved towards the rule that already holds for the corresponding feature of the majority of the (other) senses, p. 2.

[Thus there comes into view a 'pure' science of experience as a perfectly homogeneous, closed, system of reality without prejudice to its dependence on other systems of reality and to the particular changes and rules thus forced upon it.

I cannot offer any *à priori* proof of this pure science of experience. But its probability is already very great by virtue of the success which follows the application of the 'idea' to the study of sensory experience. *Ex pede Herculem.*]

III. The study of a group of simple sensations—of cutaneous and visceral origin—offers at once two easily distinguished and universally accepted attributes, quality (e.g. cold as against warmth, touch as against pain), and intensity, p. 3.

IV. The axiom of the inseparability of the attributes from one another is based on the fact that apparently constant attributes prove to be constant, and that apparently inconstant attributes belong to a different level of experience, for which the conditions of integration may not coincide with the conditions of the presence of the sensations to which the inconstant features adhere, p. 4.

V. Localisation is not an attribute, because its presence in experience involves a reference from the sensation to which it adheres to some other experience. But it must have a basis in the sensation to which it adheres; and this basis must be psychically similar, or akin, to localisation. I call this basis 'order,' p. 6.

VI. Along with order goes a fourth attribute of extensity. These two find a parallel in temporal attributes of order and durance. The latter order is distinguished from the former by the terms temporal and systemic (= system of sense organs of the same kind giving the same quality, system of orders of the same quality). The temporal attributes are not the subject of special consideration in this work, as they are equally common to all sensations, p. 8.

VII. The other four attributes—quality, intensity, extensity, and systemic order—are verifiable in the second (obscure) group of senses, comprising the articular, muscular, and organic senses. The obscurity peculiar to one or other attribute in these senses is satisfactorily explained by their lack of variation, due to physiological restrictions, p. 9.

VIII. The senses of the third group—vision, smell, and hearing— are complex and difficult. But as their difficulties do not converge, they reduce each other's effectiveness. Intensity is problematical only in vision. Extensity and order are very obscure in smell, p. 12.

[The theory advanced in this book brings hearing into clear and full conformity with the formula of attributes derived from the first two groups of senses.

Whatever be the outcome of these difficulties, the probability of the (at least approximate) correctness of the proposed list of attributes of sensation is very high.

This result is supported by the comparative study of the complex or integrative experiences which appear in the different senses and of their attributive bases. The conviction produced by the systematic consistency of all these results justifies their use as a method towards the rapid and sure advance of (pure) psychological theory.]

IX. A preliminary survey of tones is given by the tones of any musical instrument, e.g. the piano. The different series of tones given by different musical instruments may be reduced to one series of pure tones by the analysis and elimination from each musical tone of the partial pitches it contains (Helmholtz), p. 15.

X. Musical tones thus contain, or are, a group or blend of pitches. The difference between the tones of different instruments may therefore be called a difference of pitch-blend. Whether it may also be held to be a blend of tones is a special problem, not a presupposition of the psychology of hearing, p. 18.

XI. Only two attributive classifications of pitch come into account —the qualitative and the ordinal. The alternative is to be settled not merely by a direct phenomenological dictum, as it were, but by a systematic consideration of all the available evidence. The result will doubtless receive phenomenal justification, i.e. the mind will assent to the conclusion, not only because it has attained, and can again attain, that conclusion at any time, but also because that conclusion, in face of its objects, carries with it a certain self-evidence, p. 20.

XII. The ordinal classification of pitch is supported by both direct and indirect evidence. The latter includes consideration of the facts of discrimination, the typical groupings of attributes in other senses, the integrative forms of auditory experience, and the structure and development of the organ of hearing, p. 23.

XIII. Along with the ordinal differences of pitch goes a variation of volume, involving the extensive attribute. Volume is a real, not an associative, character of sounds; or rather sounds are volumes in just as real a sense as stones are masses, except that the latter are material, while the former are psychical. The evidence for the volumic nature of the 'rising' aspect of sounds falls into the classes mentioned in XII, p. 26.

[The failure of previous psychologists to find the true analysis of sensations of hearing is due to two reasons: (1) they had attained no method of dealing with the attributes; (2) they were governed by the false notion that the only kind of order and continuity admissible among sensory experiences is a spatial one. This hindrance effectually barred the way to the former method and destroyed the power of hearing itself to point to the true direction. Far from being fundamental, the space of experience is a special and elaborate kind of order and continuity, p. 28.]

XIV. Hearing thus conforms perfectly to the type suggested by the other senses, at least so far as the attributes are concerned, p. 30.

XV. The volumic nature of sounds leads us to recognise that tones are not atoms, but rather molecules of auditory sensation, the smallest masses we find before us. Pitch then appears as the intensively

13—2

predominant atom(s), order(s), of the whole volume, which is otherwise regularly and symmetrically balanced in relation to pitch.   These
results provide an adequate definition of tone, as distinct from sound
or noise, etc., p. 30.

XVI.   We can thus account for all the psychical character of tones
and of the tonal series, and for the psychical and musical status of
pitch-blends.   These are marked by minor predominances within their
total volume, which do not however affect the constancy of the latter.
Thus pitch-blends are in their musically useful forms immediately
identifiable with one another and with the perfect tone of the same
nominal pitch.   But they are much more pleasurable than the latter,
p. 32.

XVII.   The psychological study of noise has been immensely
obstructed by the unjustifiable substitution of the term 'tone' for the
term 'pitch' in the analysis of sounds.   Subsequently the term tone
is held to imply characters that belong to its proper object, but that had
never been incorporated in the term itself.   If they had, the substitution
of 'tone' for 'pitch' would have been impossible.   This surreptitious
character of tone is then made the excuse for saying that noises are
irreducible to tones, even though they contain pitches, p. 34.

XVIII.   Noises are auditory masses that are characterised by
extreme departure from the regularity and balance of tones.   This
irregularity of mass is attainable by various means, especially by the
rapid oscillation of vibratory rates, by which means the dominance
of pitch is more or less obliterated.   Tones and noises are not reducible
to one another, but to a common 'atom' of auditory sensation, p. 39.

XIX.   Vowels are not a new phenomenon of hearing.   They occupy
a place somewhere between tones and noises, being probably characterised by a slight blurring of pitch predominance.   The various theories
of vowels with the exception of Köhler's are all compatible with the
analysis of hearing here propounded, p. 41.

XX.   The theory of octave qualities is untenable.   Its formulation
is due not so much to any services it can render as to the inherent
weakness of the prevailing foundations of the psychology of hearing,
which call for any possible re-modelling, however doubtful its outlook
may be.   Nevertheless octaves do possess a kind of 'similarity,' which
is explicable on my theory in connexion with the problem of fusion, p. 44.

XXI.   When two sources of sound depart gradually from unison,
certain deviations from the regular system of the perfect tone appear,

chiefly fluctuations of intensity (beats), multiple pitches (primaries and intertones), and noises. These phenomena offer no new problems for psychological analysis, p. 53.

XXII. The same applies to the differential and other pitches which succeed or accompany them. These fall under the head of multiple pitches. Beats and differential pitches are psychically quite independent things, because beats adhere to the primary predominances, whereas differential pitches may appear far away from them, even outside the primary volumes altogether, p. 54.

XXIII. The problem of multiple pitches passes over into the problem of multiple tones or of the fusion of tones, in virtue (1) of our natural tendency to substitute the term 'tone' for the term denoting its specific characteristic—'pitch,' and (2) of the fact that in a tonal mass the pitches it contains and the 'tones' they suggest do not seem to possess the same independence and intensity as they show on successive presentation, p. 55.

XXIV. There are only three distinct and unmistakable grades of fusion—the octave, the fifth, and the fourth with all the others. These grades are so clearly fusional that they are hardly to be confused with any other difference between pairs of tones. They must therefore form the prime basis for the study of fusion, p. 57.

XXV. Stumpf's failure to attain to a psychological theory of fusion is due to the obstruction caused by the qualitative classification of pitch, the consequent confusion of pitch and tone, and the want of a proper method of analysis, p. 58.

XXVI. Stumpf's exclusion of any explanation in terms of the psychical adjuncts of fusing tones implies that the basis of fusion is to be found in these tones themselves. But it is useless to try to explain by raising the process of fusion itself in the person of the octave to the peerage of attributes, as Stumpf and others have recently done, p. 59.

XXVII. With the help of a proper method Stumpf's laws of fusion suffice to locate the basis of fusion. Stumpf's first law: that "the grade of fusion is independent of the tone-region," and the fact that fusion is not altered by the discrimination of pitches, exclude pitch as the basis of fusion, p. 60.

XXVIII. The acceptance of Stumpf's second law: that "fusion is independent of intensity, both relative and absolute," excludes the attribute of intensity. Quality and extensity drop out as invariables, so that there remains as the only possible basis of fusion the volumic differences of tones, p. 61.

XXIX. The volumic differences of single tones and the serial continuity of their pitches or predominating orders lead us to infer that simultaneous tones of neighbouring pitch are largely coincident in volume, p. 62.

XXX. The fact that simultaneous tones never seem to lie completely apart or outside of one another, no matter how different or distant their pitches may be, leads to the conclusion that the upper limiting order of all tones is identical and that the volume of any tone always falls wholly within the volume of every other lower tone, p. 62.

XXXI. The standard nature of the relations of the octave suggests that the octave is a constant and natural pattern of volumic relations. As the upper limiting orders of the two tones coincide, the most natural pattern would seem to be given by coincidence of the lower limiting order of the upper tone with the predominant order of the lower tone. This would imply that the predominant order not only seems to be, but is really, central to the whole tone, and that the tone's volume not only seems to decrease regularly with increase in the rate of vibration, but really does so.

The upper tone of the octave is distinguishable from the lower one chiefly by the second predominance it adds to the whole volume, which is identical with that of the lower tone. Some effect is doubtless produced by way of extra 'weight' in the whole of the upper half of the volume. These coincidences and slight differences seem to account fully for the phenomena of fusion in the octave, p. 63.

XXXII. A second arrangement of coincidence of volumes approximating to the symmetry of the perfect tone is given when the lower limit and the predominance of the upper tone lie equally far on opposite sides from the predominance of the lower tone. Here the upper tone adds two new points to the lower volume. There is no other outstanding form of balance of volumes. Thus we must ascribe this one to the fifth.

The psychical volumes of the octave and fifth would thus bear the same relations to one another (1 : 2, 2 : 3) as do the corresponding physical ratios. But they are educed independently of the latter. And we can obtain the proportions of any other interval either indirectly through these psychical standards or directly from the law just established that volumes decrease continuously with rise of pitch. On reflexion the methods of measuring these tonal volumes appear very similar in principle to the methods of measuring 'physical' distances, p. 65.

XXXIII. Amongst the other intervals some decrease of balance and symmetry in volumic coincidence can be traced which seems to provide a basis for the minor grades of fusion shown by them. But the conceptual reconstruction, or as it were, empathy, of these proportions is uncertain. The ear alone can settle what for it, at the best, are very slight differences, p. 66.

XXXIV. Diagrams are given to embody this theory, which presents ground upon which a special experimental study of the intensive relations within the whole volume of a tone could be built up, p. 69.

XXXV. The theory of tonal masses and fusion thus shows itself to be of a piece with the theory of the 'pure' tone. In view of the considerable symmetry and balance within the tonal mass of the parts adjacent to any pitch predominance within the mass, it is permissible to speak of the analysis of the mass by discrimination of its predominances as an analysis into tones, provided the limitations of that analysis are remembered, p. 71.

XXXVI. The experience of distance which is found in some other senses is in them based upon differences in the attribute of order. We should therefore expect to find in hearing a similar experience based upon the differences of order that are prominent in hearing, viz. differences of pitch of tones, p. 73.

XXXVII. Tonal distances do occur, but they are not comparable with such ease as in other senses. Tonal distances are most noticeable when they are quite small, and also when they show distinct variations for one and the same ratio of vibrations in different parts of the auditory range, p. 75.

XXXVIII. The chief reason for the obscurity of tonal distance is the prominence of tonal interval, which is for any ratio a constant experience throughout the musical range, p. 76.

XXXIX. Interval is the volumic outline of the whole mass of sound formed by two tones. This is always characteristic, no matter what the degree of fusion may be. Interval is concerned with the intensive outline of the mass or its proportions, fusion with its balance and symmetry, p. 77.

XL. These two different aspects of the same mass give the octave its great importance as a tonal standard. Our whole attitude to the musical range of pitches is governed by the octave fusion and interval, to which all others are subordinated. Hence the great 'similarity' of octave tones, p. 78.

XLI. In spite of the facts of the discrimination of pitch the nature of volume seems to imply that the multitude of ordinal 'atoms' constituting a volume is proportional to the size of that volume. Similarly the distance between the tones of an interval would be proportionate to the pitch of the interval, and would decrease with rise of pitch, p. 81.

XLII. The impression of increase of distance with rise of pitch may therefore well be illusory, being based upon our power of discriminating pitches, p. 82.

XLIII. If intervals are essentially constant tonal forms, any changes of distance due to the raising or lowering of an interval would be quite irrelevant as being merely a part of the whole form which must change proportionately in every part with any change of pitch, p. 83.

XLIV. Absolute ear emerges when the natural absoluteness of tonal orders maintains its efficiency in spite of the tremendous emphasis laid on relativity or proportion in music, p. 84.

XLV. The relations established between successive tones rest upon the same basis as do those of simultaneous tones and are therefore the same in nature. Thus in the octave sequence the upper orders of both tones are identical, as are also the lower order of the upper and the predominance of the lower. These successive relations are therefore also relations of form, p. 86.

XLVI. An explanation of the difficulty most felt by less musical persons in identifying and learning to name simultaneous intervals and ascending and descending successive intervals is ready to hand. These difficulties are analogous to those apparent in identifying a visual pattern with its inversion or of identifying the sum of two curves with their sequence, p. 89.

XLVII. The anomalies of pitch at the extremes of the musical range observed by v. Maltzew seem to follow naturally from the difficulty (which must ultimately emerge) of the basilar membrane's responding to high vibratory frequencies with a small enough volume, and to low frequencies with a large enough volume. Then on the upper side the octave would appear too late, on the lower side too soon, p. 95.

XLVIII. The theory of fusion given above provides an adequate basis for all the minor phenomena of fusion, p. 99.

XLIX. The experience of motion which is found in some other senses, is based upon progressive differences in the attributes of systemic and temporal order. We should therefore expect to find in hearing a similar experience based upon differences in pitch and in temporal order, p. 113.

L. A parallel can be found in hearing both to the visual motion that is founded upon an intense and obtrusive basis and to the elusive motion that connects certain motionless impressions. The former is gliding tone, the latter is an important aspect of melody, p. 115.

LI. As we know it familiarly, melody is a static 'figure' based upon the architecture of our tonal system, as well as being a motional 'figure.' But though the former has subordinated the latter to its needs, the latter was the earlier by origin and is still the essence of melody, p. 118.

LII. Certain primitive forms of music seem to show motional melody developed in relative freedom from the static demands of scales, p. 122.

LIII. The octave is the basis of standardisation of all scales whatever. Its appearance and influence are not to be ascribed to any sort of parallelistic process in hearing, not even to the parallelism or coincidence of partials (Helmholtz), p. 123.

LIV. A second, almost universal, interval, or pair of intervals, is the fifth with its reflex, the fourth. The intervals of the octave and fifth derive their impulse towards self-realisation, as it were, from their natural source, indicated in XXXI f., p. 125.

LV. If the fourth appeared as a common adjunct of the fifth, it could be precisely remembered as a volumic outline, like every other interval, p. 126.

LVI. The preferability of the fourth in practice may have been due to the ease of string division into halves and quarters, or to the serial outcome of the octave and fifth: fourth, whole tone, fourth. But the actual course of development in any particular case is a problem for ethnological study, p. 126.

LVII. From this natural basis development proceeds according to a few principles, of which the chief is the intercomplication of the foundations themselves. But this procedure must not be supposed to limit the variability of its result in the way that our mathematical conceptions of interval suggest. The deficiencies of purely auditory procedure leave room for the operation of subsidiary principles of formation, while the desire for system and fixity invite them, p. 127.

LVIII. Moreover, the method of derivation of a scale has no relevance to the musical coherence and utility of that scale, p. 128.

LIX. It follows from the theory of interval given in XXXIX that a scale is a series of more or less definite proportions (filling out the octave), whose origin lies in various principles and whose maintenance depends upon the musical stability and generative power of the scale itself. Scales differ in these latter respects, not in their nature as a series of mere intervals, p. 129.

LX. The variant scales of any people may be brought into relation to one another in a cyclical manner (Greek, ecclesiastical), or by the modifications of equal temperament (Javese, Siamese, and our own). The latter method attains thorough systematisation or reciprocity. The whole musical scale becomes again in its discrete divisions what it is originally in its continuity—a surface of constant curvature, so to speak, p. 129.

LXI. The course of discovery of equal pentatonic and heptatonic scales shows how necessary it is in the study of exotic music to inhibit the assimilative tendencies of our musical habits, formed upon our own music, and to form a notion of the nature and intentions of that music only after a meticulous study of its actual (phonographic) records, supported by a record of the conscious intentions of the best native musicians, p. 132.

LXII. The formation of pentatonic and heptatonic scales pre-supposes no new principle or method of procedure unknown in our own music. We have only to show that intervals could readily be got so nearly alike as to suggest the ideal of equality. Up to that point reduplication and repetition of the intervals given by octave and fifth—c, f, g, c',—suffice, p. 135.

LXIII. A third principle of scale development is the equal division of the playing string, while a rather vague fourth is given by the merely playful formation of small intervals, p. 137.

LXIV. The further development of music is due to an interaction of all the aspects of all its simpler structures, whereby the lines of greatest potentiality ultimately attract the greatest migration of interest. The rate of development is restrained only by the ability of the average influential listener to follow and to enjoy, p. 138.

LXV. The physiology and the psychology of hearing are essentially independent, though partially convergent, disciplines. In so far as physiology deals with the specific neural basis of auditory experiences, the dependence of experience upon organism will give psychology an inevitable primacy. Psychology sets a problem which physiology must answer to its satisfaction, p. 139.

LXVI. In the sense of this last statement a review is made of the chief physiological theories of hearing: by v. Helmholtz and others (especially A. A. Gray), by W. Rutherford and Th. Lipps, by C. H. Hurst, M. Meyer, J. R. Ewald, E. ter Kuile, A. Lehmann, and O. Göbel. In so far as these theories attempt to provide a satisfactory basis for the nature and the development of auditory experiences, they all leave much to be desired. Their different merits set their various psychological defects into broad relief, while their physiological convergence hopefully suggests the possibility of finding a satisfactory answer to the demands of experience. This convergence appears most clearly in Gray's extension of Helmholtz's resonance theory, Ewald's and Lehmann's standing-wave theory, and ter Kuile's propelled-wave theory, p. 142.

LXVII. The method of solution suggested by psychological analysis is the direct deduction of a physiological result which would form an exact parallel to the results of psychological analysis and the search for a complex of physical processes which would yield that result, p. 162.

LXVIII. This leads to the acceptance of the advancing-wave type of theoretical basis, first suggested by Hurst, and given in a better form by ter Kuile, as the most promising for theoretical construction. The basilar membrane is supposed to be of uniform, or nearly uniform, elasticity in the transverse direction (with considerable freedom in the longitudinal direction). Any defect from uniformity would probably give a gradual increase of elasticity (sensitivity) towards the apex of the cochlea, p. 162.

LXIX. Consideration of the dissipation within the cochlea of any momentary pressure exerted by the stapes and of the interaction of a series of dissipating pressures with the series of subsequently impinging pressures leads to the conclusion that the effect of a regular periodic vibration of the air upon the basilar membrane would be to produce upon it a bulge beginning at the basis of the membrane, reaching along it in proportion to the length of the air wave, and possessing a point of maximal bulge in the centre of the length affected or approximately so, p. 163.

LXX. The effect of a periodic series of pressures on the basilar membrane will not be totally annulled by the end of each period, but will only be brought into a condition of longitudinal equilibrium round the central maximum of intensity. This leaves room for the initiatory increase of excitation, which is complete when perpendicular equilibrium has been reached after several periods between the longitudinal, balanced system of pressures exerted upon the basilar membrane and the reactive elasticity of the length of basilar membrane affected, p. 167.

LXXI. The broadening of the basilar membrane towards the apex of the cochlea seems most probably to be a device for securing greater sensitivity to the pressures that survive the passage of so much of the cochlea. Remarks concerning bone conduction, combination tones, etc., p. 168.

LXXII. Analysis of irregular periodic waves follows as a matter of course upon the process of longitudinal equilibrisation of pressures described in LXIX. Such equilibrisations will take place in so far as the conditions are provided for them in any periodic wave, just as they do in Fourier's analysis. Only the process is mechanical, as is that of an adding machine. Thus all phase relations become ineffective in so far as uniaural hearing is concerned, p. 169.

LXXIII. This physical construction seems compatible with the results of the investigations into the localisation of tones (pitches) on the basilar membrane (experimental injury) and with the number of transverse fibres on the basilar membrane or of neural receptors connected therewith, p. 171.

LXXIV. If these numbers seem too small, their scope may be widened by the hypothesis of uniformly decreasing elasticity of the basilar membrane indicated in LXVIII and LXXI. This hypothesis is not inconsistent with the psychological analysis already given, especially with XV and XXXI ff. For the introspective facts show that the departure from an equal elasticity cannot be great, and some departure from equality with maintenance of uniformity is in perfect accord with the proportional nature of interval expounded in XXXIX and XLIII; cf. LXXVII, p. 174.

LXXV. The problem of binaural hearing for pure psychological theory is to show that the ordinal differences of the elements of hearing are an adequate basis for the bi-systemic phenomena of hearing, especially the 'localisation' of sounds. Compare the psychological problem of binocular vision, p. 175.

LXXVI. The coordination of the two uniaural systems must not be presupposed. It must have imposed itself upon the ordinal differences of the two systems in virtue of the approximately identical forms evoked in each by their relations to the common stimulus, p. 177.

LXXVII. A certain amount of natural incoordination of the two ears is found in cases described as showing a pitch difference between the two ears. These cases do not by any means involve the assumption of a 'mixture' of tonal qualities like that of visual qualities. Their proximate cause is probably a certain variation in the texture, or in the uniformity of elasticity of, the basilar membrane, p. 179.

LXXVIII. The facts of binaural 'mixture' and the binaural summation of intensities presuppose not only a longitudinal overlapping of uniaural volumes, but also and especially a transverse overlapping of these volumes, which can, moreover, only be partial. If it were complete, the distinction of the two ears from one another would be impossible (except perhaps on successive stimulation of the ears), as would be also binaural localisation. If there were no overlapping, summation of intensities and binaural 'mixture' would be impossible, p. 182.

LXXIX. These assumptions are supported both by anatomical or physiological, and by introspective, psychological evidence, p. 182.

LXXX. Binaural integration does not give rise to a really new system or dimension of orders, as does binocular integration. It means at most only the mobilising, as it were, of the transverse uniaural volumes in their own plane, not in any new direction. The two uniaural systems, then, really remain coordinate parts of an inclusive system— the binaural—not coordinate contributors to a new integrative level, as are the two binocular systems, p. 184.

LXXXI. The oscillation thus produced is such as may combine with simultaneous oscillations in other senses to produce the localisation of sounds, p. 185.

LXXXII. Thus the intensive difference of uniaural impressions is not the direct, but only the indirect basis of binaural localisation, in so far as it procures a variation of obtrusiveness of uniaural differences of transverse order, p. 186.

LXXXIII. An analysis of the experimental observations of binaural localisation shows that the latter does not primarily involve more than can be provided by the theory just developed, namely an oscillation of (spatial) orders ('directions') from one end of a series ('opposite the left ear') to the other ('opposite the right ear'), p. 187.

LXXXIV. The only improvement in the direct basis of localisation procured by other factors than mere interaural difference of intensity is that produced by complexity of pitches (pitch-blends and noises). This seems due to the great repetition of predominances, which would give a much more detailed basis for the observation of interaural difference of emphasis than that given by a pure tone. All other improvements are secondary, being based upon cognitive correlations and thus lying outside the range of sensory processes, p. 189.

LXXXV. Analysis thus shows the auditory localisations of the mosquito and of man to be processes whose identity is obscured only by the complicated nature of our uniaural systems, p. 191.

CHAPTER XI

SHORT SUMMARY

1. A purely psychological science of experience is possible and necessary. It calls for a reform of the psychology of hearing by the help of the method of systematic comparison of hearing with the probably typical structure of the other senses.

2. Comparative study of the senses in their simpler forms and aspects yields a probable type of elementary sensation possessing six attributes: quality (cold, warm, red, bitter, etc.), intensity, systemic order (underlying all localisations and positions), extensity, temporal order and durance. This type is the key to the theoretical gates of hearing.

3. The tonal series, reduced by the elimination of partials, conforms to this type by the classification of pitch as systemic order, the extensive implication of the volumes of tones, the obvious intensity, and the one and equal quality of all tones.

4. Tones, being volumes, are not 'atoms,' but rather regular balanced 'molecules' of sound in which the central 'atom' predominates, thus giving the whole a pitch.

5. Noise is a very irregularly balanced mass of elementary sound 'atoms' in which more or less vaguely defined predominances (pitches) may appear. It is coordinate with, not reducible to, tone. Vowels form another coordinate.

6. It is a problem, not a presupposition of the psychology of hearing that pitch is to be identified with 'tone' in the analysis of tonal masses. This problem is the problem of fusion, which the method of analysis followed shows to be due to coincidence of volumes. The

proportions of the coinciding volumes can be obtained by purely psychological analysis and are strictly proportionate to the physical rates of vibration. All the phenomena of fusion are explicable on this basis.

7. All simultaneous tones have a common upper limiting 'atom' of sound and coincide downwards from that point in the proportion of their relative volumes. Their predominances or 'pitches' stand centrally in their volume. Fusion is determined by this coincidence and the resulting balance of the lower limiting and predominating points of the higher tone round the predominance of the lower.

8. The theory of tone thus runs gradually and continuously into the theory of pitch-blends ('timbre'), fusion, and consonance. No new principle separates the sensations of tone, as we know them, from their conjunction in groups.

9. The experience of distance is found in hearing and is there based, as in the other senses, on differences in the ordinal attribute. But its value is far outweighed by that of interval, the constant proportion of volumic outline or stress. With the help of the preferences given by fusion, interval is responsible for the standardisation of the whole musical range. Or rather the musical range is the range of constancy of interval proportions.

10. The explanation of the problems of tonal sequences involves no new principle and no change of basis of explanation.

11. The experience of motion found in other senses is confirmed in hearing both in the obtrusive form of gliding tones and in the elusive form of 'passage' between successive tones. The latter is an important aspect of melody, independent of laws of proportional progression (scales) to which it has been made completely subordinate in almost all forms of music.

12. The octave and the fifth, with its common adjunct the fourth, as being the only distinct, naturally (fusionally) determined, intervals, are the probable ground of development of all specific scales.

13. A scale is a series of intervals or volumic proportions whose value lies in the basis of familiarity and guidance it supplies to the listener's attention. Its musical coherence and potentialities do not emanate from any of its probable or possible sources, but are intrinsic.

14. The further determination of scales proceeds according to two principles, directly issuing from this natural basis: namely, the intercomplication (1) of the foundations themselves by repetition, and (2) of the products of that manipulation by equalisation of approximately

equal intervals. Two extrinsic sources of small intervals are the subdivisions of strings and the playful formation of small intervals.

15. The most acceptable type of physiological theory of hearing is that which assumes the propulsion of a wave along the basilar membrane. Consideration of the elasticity of the membrane and of the interaction of the pressures set up within the cochlea before any moment with those set up in the remainder of the period shows that every physical tone produces a wave of depression of the basilar membrane beginning from the basis and extending along in proportion to its pitch, with a point of maximal depression in the centre round which relative intensities are arranged symmetrically and decreasingly. This deduction forms a satisfactory parallel to the psychological facts of hearing and seems physically probable.

16. The preceding psychological theory of hearing seems to present a sufficient basis for a complete theory of binaural integration.

17. The binaural systems are really as identical as they appear to us to be, in virtue of the volumic forms which are evoked in them by their relations to the common stimulus, and in spite of the original differences of their ultimate elements.

18. The facts of binaural 'mixture' of tones, the binaural summation of intensities, and the discriminability of the two ears show that uniaural volumes 'overlap' transversely, but only partially so. The differences of emphasis produced in each system by the intensive differences of uniaural stimulation seem to provide a sufficient basis for all the direct localisational efficiency of hearing.

CHAPTER XII

UNTECHNICAL ACCOUNT OF RESULTS

In order to help those who are not familiar with the niceties of psychological terminology I shall now attempt to state the results of my theory in the terms of common knowledge. But I explicitly decline to accept any responsibility for misunderstandings that may thus arise. A science can be advanced only upon the conceptions that are most adequate to its objects. I have shown repeatedly throughout this work how insufficient care in the use of popular or generally accepted notions regarding auditory experiences may raise barriers to progress that can be removed only with great difficulty and with the closest scrutiny of the implications of all conceptions adopted in explanation. I believe that of the new conceptions used by me those of order and volume will appear most strange to those not accustomed to philosophical and psychological terminology. They are also in themselves the ground of the greater part of the theoretical reconstruction I offer.

It is commonly held that the visual parallel to the pitch differences of musical tones is the series of colours in the spectrum or at least a series of colours of different kinds. Francis Galton (21) gave an interesting account of certain peculiar people who assert that they have coloured hearing as it were; when a certain vowel or word is sounded they have at once in mind a certain colour, which always appears with that sound; for other words or vowels other colours will come to their mind. In some people colours are associated with different keys of music or with different notes of the scale (cf. 83; 86; 87, 81 ff.; 78; the discussion appended to 78 shows how difficulties arise as soon as the analogy is pushed beyond the basis of the vibrational series). Instruments have been constructed on which music can be played in colour; each ivory of the keyboard is connected with an electric lamp of a certain colour, so that when chords and melodies are played, not only are the usual sounds heard, but also groups of coloured discs or the like are illuminated. The constructor's idea evidently is that music may thus be translated into the equivalent terms of our other most developed and artistically most useful sense[1].

I consider this view to be entirely wrong. And it is inconsistent unless all local differences in the colours are eliminated. Tones do not appear at different places; they all blend together. And so, if colours are the parallel to pitches, the colours should all be made to illuminate only one constant surface. But every one knows that if they did so,

[1] Cf. 144. Rimington's colour organ is constructed to bring out analogies between the spectrum band and the musical octave. These analogies and the resulting colour changes are held to be the basis of a probable art of pure colour of the future. It is said to be very interesting to watch the ever-varying combinations of colours. For another attempt v. *Athenaeum*, 1913, no. 4483, p. 322: "A corresponding arrangement of colours is shown at the same time by means of wires connected with rows of twelve electric lamps in coloured screens. There are in all seven such rows, placed one above another in a spiral....The intensity of light in the seven rows of lamps varies according to the intensity" of the sounds played.

only one colour at a time would be visible. In fact the colour disc should be reduced to a spot of just visible size; for tones are not commonly, or at least on the basis of this analogy, supposed to have any size at all. So it would seem that if this analogy between hearing and vision is carried out strictly, the colour organ would make a very poor show. This shows how even a popular notion about the properties of sounds and colours can involve itself quickly in the greatest difficulties.

One who defends the parallel between pitches and colours might then proceed to prop up his claim by various assertions about the nature of sounds. If he did so, he would only work himself further and further into a quagmire of difficulties. We will not try to follow his efforts. The various psychologists we have discussed have made such efforts in the best possible way, and have not succeeded with them. Of course it is hard for those who set out from a knowledge of the physical basis of sounds and colours, to give up the preconception suggested by the octaves of vibrations. Colours correspond to different wave-lengths of ethereal vibration and pitches to different wave-lengths of aerial vibration. To part from the parallelism of these series in favour of similarities established by comparison of the sounds and colours as they appear to us subjectively, seems—well, it may seem to some like giving up knowledge or even Science in favour of mere opinion. "People," they may say, "who start analysing their feelings, as they appear to them, can get anything out of them. And that's all there is in 'psychology,' anyway."

Others, who are more respectful, may attempt to evade the difficulties they encounter by admitting the hopelessness of establishing a true parallel between vision and hearing. But they will take their stand by the knowledge that they deem 'attainable and sure'—physical or physiological knowledge for example; and say: the work of 'psychology' is to find out what organs our senses depend upon, how these organs are affected by physical sounds and lights, etc., how they work to give us our sensations, and upon what parts of the brain our other experiences, such as feelings and thoughts, are dependent. As for us, they will say, we will abide by our physical knowledge and believe that the parallel of pitches and colours is well founded in nature and, anyway, cannot be proved to be wrong. How could we start making a pure science out of mere experiences? They are so fleeting and elusive, so intangible, so undemonstrable. Anyone could believe anything about them. And as a matter of fact, every sort of thing has been said about them by philosophers and psychologists. One

says one thing, another another; and together they never get on at
all. Whereas physical processes and the workings of the body are
things we can really study and understand[1].

It is useless to attempt to meet these arguments. For much of
the indictment is true. The only possible answer is to present what
results can be attained and invite comparison of them and the methods
of their discovery with those of any reputable science.

My claim is that the true parallel between music and pictorial
art rests on the basis of form. Music as an art is more like the arts
of etching or drawing which dispense with all change of colour, except
the series from white to black. Music is like a higher elaborate art of
ornamentation devoid of all representation of objects. No true parallel
between music and any of the forms of pictorial art can be established;
but it is right to say that, if differences of visual colour are left out
of account, both are arts of pure form.

Sounds are not the parallel of colours. But sounds are like colours
in being spread out; in the act of vision colours are spread over a
certain extent of sensitive surface in the eye, the retina; in the act
of hearing sounds are spread over a certain extent of the sensitive
surface in the ear, the basilar membrane, etc. But colours all lie side
by side, or we cannot distinguish them from one another; they mix
then to form other colours. Sounds always overlap each other more
or less, though never completely so long as they differ in pitch. We
distinguish them by the different way they affect the basilar membrane;
one sound makes the most intense impression at one point of the
membrane, another sound at another point. The most intense points
for the series of tones from highest to lowest pitch lie along the basilar
membrane, beginning from the one end (the basis) and running towards
the other end. The most intense point for any one tone lies in the
middle of the extent of the basilar membrane affected by it.

Is this not also true, merely as we hear it? High tones are small

---

[1] The paragraph represents no special point of view, but only an average. But I am
not overstating. Even from the pen of an excellent psychologist we have recently read:
"I am not one of those high and dry theorists who hold that physiology and psychology
must be kept strictly apart as independent disciplines." If that does not mean that
psychology is not an independent discipline whereas physiology is, I am much mistaken.
But if each can be an independent discipline, each *must* be it, however much the two
may finally cooperate. If one of them cannot be independent, I do not know who would
yet suggest that physiology is the dependent one. And if psychology is dependent, the
point of view is essentially that sketched in the text.

and thin; the lower a tone gets, the bigger and bulkier it becomes. And pitch moves progressively to one side of a series, as we listen to the tones of the piano played from the high to the low end of the keyboard. Moreover, tones played together always seem to be together, unseparate, blended or fused, no matter how different their pitches may be. One can never get two tones entirely away from one another, as one separates two patches of colour.

When octaves are played, the upper tone coincides with the upper half of the lower tone, making that half more intense; with a special point of intensity at the middle of this upper half. If the octave above that again is added, a third notch of intensity appears an eighth of the length of the lowest tone from the upper end of it. If a fifth is played the notch of the upper tone and its lower end lie equally far apart on either side of the notch of the lowest tone. And so on. These notches are the pitches of the tones. So that harmonies and the musical 'colours' of tones are like an ornamentation of the outline of the volume or extent of the lowest tone that is played or heard.

As music is played, the ear follows all the prominences in the main volume of sound as they appear, to the extent that it endeavours or is accustomed to do so. All other prominences and the volumes around them it hears only in bulk. They make a characteristic and recognisable mass-impression and are more or less pleasant. That, then, is the reason why I say that music is like an art of ornamentation; it is an art of form. If music is to please, it cannot change at random the ornamental outline of the masses of sound that it gives in succession; it must do that in such a way as to let the ear follow and apprehend all the important changes in the prominences of the outline, i.e. all the important changes of pitch; and all pauses and final sounds must leave the ear with a nicely proportioned, well-balanced, regular mass of sound before it.

When we look at a beautiful etching, we do not think of the points and lines in it as places on the printed paper. Of course we cannot abstract entirely from the interest of the places represented in an etching. But if it gave us no more than that, the work would be a mere illustration, of no artistic value as such. The artistic basis of every picture is the whole mass of points, lines, and surfaces it presents: as a mass of forms, not as a mass of represented physical distances or places. It is the agreeableness of all we see before us, merely as visual experience, that forms the first ground of the art. Much may then be added because of the representational interests of the subject. But the former purely visual 'harmony' is essential to the work of art.

We say harmony here, simply because that word takes us away from real interests, the interest in houses, places, persons, etc. to the agreeable unity of what we merely feel and experience through sense. The beauty of musical harmonies does not rest upon the interests of representation, but merely upon the intrinsic relations of sounds as heard.

This process of abstraction leads to a notion of what I mean by order. It is not places or spatial positions; but just this purely psychical (seen or heard) arrangement common to the distinguishable components of the artistic etching and to the pitches of music. These components of the etching may take on in our minds the significance of places, things, persons; just as pitches may take on, at times, the significance of speeds of motors, engines, persons' voices, birds, etc. But they do not begin thus in our minds.

It fascinates me to think of an art that deals with purely psychical volumes and prominences in these volumes, and that delights us by leading us about amongst these volumes in an endless variety of rhythms, and speeds, sometimes complex, sometimes clear, now smooth and fluent, now strained, involved, and restless. It is an art which can embody the manners of all our bodily and mental activities without actually presenting us with these in representation. If there is a way in which we can move about in the world, that way can be depicted in the bulks and volumes of sounds; we can be brought to move about in them in just such a way. All our activities can be brought home to our minds with never a word or picture by which we could recognise them and perhaps forget the interest of the mere manner of our soul's life. All this can only be if sounds share a common basis with the space in which all our daily activities are performed.

It gives a new pleasure to tone to think of it as, not merely a speck of quality, whose relation to a kindred quality we cannot understand, but as a volume, a perfectly regular, balanced volume of 'atoms' of hearing which may be varied, and so made the basis of great pleasure by certain minor alterations of the balance of its volume (partial pitches). We can understand the relations of tones to one another; for they all reduce to one identical series of atoms of hearing. We have had no unalterable discords and noises thrust as eternal 'qualities' upon our soul. All our hearing can be used for beauty and we can understand this beauty. Our art is not a creation of biological chances. It is ordered and intelligible and yet natural; as much a part of the natural world as are the heavens and our bodies.

For in spite of the seeming abandonment of the results of physical science, the purely psychological analysis of hearing offered in this work conforms much more closely to the physical and physiological basis of hearing (at least) than does the parallel between hearing and vision based upon the serial systems of the vibrations that cause them. How our sensations of colour are to be analysed so as to appear equally conformable to their physical basis, does not concern us here. In the physical plane we have (1) aerial medium, (2) amplitude of oscillation, (3) wave length with (4) one maximum of condensation. On the physiological plane we have (1) the specific function of hearing, (2) amplitude of displacement of the basilar membrane, etc., (3) length of membrane affected, and (4) point at which membrane is maximally affected. In the psychical plane we have (1) quality of hearing, (2) intensity, (3) volume of sound, (4) predominance of intensity within this volume, or pitch. To each point of the basilar membrane affected or rather to each neural terminal attached to the organs of the basilar membrane, there corresponds in the psychical realm an 'atom' of hearing; although we probably never experience these single atoms, but only more or less regular 'molecules' or volumes of sound, i.e. tones or noises, or masses of tones and noise.

The musical 'ideal' is the perfectly pure tone, devoid of all upper partials. It is perfectly balanced, regular, and continuous, a perfect system of 'atoms' of sound. But no instrument naturally produces or can conveniently be made to produce such perfect tones. Many instruments produce tones, which, though they contain upper partial pitches, nevertheless approximate closely to the perfect balance of the pure tone. For this purpose the partials must be so produced that they are completely subordinate to the proper pitch of the tone played and do not draw away the attention from the pitch of the latter to their own pitches or otherwise upset its balance. If this restriction is observed, a great many beautiful variations upon the 'ideal' perfect tone can be obtained. These indeed are so interesting in their variety that they supersede the pure tone in musical value. They are also probably easier to recognise and to follow than the perfect simplicity of the pure tone would be, were it readily producible.

When several tones are produced after one another, variations in volume of tone are produced. These create a special interest through the experience of motion which arises from successive changes of pitches (orders). This motion may be compared with the motion of a point of light from one place to another; or in an art, to the motion of the defining points of a dancer's limbs. The relation of this motional aspect of melody to the motions of vision is not mere analogy, but has a very real psychical foundation, which entirely justifies the terms applied by musicians to melodies, such as outline, wave, progression, speed, etc. This real foundation is that pointed out above with the help of the comparison of etching and music. The motion of the dancer's limbs from place to place is not our interest; the mere places they occupy are quite irrelevant. What interests us artistically is the mere motion as an experience, the relations of the various motions as regards speed, distance traversed (merely for the 'eye,' i.e. as experiences, not as physical distances) and the forms built up by them all at once and in succession. So too in the music; the tones do not move about; they only give experienced motions, which are as truly motions as those of the dancer, even although we can, and usually do, apprehend the dancer's motions at the same time as motions in space, i.e. as real motions, not experienced motions.

Successive tones also provide an interest through the relations of their volumes to one another. Some volumes pass easily into one another, e.g. octaves and fifths; for the pitch of the lower tone of an octave falls just at the end of the whole volume of the upper tone; while the pitch of a fifth down falls just half-way between the middle and end of the volume of the upper tone. These special relations between successive volumes make certain sequences of tones preferable to others. For they enable us to prepare for the tone next to come by giving us a lead to the points (orders) at which its characteristic features will appear. We bear these relations in mind all the way through a melody and see the melody as a whole in relation to them. From them in various ways other relations are built up, till a useful rounded off system of them is gained (a scale). Each member of this series and its relation to the others can be learned so that we can acquire a high degree of preparedness for any melody and remember it more readily, than we would if its successive tones jumped about anyhow. We can change gradually into other systems of tones by certain methods; and sudden changes may be made to serve artistic ends by the shock they give to our attention and preparedness.

The relations which bind simultaneous tones together rest on this same basis, although it acquires certain new influences when tones are given together. Certain pairs or sets of tones when given together approximate much more closely to the perfect balance of the pure tone than do others. These special pairs make certain groupings of tones much more preferable than others. For they enable us to follow the pitches that appear in successive tonal masses by leading the expectation forwards along recognised lines. We learn to know and recognise the various sets of tones in common use, just as we learn the forms of familiar signs, symbols or words. Considerable departures from balance in tonal mass can be used, if they help to lead over from one well balanced mass to another. But they must not be used at random, but according to certain methods which ensure both pleasant variety and sequence, and enable the listener to follow their changes. Of course here again it may be of artistic value at times to baffle the listener, so as to give him the experience of difficulty and obstruction.

The growth of the power to build up masses of tone, both harmonic and melodic, and the discovery of the best and most variable ways of treating them requires much time. The listener also requires to gain practice in hearing and analysing what the composer puts before him. He has to be educated to the style and complexity of the art. These demands sufficiently explain the slow development of the art of music without our appealing to any development of the ear or its central neural attachments at all. There is no more substantial evidence from the development of the musical art that the organs of hearing have developed than there is from the course of pictorial art that the organs of vision have developed. Everything goes to show that it is rather the complexity and probable pleasantness of what is set before the spectator and the complexity of the demands made upon his attention and experience that have developed.

CHAPTER XIII

'PURE' PSYCHOLOGY

The theory expounded in this book has been devised by the writer not in the interest of a study of hearing as such, but for the sake of the more inclusive study of the whole range of sensory experience. This work in hearing is thus only an episode in a larger effort. It is my firm belief that all our sensory experiences can be completely accounted for in general systematic terms without our having recourse

to the discoveries of physics or physiology at all. Sensory experience
would then appear as a perfectly self-complete, closed, system of reality,
as is for example the system of the elaborations of matter included
in the scope of chemistry. No doubt the universe has much travail
to reach the height of complexity at which experiences emerge. But
puny as our human cognition may be, we can now surely dare to say:
let the creating spirit move over the face of matter and inspire it to
the complexity that is experience; we, who are children of that spirit,
will unravel the plan of as much of it as is within our ken, although
we cannot with our thought add an inch to the stature of experience
and can only take, never make, even what we may call our own. Let
us dare to say it. If we do not seek with all our strength we can never
hope to find the plans of all experience. And proof of some plan com-
mensurate with our cognitive powers of reconstruction is evidence
of much more. We shall perhaps be unable to depict the whole of our
experience upon the canvas of cognition, but we do not yet know the
limits of our powers and what is beyond us can well be thought in
the fashion of our achievements. The knowledge whose ideal exceeds
itself is faith.

Many theories have been propounded regarding the nature of
experience. Many of them have been hardly more than expressions of the failure of theorists to attain to a knowledge of the nature
of experience. Especially great has been the emphasis laid upon the
vast differences that separate the worlds of matter and mind. This
again was often hardly more than the admission that no success had
been won in the application to experience of the methods already
successfully applied to matter. In this work I have shown on the basis
of a special department of sensory experience that conceptions and
methods can be applied to experience that have been successfully
applied to matter. In philosophical work it seems to me that a piece
of detailed and exhaustive treatment is always of much more value
in its general significance than is a piece of general and superficial
treatment of wide scope. It is not my present task to develop fully
the general philosophical implications of the methods I have applied
to hearing and of the success of their application. If my work is in the
main successful, these implications will inevitably follow of themselves.
But I feel it is important to draw some measure of attention to these
things, if only to emphasise the importance for philosophy of the
results of special psychological investigations.

For instance, I think I have shown convincingly that noises (vowels) and tones consist of a common stuff; in other words that they are made up of identical particles of auditory stuff, which differ only in order and intensity. In so far then as sounds are simultaneous and overlap, they consist strictly of the same psychical stuff. I say stuff deliberately; I will not use the word matter, because that is reserved for the realm specifically known as material. But as I conceive it, tones and noises consist of particles of auditory stuff, of particles of experience, in just as true a sense as water consists of particles of oxygen and hydrogen. And these again of smaller particles, and so on. Our knowledge of experience differs no doubt from our knowledge of matter. We may know of experience what we can never know of matter, e.g. its qualities. We may know of experience what we can never know directly of matter, e.g. its intensities. We may know of experience what we can never know phenomenally of matter, e.g. the essences of its integrative unities. We know that atoms, molecules, cells, lives, are unities; but we do not apprehend that unity essentially, as we apprehend the unity of a thought, a concept, a feeling. And so on. But apart from all that, it seems to me that we have as much right to talk of psychical stuff and to treat it as a real object, having properties we can only discover through careful cognitive investigations, as we have to talk of matter as we do. And from that I can see forwards to a perfectly continuous treatment of matter and experience. We shall perhaps not say that a thought consists of the experiences upon which it is based; but it certainly unifies them. And if we say a molecule consists of its atoms, that is only a tautology in full knowledge; we do not know what its unity is; if that unity is an essence, it is entirely real to us, it is in no respect phenomenal to us. The only difference between the worlds of matter and experience would therefore be, that the world of experience is at least partly phenomenal for us, whereas the world of matter is entirely real for us. No doubt laws may emerge in certain relations between objects that are entirely real for us, that never emerge amongst those objects that are partly phenomenal for us. That should not disturb us. Probably new laws emerge at each different level of integration. That will appear clearly as knowledge becomes fuller. But that certain laws run throughout long chains of integrations, seems to me highly probable. And as far as I can see, it seems probable that our psychical integrations form chains that reach back into the physical world.

It may seem, then, that the time has come to throw away our preconceptions regarding the psychical world and its connexion with the material world that are based on previous imperfect or wrong methods and knowledge. If the methods I have advocated and applied, and their results, stand in the main—and I do not expect more,—it is surely time that the fullest scope and opportunity were given to psychological science, and that it were encouraged in every possible way, instead of being ignored, or hampered by the propagation of systems of philosophy and even of psychology that have outlived their value and efficiency. In so far as philosophy is concerned with experience and is in principle inductive, the progress of pure psychology is vital to its development. I make no assertions regarding the other scope and contents of philosophy. But in this country philosophy has always included much of the science of mind or experience. It is a plain duty laid upon those of us who are interested in mind to maintain the excellent tradition of British philosophy in its dealings with mind, to have a clear eye for what is a furtherance of knowledge and for what is a mere pawing of the air and a wind of words. We should hesitate at nothing, neither fearing to doubt, or to deny, nor tiring of trying to encompass the mysterious with knowledge.

WORKS CITED

(1) ABRAHAM, O. AND BRÜHL, L. J.   Wahrnehmung kürzester Töne und Geräusche. *Ztschr. Psychol.* 1898, **18**, 177–217.

(2) ABRAHAM, O. AND SCHAEFER, K. L.   Ueber die maximale Geschwindigkeit von Tonfolgen. *Ibid.* 1899, **20**, 408–416.

(3) BALEY, S.   Versuche über die Lokalisation beim dichotischen Hören. *Ibid.* 1915, **70**, 347–372.

(4) —— Versuche über den dichotischen Zusammenklang wenig verschiedener Töne. *Ibid.* 1915, **70**, 321–346.

(5) BERGSON, H.   *Les données immédiates de la conscience.*   Paris, 1888 (9th ed. 1911).

(6) BEZOLD, F.   Weitere Untersuchungen über "Knochenleitung" und Schall-leitungsapparat im Ohr.   *Ztschr. Ohrenhlk.* 1904, **48**, 107, cited from *Zentralbl. Physiol.* 1904, **18**, 725.

(7) BÖNNINGHAUS, G.   Ein Fall von doppelseitiger zerebraler Hörstörung mit Aphasie. *Ztschr. Ohrenhlk.* 1905, **49**, 165–170.   *Arch. of Otol.* 1906, **35**, 517 –522.

(8) BRENTANO, F.   *Untersuchungen zur Sinnespsychologie.*   Leipzig, 1907.

(9) BÜHLER, K.   *Ueber Gestaltwahrnehmungen.*   Stuttgart, 1913.

(10) DENKER, A.   Die membrana basilaris im Papageienohr und die Helmholtzsche Resonanztheorie.   *Biol. Centrbl.* 1906, **26**, 600–608.

(11) DUNLAP, K.   Extensity and pitch.   *Psychol. Rev.* 1905, **12**, 287–292.

(12) —— The extensity theory of pitch.   *Psychol. Bull.* 1909, **6**, 58.

(13) v. EHRENFELS, C.   Ueber Gestaltqualitäten.   *Vierteljahrsschr. f. wiss. Philos.* 1890, **14**, 249–292.

(14) ENGEL, G.   Ueber Vergleichungen von Tondistanzen.   *Ztschr. f. Psychol.* 1891, **2**, 361–378.

(15) EWALD, J. R.   Zur Physiologie des Labyrinths.   6. Mittheilung.   Eine neue Hörtheorie.   *Arch. ges. Physiol.* 1899, **76**, 147–188.

(16) —— 7. Mittheilung.   Die Erzeugung von Schallbildern in der camera acustica. *Ibid.* 1903, **93**, 485–500.

(17) —— Ueber die neuen Versuche die Angriffsstellen der von Tönen ausgehenden Schallwellen im Ohre zu lokalisiren.   *Ibid.* 1910, **130**, 188–198.

(18) EWALD, J. R. AND JÄDERHOLM, G. A.   Die Herabsetzung der subjectiven Tonhöhe durch Steigerung der objectiven Intensität.   *Ibid.* 1908, **124**, 29–36.

(19) FAIST, A.   Versuche über Tonverschmelzung.   *Ztschr. Psychol.* 1897, **15**, 102.

(20) FISCHER, O. Ueber ein von Max Wien geäussertes Bedenken gegen die Helmholtzsche Resonanztheorie des Hörens. *Ann. Physik.* 1908, **25**, 118–134.

(21) GALTON, F. *Inquiries into Human Faculty and its Development.* London, 1883. Passage on "Colour Associations."

(22) GÖBEL, O. Ueber die Tätigkeit des menschlichen Hörorgans. *Arch. Ohrenhlk.* 1911, **87**, 42–60, 89–122, 280–302; 1912, **90**, 134–153, 155–171.

(23) —— Ueber die Ursache der Einklangsempfindung bei Einwirkung von Tönen, die im Oktavenverhältnis zueinander stehen. *Ztschr. Sinnesphysiol.* 1911, **45**, 109–116.

(24) —— Ueber die Art der Labyrinthtätigkeit. *Berl. Klin. Wochenschr.* 1914, nos. 19, 21.

(25) GRAY, A. A. A modification of the Helmholtz theory of hearing. *J. Anat. Physiol.* 1900, **34**, 324–350.

(26) —— The theories of hearing. *J. Laryngol. Rhinol. Otol.* 1905, **20**, no. 6.

(27) —— *The Labyrinth of Animals.* London, 1907, **1**; 1908, **2**.

(28) GURNEY, E. *The Power of Sound.* London, 1880.

(29) v. HELMHOLTZ, H. Die Lehre von den Tonempfindungen. Braunschweig, 1870, 3rd ed.

(30) —— *Sensations of Tone.* Trans. by A. J. Ellis, London, 1895.

(31) HOCART, A. M. AND McDOUGALL, W. Some data for a theory of auditory perception of direction. *Brit. J. Psychol.* 1908, **2**, 386–405.

(32) v. HORNBOSTEL, E. M. Ueber vergleichende akustische und musikpsychologische Untersuchungen. *Ztschr. angew. Psychol.* 1910, **3**, 465 ff. Also in *Beitr. Akust. Musikwiss.*

(33) HURST, C. H. A new theory of hearing. *Trans. Liverpool Biol. Soc.* 1895, **9**, 321–353.

(34) JAENSCH, E. R. Die Natur der menschlichen Sprachlaute. *Ztschr. Sinnesphysiol.* 1913, **47**, 219–290.

(35) —— Untersuchungen zur Tonpsychologie. *Ber. 6 Kong. exp. Psychol. Leipzig,* 1914, 79–86.

(36) JAMES, W. The spatial quale. *J. specul. Philos.* 1879, **13**, 64–87.

(37) JUDD, C. H. *Psychology.* General Introduction. New York, 1907.

(38) KATZ, D. Ueber einige Versuche im Anschluss an die Tonwortmethode von Karl Eitz. *Ber. 6 Kong. exp. Psychol. Leipzig,* 1914, 86 f.

(39) KELLER, H. Sammelreferat über die Neuerscheinungen der Akustik in den Jahren 1903–1905. *Arch. ges. Psychol.* 1908, **13**, Litber. 43–117.

(40) KEMP, W. Methodisches und Experimentelles zur Lehre von der Tonverschmelzung. *Ibid.* 1913, **29**, 139–257.

(41) KLEMM, O. Ueber die Lokalisation von Schallreizen. *Ber. 6 Kong. exp. Psychol. Leipzig,* 1914, 169–258.

(42) KÖHLER, W. Akustische Untersuchungen. *Ztschr. Psychol.* 1910, **54**, 241–289; 1911, **58**, 59–140; (1913, **64**, 92–105).

(43) v. KRIES, J. Ueber das absolute Gehör. *Ztschr. Psychol.* 1892, **3**, 257–279.

(44) KRUEGER, F. Zur Theorie der Combinationstöne. *Philos. Stud.* 1901, **17**, 185–310.

(45) KRUEGER, F. Die Theorie der Consonanz. Eine psychologische Auseinandersetzung vornehmlich mit C. Stumpf und Th. Lipps. *Psychol. Stud.* 1907, 2, 205–255.

(46) KÜLPE, O. *Outlines of Psychology.* (Trans. by E. B. Titchener.) London, 1895.

(47) TER KUILE, E. Die Uebertragung der Energie von der Grundmembran auf die Hörzellen. *Arch. ges. Physiol.* 1900, 79, 146–157.

(48) —— Die richtige Bewegungsform der Membrana Basilaris. *Ibid.* 1900, 79, 484–509.

(49) LARIONOW, W. Ueber die musikalischen Centren des Gehirns. *Ibid.* 1899, 76, 608–625.

(50) LEHMANN, A. Ueber die Schwingungen der Basilarmembran und die Helmholtzsche Resonanztheorie. *Folia Neurobiol.* 1910, 4, 116–132.

(51) v. LIEBERMANN, P. Ueber das Wesen des Vokalklanges. *Biol. Centbl.* 1912, 32, 731–748.

(52) v. LIEBERMANN, P. AND RÉVÉSZ, G. Ueber Orthosymphonie. Beitrag zur Kenntnis des Falschhörens. *Ztschr. Psychol.* 1908, 48, 259–275.

(52 A) —— Experimentelle Beiträge zur Orthosymphonie und zum Falschhören. *Ibid.* 1912, 63, 286–324.

(53) —— Ueber eine besondere Form des Falschhörens in tiefen Lagen. *Ztschr. Psychol.* 1912, 63, 325–335.

(54) —— Ueber binaurale Tonmischung. *Ges. Wiss. Gött. Math. Physik.* 1912, 676–680.

(55) —— Die binaurale Tonmischung. *Ztschr. Psychol.* 1914, 69, 234–255.

(56) LIPPS, TH. *Grundtatsachen des Seelenlebens.* 1883.

(57) —— Zur Theorie der Melodie. *Ztschr. Psychol.* 1902, 27, 225–263.

(58) LORENZ, C. Untersuchungen über die Auffassung von Tondistanzen. *Philos. Stud.* 1890, 6, 26–103.

(59) LUCAE, A. Zur Physiologie des Gehörorgans. *Arch. Physiol.* 1904, Suppl. Bd. 490–495.

(60) MACH, E. *Beiträge zur Analyse der Empfindungen.* Jena, 1886.

(61) v. MALTZEW, C. Das Erkennen sukzessiv gegebener musikalischer Intervalle in den äusseren Tonregionen. *Ztschr. Psychol.* 1913, 64, 161–257.

(62) MARBE, K. *Theorie der kinematographischen Projektionen.* Leipzig, 1910.

(63) MAYER, A. Researches in acoustics. *Amer. J. Sci. Arts,* 1874, 8, 81–109.

(64) MEINONG, A. AND WITASEK, S. Zur experimentellen Bestimmung der Tonverschmelzungsgrade. *Ztschr. Psychol.* 1897, 15, 189–205.

(65) MEYER, M. Ueber Kombinationstöne und einige hierzu in Beziehung stehende akustische Erscheinungen. *Ibid.* 1896, 11, 177–229.

(66) —— Zur Theorie der Differenztöne und der Gehörsempfindungen überhaupt. *Ibid.* 1898, 16, 1–34.

(67) —— Ueber die Unterschiedsempfindlichkeit für Tonhöhen nebst einigen Bemerkungen über die Methode der Minimaländerungen. *Ibid.* 1898, 16, 352–372.

(68) —— Ueber die Intensität der Einzeltöne zusammengesetzter Klänge. *Ibid.* 1898, 17, 1–14.

(69) MEYER, M. Ueber Tonverschmelzung und die Theorie der Consonanz. *Ibid.* 1898, **17**, 401–421; **18**, 274–293.

(70) —— Ueber die Funktionen des Gehörorgans. *Verh. Physik. Ges. Berlin*, 1898, **17** (5), 49–55.

(71) —— Zur Theorie des Hörens. *Arch. ges. Physiol.* 1899, **78**, 346–362.

(72) —— E. ter Kuile's Theorie des Hörens. *Ibid.* 1900, **81**, 61–75.

(73) —— Contributions to a psychological theory of music. *Univ. Missouri Stud. Sci. Ser.* 1901, **1**, no. 1, 80 pp.

(74) —— Ueber Kombinations- und Asymmetrietöne. *Ann. Physik.* (4), 1903, **12**, 889–892.

(75) —— Experimental Studies in the psychology of music. *Amer. J. Psychol.* 1903, **14**, 192–214.

(76) —— Zur Theorie der Geräuschempfindungen. *Ztschr. Psychol.* 1903, **31**, 233–247.

(77) —— An introduction to the mechanics of the inner ear. *Univ. Missouri Stud. Sci. Ser.* 1907, **2**, no. 1, 140 pp.

(78) MONTEITH, E. R. Colour-music: experiments in the educational value of the analogy between sound and colour. *Proc. Mus. Ass.* 1913, **39**, 85–102.

(79) MOORE, H. T. The genetic aspect of consonance and dissonance. *Psychol. Monogr.* 1914, **17**, no. 73, 68 pp.

(80) MORROW, W. The trumpet as an orchestral instrument. *Proc. Mus. Ass.* 1895, **21**, 133–147.

(81) MÜLLER, G. E. Zur Psychophysik der Gesichtsempfindungen. *Ztschr. Psychol.* 1896, **10**, 1–82.

(82) MYERS, C. S. *Textbook of Experimental Psychology.* Cambridge, 1911, 2nd ed.

(83) —— A case of synaesthesia. *Brit. J. Psychol.* 1911, **4**, 228–238.

(84) —— Experiments on sound localisation. *Brit. Ass. Rep.* 1913, 679 f.

(85) —— Are the intensity differences of sensation quantitative? *Brit. J. Psychol.* 1913, **6**, 137–154.

(86) —— Two cases of synaesthesia [A. Scriabin and another]. *Ibid.* 1914, **7**, 112–117.

(87) MYERS, C. S. AND VALENTINE, C. W. A study of the individual differences in attitude towards tones. *Ibid.* 1914, **7**, 68–111.

(88) OGDEN, R. M. A contribution to the theory of tonal consonance. *Psychol. Bull.* 1909, **6**, 297–303.

(89) PEAR, T. H. The experimental examination of some differences between the major and the minor chord. *Brit. J. Psychol.* 1911, **4**, 56–88.

(90) PETERSON, J. The place of stimulation in the cochlea versus frequency as a direct determiner of pitch. *Psychol. Rev.* 1913, **20**, 312–322.

(91) PIERCE, A. H. *Studies in Auditory and Visual Space Perception.* New York, 1901.

(92) RAYLEIGH, LORD. Acoustical observations. Perception of the direction of a source of sound. *Phil. Mag.* (5), 1877, **3**, 456–464.

(93) RETZIUS, G. *Das Gehörorgan der Wirbeltiere. Morphologische-histologische Studien.* Stockholm, 1881–4.

(94) Révész, G. Nachweis, dass in der sog. Tonhöhe zwei voneinander unabhängige Eigenschaften zu unterscheiden sind. *Ges. Wiss. Gött. Math. Physik*, 1912, 247–252.

(95) —— *Zur Grundlegung der Tonpsychologie.* Leipzig, 1913.

(96) —— Neue Versuche über binaurale Tonmischung. *Ber. 6 Kong. exp. Psychol. Leipzig*, 1914, 90–92.

(97) Rutherford, W. *The Sense of Hearing.* Brit. Ass. Lecture, 1886, 24 pp.

(98) —— Idem. *J. Anat. Physiol.* 1886, **21**, 166–168.

(99) Schaefer, K. L. Ueber die Wahrnehmung und Lokalisation von Schwebungen und Differenztönen. *Ztschr. Psychol.* 1890, **1**, 81–98.

(100) —— Neue Erklärung der subjektiven Kombinationstöne auf Grund der Helmholtzschen Resonanztheorie. *Arch. ges. Physiol.* 1900, **78**, 503–526; **83**, 73–80.

(101) —— Der Gehörsinn. *Nagel's Handbuch d. Physiol. d. Menschen.* Braunschweig, 1905, **3**, 476–588.

(102) —— Psychophysiologie der Klanganalyse. *Erg. Physiol.* 1909, **8**, 1–25.

(103) Schaefer, K. L. and Guttmann, A. Die Unterschiedsempfindlichkeit für gleichzeitige Töne. *Ztschr. Psychol.* 1903, **32**, 87–97.

(104) Seashore, C. *Elementary Experiments in Psychology.* New York, 1908.

(105) Sewall, E. Beitrag zur Lehre von der Ermüdung des Gehörorgans. *Ztschr. Sinnesphysiol.* 1908, **42**, 115–123.

(106) Sherrington, C. S. *The Integrative Action of the Nervous System.* London, 1906.

(107) Smith, F. O. The effect of training in pitch discrimination. *Psychol. Monogr.* 1914, **16**, no. 69, 67–103.

(108) Southgate, T. L. (Discussing) The vagueness of musical nomenclature. *Proc. Mus. Ass.* 1908, **34**, 74 f.

(109) Starch, D. Perimetry of the localisation of sound. *Psychol. Monogr.* 1905, **6**, no. 2.

(110) Stücker, N. Ueber die Unterschiedsempfindlichkeit für Tonhöhen in verschiedenen Tonregionen. *Ztschr. Sinnesphysiol.* 1908, **42**, 392–408.

(111) Stumpf, C. *Tonpsychologie*, vol. **1**. Leipzig, 1883.

(112) —— *Ibid.* vol. **2**. Leipzig. 1890.

(113) —— Ueber die Vergleichung von Tondistanzen. *Ztschr. Psychol.* 1890, **1**, 419–462.

(114) —— Neueres über Tonverschmelzung. *Ibid.* 1897, **15**, 280–303.

(115) —— Konsonanz und Dissonanz. *Beitr. Akustik u. Musikwiss.* 1898, **1**, no. 1, 1–108.

(116) —— Tonsystem und Musik der Siamesen. *Ibid.* 1901, **1**, no. 3, 69–138.

(117) —— Ueber das Erkennen von Intervallen und Akkorden bei sehr kurzer Dauer. *Ztschr. Psychol.* 1902, **27**, 148–188.

(118) —— Differenztöne und Konsonanz. *Ibid.* 1905, **39**, 269–283.

(119) —— Beobachtungen über Kombinationstöne. *Ibid.* 1910, **55**, 1–142.

(120) —— *Die Anfänge der Musik.* Leipzig, 1911, 209 pp.

(121) —— Konsonanz und Konkordanz. *Ztschr. Psychol.* 1911, **58**, 321–385.

(122) —— Differenztöne und Konsonanz. 2ter Artikel. *Ibid.* 1911, **59**, 161–175.

(123) STUMPF, C. Ueber neuere Untersuchungen zur Tonlehre. *Ber. 6 Kong. exp. Psychol. Leipzig*, 1914, 305–344.

(124) SULLY, J. *Outlines of Psychology.* 1884.

(125) TITCHENER, E. B. *Experimental Psychology.* New York, 1905, vol. 2, pt. 1.

(126) —— *Textbook of Psychology.* New York, 1910.

(127) TOMINAGA, K. Eine neue Theorie des Hörens. *Zentrbl. Physiol.* 1904, **18**, 461–466.

(128) VALENTINE, C. W. The aesthetic appreciation of musical intervals among school children and adults. *Brit. J. Psychol.* 1913, **6**, 190–216.

(129) VANCE, T. F. Variation in pitch discrimination within the tonal range. *Psychol. Monogr.* 1914, **16**, no. 69, 115–149.

(130) WAETZMANN, E. Ueber die "Ausdehnung" der Töne. *Folia Neurobiol.* 1912, **6**, 24–26.

(131) WATT, H. J. Beiträge zu einer Theorie des Denkens. *Arch. ges. Psychol.* 1904, **4**, 289–436.

(132) —— Experimental contribution to a theory of thinking. *J. Anat. Physiol.* 1906, **40**, 257–266.

(133) —— The elements of experience and their integration. *Brit. J. Psychol.* 1911, **4**, 127–204.

(134) —— The psychology of visual motion. *Ibid.* 1913, **6**, 26–43.

(135) —— The main principles of sensory integration. *Ibid.* 1913, **6**, 239–260.

(136) —— Are the intensity differences of sensation quantitative? *Ibid.* 1913, **6**, 175–183.

(137) —— Psychological analysis and theory of hearing. *Ibid.* 1914, **7**, 1–43.

(138) WEINMANN, F. Zur Struktur der Melodie. *Ztschr. Psychol.* 1904, **35**, 340–379; 401–453.

(139) WERTHEIMER, M. Experimentelle Studien über das Sehen von Bewegungen. *Ibid.* 1912, **61**, 161–265.

(140) WIEN, M. Ein Bedenken gegen die Helmholtzsche Resonanztheorie des Hörens. *Wüllner Festschrift.* Leipzig, 1905.

(141) WITTMAACK, K. Eine neue Stütze für die Helmholtzsche Resonanztheorie. *Arch. ges. Physiol.* 1907, **120**, 249–252.

142) ZIMMERMANN, G. Der physiologische Werth der Labyrinthfenster. *Arch. Physiol.* 1904, Suppl. Bd. 193–202.

(143) ELLIS, A. J. On the musical scales of various nations. *J. Soc. Arts*, 1885, **33**, 485–527, 1102–1111.

(144) RIMINGTON, A. W. *Colour-music, the Art of Mobile Colour.* London, 1912, 188 pp.

(145) STUMPF, C. AND V. HORNBOSTEL, E. Ueber die Bedeutung ethnologischer Untersuchungen für die Psychologie und Aesthetik der Tonkunst. *Ber. 4 Kong. exp. Psychol. Leipzig*, 1911, 256–269.

(146) STUMPF, C. AND MEYER, M. Maasbestimmungen über die Reinheit consonanter Intervalle. *Ztschr. Psychol.* 1898, **18**, 321–404.

(147) BINGHAM, W. D. Studies in melody. *Psychol. Monogr.* 1910, **12**, no. 50, 88 pp.

(148) WATT, H. J.   Stereoscopy as a purely visual, bi-systemic, integrative process. *Brit. J. Psychol.* 1916, **8**, 131–169.

(149) HENSEN, V.   Physiologie des Gehörs.   Hermann's *Handbuch der Physiol.* 1880, **3**, pt. 2.

(150) WITTMANN, J.   Neuer objektiver Nachweis von Differenztönen erster und höherer Ordnung.   *Arch. ges. Psychol.* 1915, **34**, 277–315.

(151) MEYER, M.   Die Morphologie des Gehörorgans und die Theorie des Hörens. *Arch. ges. Physiol.* 1913, **153**, 369–384.

(152) WALLER, A. D.   *An introduction to human physiology.*   London, 1896.

(153) MCDOUGALL, W.   *Physiological Psychology.*   London, 1899.

(154) AYERS, H.   Vertebrate Cephalogenesis.   II.   A contribution to the morphology of the vertebrate ear, with a reconsideration of its functions. *J. of Morphol.* 1892, **6**, 1–360.

(155) WATT, H. J.   The typical form of the cochlea and its variations.   *Proc. Roy. Soc.* 1917.

(156) KÖHLER, W.   Akustische Untersuchungen III.   *Ztsch. Psychol.* 1915, **72**, 1–192.

(157) SHAMBAUGH, G. E.   A re-study of the minute anatomy of structures in the cochlea with conclusions bearing on the solution of the problem of tone perception.   *Amer. J. Anat.* 1907, **7**, 245–257.

(158) KISHI, K.   Corti'sche Membran und Tonempfindungstheorie.   *Arch. ges. Physiol.* 1907, **116**, 112–123.

(159) MYERS, C. S.   The influence of timbre and loudness on the localisation of sounds.   *Proc. Roy. Soc.* 1914, **B**, **88**, 267–284.

APPENDIX

In an investigation begun since this work was written and to be published soon (155), I have been able to prove (1) "that the cochlea is built according to a constant plan, of which the scale alone varies from case to case. This scale shows a decidedly high correlation with the size of the organism as a whole. A change of scale will obviously alter all the dimensions recorded except the number of whorls. But even that number, when it varies independently, does not alter the other dimensions of the cochlea. The only other variant thus far detected is the rate of curvature of the spiral, which is greater in the bigger scale organs"; and (2) "that there are two sources of change in the length of the basilar membrane. The chief one is its own absolute increase in length, which appears in a greater number of whorls than usual. The other is the increase in the relative thickness of the tube of the cochlea. There are no other internal variations in the dimensions of the cochlea than these."

There seems thus to be "an increased rate of curvature for absolutely long basilar membranes (large cochleas) and a decreased rate for relatively long ones." I should favour the theory regarding the curvature of the cochlear spiral put forward by Hurst (v. p. 148 f. above). Curvature could hardly be, as M. Meyer suggests (151, 376), a mere matter of the "mechanics of development," e.g. a device for stowing the long cochlear tube into little space and so devoid of all effect upon hearing.

It appears that man stands rather low among the animals in respect of the length of his basilar membrane relatively to the dimensional scale of the whole cochlea. Any arguments based upon the supposition that the elementary efficiency of the hearing of man is finer or further developed than is that of the animals would thus be rendered groundless. Gray's photographs, besides (27), show that for delicacy and regularity of structure man's cochlea cannot compete with that of many animals. All that we can do cognitively and artistically with what we hear, must be done in spite of the roughness and restrictions of our receptory apparatus.

These new data and conclusions fit in well with the theory of hearing developed in this book. The work of the basilar membrane can readily be adjusted to any scale of dimensions of the cochlea as a whole without any change of basilar length being required. At the same time it is evident that a greater tension of elasticity would spread the same range of tones over a greater length of basilar membrane; or, if the elasticity remained the same, the greater length would give a greater range of hearing. A greater basilar length would, therefore, in either case imply greater efficiency of hearing, as seems otherwise to be the case.

I was unfortunately unable to obtain Dr Köhler's third paper (156) until the present work was passing through the press. The paper was published in June, 1915, while it was received by the editor of the *Zeitschrift für Psychologie* on 14th Nov., 1914. As the views propounded in this paper differ in certain most important aspects radically from the general psychological theory of Dr Köhler's earlier papers (42), I feel it necessary to recall that my first paper dealing with the attributes of sound from the point of view of a systematic treatment of all the senses (133) was published in September, 1911, while my second, devoted solely to the systematic problems of the attributes and integrations of sound (137) was published in May, 1914, when I sent a copy of it to Dr Köhler at Frankfurt a. M.

In this latest paper Köhler gives himself considerable trouble to show that "phenomenally pitch has not the character of a quale, but of a space point, degree, niveau, in which a tone is" (p. 187). In view of the novelty and importance of this view, it might seem natural that Köhler should have taken the trouble to refer to those of his predecessors who had expressed similar conclusions, however distantly they resembled his own, even if he had only glanced at the latest literature in his hands. But it is fair to Dr Köhler to observe that he expressly cultivates independence of thought and argument. Thus in a note on the first page of this paper he writes: "The following investigations are entirely independent of those published by Révész and v. Liebermann in recent years. In order to preserve this independence I have up till the closure of this work not yet read Révész's *Grundlegung der Tonpsychologie*" (1913, 95). Then on p. 157, when actually discussing the validity of Révész's view of pitch as quality, he points out in a footnote that "as already emphasised, the arguments in Révész's larger work are still unknown to me." Probably I ought to infer from this that, in omitting to refer to my analysis of hearing, Köhler does not mean to claim any priority for his classification of pitch as an attribute, but is only working at the matter independently, in order that there may be the greater diversity of effort and, as a consequence, the greater gain of truth. I fully appreciate the restraint and self-sacrifice involved in this method. The conclusion regarding pitch must seem novel and striking to anyone familiar with the psychology of the senses and with sound in particular. It certainly seemed so to me when I first came upon the obvious need for it and felt the overpowering certainty of its correctness in the autumn of 1910. It was an exciting task to work out the implications of the change as far as they could rapidly be traced. I have not the slightest doubt that Köhler feels it so too and is busily engaged on the work. But surely the question was as irresistible to him as to me: has anyone ever held this theory before, and, if not, why not? After all it is a very remarkable fact that such an elementary distinction, such a ground fact, of hearing should have been kept in hiding all this time for us twentieth century folk to discover. Professor Külpe said to me in July, 1914, when we were talking about my paper (137): "I should never have thought that the foundations of the psychology of sound could still have been shaken in that way."

However it may be, I feel it right and proper to emphasise not only my own originality and priority of method and result, but also the considerable development I have given to the method and the wide scope I have justified for the results; and to use Dr Köhler's paper as a means of showing up these merits of my labour.

The method I adopted and urged from the beginning is a systematic consideration of the attributes and integrations of all the senses. In an illustrative fragmentary way Köhler follows that method in his discussion of the attributive classification to be given to pitch and (more briefly) to the brightness and vocality of sounds. In so far as he classifies pitch with the place-values of vision (pp. 22, 37, 119, 184 ff.)—otherwise he speaks of it as something degree-like or niveau-like (pp. 36, 184 ff.) or, as it were, mathematical (pp. 36, 145 f., 184 ff.)—he seconds my own result, although he omits to make the very necessary and highly significant distinctions required, if pitch and *place*-value are to be identified. The last passage of his paper is entitled "Objective justification of terminology"; but it is mainly occupied with justifying his classification of pitch with the place-values of vision. That is no justification of his terminology; the word he constantly uses—"tone-body"—means "brightness and vocality taken together" (p. 3). The only justification of that strange term and its stranger use is contained on the last two pages of his paper. The reason given is that brightness and vocality as qualities in the narrower, stricter, sense, stand closer to one another than does each to pitch; they are the real 'content' of sound. "The name 'tone-body' seems to me to signify somewhat the qualitative totality of a sound phenomenon, especially as this totality, as is well known, 'occupies a volume,' and in many cases is allocated to a 'pitch'" (p. 192). But he has nowhere explained or justified this term "volume" or what it implies. His whole paper set out to show, and shows, to his satisfaction, that "musical pitch is not [to be] reckoned as belonging to the tone-body" (p. 3).

This poorly justified, and, perhaps especially, phenomenologically unjustified, habitual terminology, as well as the few references to the new interpretation of pitch in the main text (pp. 22, 36 f., 119?) besides other reasons that will presently appear, lead me to believe that the classification of pitch with place-value was an after-thought of Köhler's[1].

It is interesting to me to see that Köhler gladly notes (p. 185) how the Greek comparison of pitch with a ποσόν rather than with a ποιόν, fits our common cause. I myself found that valuable note in Stumpf's work and referred to it in 1911 (133, 143). There is a difference, however; for the Greeks evidently thought of tones as quantitative, more as what Köhler has reckoned in with tone-body than as localisational. And, although the terms 'degree-like' and 'niveau-like' seem at the first glance to have a more quantitative significance than have 'place-values,' they are really just the same; for a degree or a niveau is only a surface or a mark of height, whereas only the distance or volume between two surfaces can properly be held to be a quantum. But I do not know how seriously the inclusion of "volume" in 'tone-body' is to be taken; in his lengthy paper Köhler might have found space to explain what he meant by that; perhaps by including "volume, occasionally also further aspects, which, to avoid confusion I here leave quite aside," he meant merely to draw his terminological net close enough for all eventualities.

That the place-value view of pitch is an after-thought is borne out by the fact that Köhler has hardly begun to appreciate the significance of that theory. Thus he rightly appreciates the value of the lines of classification he has touched upon, in the following words (p. 184 f.): "One need only think of the problems that will later on emerge for the physiological study of the brain to recognise what importance accrues to the phenomenologically adequate correlation of the various aspects of different sensory fields: the inductions of the physiologists will then find support in our correlations and grievous fallacies will be possible, if we do not properly consider phenomeno-logical correspondences, to which the physiological must of course run parallel." That is a sort of principle of discovery. Three pages earlier he had stated positively that "a *bright* tone is *similar* to a bright optical picture," i.e. it is directly or phenomenologically similar, not merely indirectly associated for any sort of subsidiary reasons. Now it is a familiar fact that "optical brightnesses correspond to intensities, but so-called acoustical brightnesses correspond to frequencies" of vibration (p. 183). To get over this psychophysical discrepancy Köhler then proceeds to invent a speculation about some possible chemical processes of identical nature, arising centrally from these different peripheral excitations. But if there is anything in the idea of parallelism at all, we may expect the parallelism to hold over the whole journey from the periphery to the experience. That would lead us to

---

[1] Cf. 42 (1911), 102: "everything that is to be said in a later paper on the concept of pitch will, from the negative side," etc. So Köhler did not, then, anticipate any *positive* thesis about pitch, and, true to his anticipation, his whole third paper is built up on a negative treatment of pitch.

suspect the phenomenological identity of visual brightness and "so-called acoustical brightness."

This leads on to the general problem of phenomenology. Köhler seems to share the notion that phenomenology is a discipline like the laws of the Medes and Persians. You have only to point to two amongst other objects and in a disinterested manner to ask: aren't these two much more like one another, don't they belong more obviously to one another, than does either to any of the rest? The answer is in the affirmative, of course. And no consideration from any other source can change the verdict, whether contradiction appear or not. That is more or less the manner in which Köhler comes to identify pitch and place-value, brightness in sights and "so-called brightness" in sounds. As a result, the reader may either yield to the suggestion, or, remembering the number of other different views about brightness and pitch, incline to be sceptical of the method of procedure. Why should he yield so easily to such suggestive questions? If the things suggested are so obvious why were they not generally admitted long ago? Probably because they are not just a matter of this very modern phenomenological activity.

Unless we are to open the door of psychological study to a confusion of arbitrary classifications and theory, we must take our phenomenology scientifically and proceed to establish our classifications on as broad a basis as possible. For an example of this method I may refer to my discussion of the proper classification of pitch and volume, above, p. 23 ff.

The following are amongst the special 'qualities' of sound claimed by Köhler in this paper: all the simple vowels *m*, *u*, *o*, *a*, *e*, *i*, the two pitch-less sounds *s* and *f*; the rolling *rr*; the explosives *p*, *t*, *k*, etc.; and many others only faintly indicated. The number of possible qualities seems unlimited. The *rr* quality arises with a certain rapidity of beats, which are well-known to be essentially a more or less rapid oscillation of the intensity of sound; at slow rates in fact they are obviously so; but at faster rates we do not so obviously hear them as fluctuations of intensity; but we do hear them as '*rrr...*' "I do not know," says Köhler (p. 93), "if there are now many psychologists who would still consider debatable any such statement as: the *rr* quality is nothing but an oscillating of heard intensity,—when it is, as it is here, a question of *description*." If you do hear oscillations of intensity, they are not the substance or the basis of *rr*, but only accompany it, being due to other causes than those directly responsible for *rr*.

Similarly (p. 109) when you listen to the cadences of speech, it is possible to isolate in attention the changes of pitch. "But the important point is: as soon as you succeed in hearing pitches, the phenomenal character of the heard sentence has been radically changed, the *spoken* sentence has become a *sung* sentence and the contrast between these two phenomenal forms is so great that it can hardly be easily overlooked by anyone." Therefore spoken speech has no pitches (p. 112).

This latter conclusion agrees with the idea of depreciating the importance of pitch in sound that is the fundamental motive of Köhler's work in this paper. And it seems to make hay of older views promulgated by Helmholtz and his successors, according to which spoken speech has a more or less indefinite form of pitch which can be apprehended by special analytic effort and noted roughly in musical notation. But these older views had a very good purpose, which can still be encouraged and furthered. In fact Köhler's work may be looked upon—apart from phenomenological considerations— as but a more successful continuation of that earlier work. When he finds an optimal *a* or *o* in a pure tone of so and so many vibrations per second, we may recognise that he is doing for vowels further service of the same kind as Helmholtz did for both vowels and for spoken speech in fixing their pitch variations in musical notation. And after his criticism of Helmholtz's efforts, he is surely not going to ask us to believe that pure tones and vowels are phenomenologically identical.

Helmholtz, of course, never meant his notation examples to be *sung*. The pitches indicated were intended to be approximately those of spoken speech, according to the difference between spoken and sung pitches. How will Köhler represent the pitches of spoken speech? The question is, of course, mistaken; "spoken speech has no pitches." It consists of vowels, and consonants, etc., in a peculiar stream. True: but all these vowels and consonants have optimal relations to pure tones and other sounds, which can to some extent be indicated in musical notation, as also can the approximate niveau of the voice sounds. Then we are back on Helmholtz's lines again. I suppose every reader used to give these notational illustrations of the intonation of sentences in his own or other languages the same sort of criticism as Köhler gives them: I don't *sing* like that, but it's funny how like the singing is to my accent or to that of these foreigners. The problem is to do Helmholtz's service better than Helmholtz.

Besides if a certain tone has an optimal resemblance to a given vowel, that vowel has an optimal resemblance to the tone, the more certainly so since the two sets of variants are linear series. So if the vowel is devoid of pitch, then the pitch is devoid of vocality; the resemblance must be due to a third common element—presumably Köhler's brightness. Then if the vowels are amongst the qualities of sounds, and pitches are not qualitative, tones will have no quality, or merely brightness. That reminds one of the 'colourless' visual phenomena. But these are only popularly considered 'colourless' or devoid of quality. They really have quality as much as the colour-hues do. Then pure tones will have a quality too—apart from their brightness. But what can this quality be? It must be a quality that is unlike the vowel qualities that are so beautifully periodic from octave to octave of vibratory frequencies[1], like the colours of the colour figure, one quality passing gradually over into another. Then this tone quality cannot fall into one system with the vowel qualities. And what of the *rr* quality and the explosive qualities and all the other innumerable noise qualities? Do they form a system like the colour figure, or are there just a host of them? Or is brightness really the quality that is common to them all?

In fact Köhler does assert a view like this last. Brightness and vocality are to be *taken together* as qualities; that is a change upon his earlier view which regarded vocality as the only kind of quality. These two "appear in a relation of most intimate penetration" (p. 191). But where has vocality gone to in pure tone? Or is it not absent there (as I argue), but really there in full form, the only difference being that tone has a pitch whereas the ordinary vowel has not? Then we need some knowledge of the conditions under which pitch appears. This really does become a rather mysterious problem for Köhler. He speaks vaguely of some special peripheral simplicity in the conditions underlying pitch (pp. 102 f., 180). To say the least, Köhler's views bristle with difficulties.

Incidentally Köhler makes a notable remark about Jaensch's work. The *s* given by the Galton whistle, which causes a periodic vibratory process, can be made more lifelike, Köhler finds, "if one sounds on two Galton whistles simultaneously two tones of this region that lie far enough apart not to give any distinct beats." "In similar manner one can more or less increase the speech likeness of all simple tones." "This is how *all* the experiments lately published by Jaensch are to be interpreted." In my opinion it is rather the other way about. The work that Köhler has recently published on vowels is better interpreted according to the indications of Jaensch's work. Vowels are (partial) sounds of a somewhat indefinite pitch, which lies about the point of the range of pure tones of definite pitch where the greatest resemblance to these vowels is to be found. Thus phenomenological resemblances and physical connexions are brought into parallel.

With Jaensch's leading then we can begin to understand the phenomenological difference *and connexion* between vowels and tones. Indefiniteness of pitch is a category that will include many progressively variant forms, and yet remind us that indefiniteness can be attained in a multitude of ways which may be characteristic of the vowel sounds produced by cats, dogs, monkeys and men. A study after this method may teach us in the end that

[1] The new values reported found in this paper are: vowel *i*—16 × 261·3 vbs, ± 62 vbs; sound or consonant *s*—32 × 264·4 vbs, ± ca. 200 vbs; sound or consonant *f*—ca. 64×260. Compare Table 1, p. 43, above. The sound *ch*, as in German *ich*, is believed to lie in the octave higher.

vowel sounds and the like are not to be classed with the qualities of other senses, but with their forms, surfaces, textures; and that we must look *else-where* for the qualities or quality of sound.

It is a familiar fact that these forms have often been called qualities—figure-qualities. They were obviously figures, but in order to express their unity and individuality they were also called qualities. Some experiences, such as these of Köhler, may for the same reasons make claim to the name of quality and also, but less obviously so, be figures or forms. And yet it be wrong to call either set qualities. The proof of their nature as ' forms ' depends on broad theory such as I have advocated in this volume.

Of course Köhler's brisk and vivid phenomenology may see differently. What I want to urge is a broad, contemplative, judicial, scientific, pheno-menology. In fact, I do not see that there is anything specially to be gained by speaking of phenomenology. As I have said above (p. 23) even phenomena are to all intents and purposes realities when we come to study them scien-tifically. We have to look around so carefully and deliberately and trace connexions amongst the phenomena as if they were more than phenomena. Whereas, the word phenomenology suggests that a reliable study of pheno-mena can be made without their being considered as realities and without concern for their relations to realities. The word psychology in the sense of pure psychology seems to me to cover the whole field of inquiry sufficiently, whether it be phenomenal or real. It certainly does not suggest such flights of descriptive and classificatory fancy as does the other term, but a more cautious and critical spirit.

Köhler suggests various changes in the point of view from which we approach the problems of sound. These are quite clever and suggestive in many ways. But in various cases it is not clear that any important alteration in the 'traditional' attitude or knowledge has been effected. Nor do the hypotheses suggested by the change go beyond the vaguest indications. A discussion of them would hardly be profitable.

The main purport of Köhler's paper is to prove that most forms of sound are devoid of pitch, or rather, as he so often more particularly says, of "musical pitch." In the theory developed in this book these two things are by no means synonymous, and to some extent it is certainly true that everyone has been distinctly aware that many of the forms of sound mentioned by Köhler had no "musical pitch." One has to be careful in reflecting on Köhler's argument not to suppose that in all cases he has proved these forms of sound to be devoid of pitch, simply.

Thus very high tones lose their 'musical pitch' long before they could reasonably be supposed to lose their pitch. I should rather incline to the view that they first lose their volume, in the sense that it gets so small as to be no longer efficient as a standard by which the relative *musical* place of the tone is determined. Very high tones are as pointed and mathematical as one could desire. The difference between the vowel *i* and the consonant *s*, as Köhler expounds them, is that between tone with pitch (but not necessarily 'musical pitch') and noise (whether the latter has any sort of pitch or not); or in my own terminology the difference between regular balanced sound volume and irregular sound volume of very small extent.

Some doubt arises with the problem of the criterion of the optimal form of a vowel in relation to pure tones. Köhler himself points out (p. 31 f.) "that a decided vowel or consonant is really very seldom exactly the same in character as one of the optimal points." "Especially amongst men— who have produced the most of the vowels examined—a pure *i* is hardly ever heard, but strictly always a sound midway between *i* and *e*," etc. And the ear is so easily fatigued, that the *i*-character quickly changes towards the *e*-character.

I suppose Köhler would reply that the progressive change from one quality to another, from *a* to *e*, and then from *e* to *i*, as from red to yellow, is obvious to anyone who has a phenomenological ear, and that the validity of the point he selects for *i* or *e* purity, is greatly increased by this serial nature of qualitative changes. Only, we must not forget, the serial nature must be first definitely established with all the rigour of incognitive methods as generally valid. Even then, however, the series would not decide as to the qualitative classification. There are many series of visual geometrical forms that are not qualitative; *e.g.* squares within squares, where the angle of one rests on the middle point of a side of another, etc.

As regards the hearing of Dr v. Liebermann, which shows an abnormal displacement of pitch over against the volume of tone (*v.* above p. 50 f.), Köhler's demonstration that v. Liebermann hears vowels and selects the optimal frequencies for them very much as persons with normal hearing do, must be kept in relation with the fact that v. Liebermann hears intense and well sustained tones and chords in the normal way as regards pitch, and that as the subject is very deaf Köhler had to "present the tones relatively loud to the ear" (p. 12).

Köhler's observations on a very unmusical subject (p. 53 ff.) are of much interest. He shows that that subject probably hears no pitches, as he does not understand the term and the adjectives 'high' and 'low' applied to them. That seems to me a natural consequence of the absence of pitch, which alone would give the idea of a definite series moving, as 'brightness' increases, or volume decreases, towards one side progressively, which side is then called 'high' by associative connexions. For the unmusical person the series of change is exhausted by degrees of brightness or dullness. He hears no moving to one side, though it is still possible that he might be brought to hear it. It must be there in some rough form. On the other hand he would probably never attain to an appreciation of interval, because his volumic proportions are always rough and irregular. And yet Köhler has not proved that the absence of pitch is without influence upon the tone-body; its 'absence' merely does not disable a man from distinguishing vowels and noises; these, however, are probably in any case rough or irregular 'tone-bodies,' and while there is only one perfection, there may be many serviceable approximations to it. It is not certain that a very unmusical person hears vowels, etc., exactly as we others do, although he can operate correctly with them.

I have already suggested that the absence-argument cuts two ways. If pitch is absent in the unmusical person, vocality is absent for the musical person when he is listening to music. It is not phenomenologically there. So, if the traditional pitch qualities gradually vanish as we pass from the normal to the abnormally unmusical person, then none the less the new Köhler vowel qualities must gradually vanish as we pass from the musical person's vowels to the musical person's musical tones. If the old way is so wrong, can Köhler's way be so right? I think Köhler's arguments show that both are equally wrong.

Köhler's work on absolute ear does not yet prove, I think, more than was already known as fact regarding the process. If a change of tone-colour puts to confusion most persons who profess some degree of absolute ear, this is not therefore necessarily a matter of 'tone-body.' For if the pitch seems to be eliminated by the permanence of the fundamental in spite of change of timbre, so might one think that 'tone-body' is eliminated, because the tone-body of the fundamental remains unaltered. (Köhler would not argue thus, but another might well do so.) And if it is argued that the peculiar complex tone-body characteristic of a tone rich in partials is the basis of the recognitions of the lesser absolute ears, it must be emphasised that one might just as well argue that the peculiar group of partial pitches of the tone is the basis sought. For in the pure tone this group is removed.

At this point Köhler has two lines of objection. The first is that the complication of tone-body in compound sounds—clangs and chords—is of a special kind. He does not give any account of this that is clear enough to reproduce. But for his account see pp. 59 f., 150 ff., 166 ff.

The second objection is that "of the pitch effects which the components of a chord would each produce in isolation, only one is at any one time realised in the unanalysed chord" (p. 155). That sentence reads like a tautology: when a chord is unanalysed, when only one pitch is heard, then only one pitch is heard. But from the context Köhler obviously means: only one pitch *can* be heard *at one and the same moment*, no matter what effort is made or how musical or practised the observer is. That I do not believe, though I readily grant that it is much easier to attend to the pitches successively. I explained that above (p. 102 f.) by pointing out that the pitch series is an ordinal system in which the attention moves from point to point. But although in vision it is much easier to attend to points in the visual field successively, no one doubts that one can attend to several points at once and see them at one and the same moment without movement of the attention.

In this connexion Köhler actually states "that for each person there are only as many pitches as he can produce by voice, and that all high and very low tones that the singing voice would not reach, in so far 'borrow' their pitch from the field of possible singing tones as necessarily an automatic 'sliding of the pitch' over octaves and into the singing range takes place, as soon as the objective tones exceed the limits of that range" (p. 158). This view reminds one of the curious notions that only recently held their place with great tenacity in psychological literature; such as, that smaller differences than quarter tones were not distinguishable because they could not be sung, and that no tone beyond the voice range could be imaged by the mind's ear. The idea is not only manifestly absurd to anyone who has for a moment considered the phenomenology of pitches, but is utterly irreconcilable with all Köhler's speculations regarding pitch. On the other hand it is clear on my theory that such an opinion could be formed only because musical matters are largely independent of the brightness or volume level at which music is played. Relative proportions of musical volume are so very important. Absolute degrees of volume are, of course, also important; but we can very often abstract from them entirely and some people may do so almost always, unless the difference is forced upon their attention by rapid comparison or by verbal instruction.

Köhler's work on absolute ear then, does not prove that absolute ear rests less on pitch than on volume or *vice versa*. We do not get with his help beyond the fact that in its lesser degrees it is very dependent upon pitch-blend or timbre.

As conclusion and summary I think I may say that apart from the classification of pitch with the place-values of vision, Dr Köhler's paper does not carry us any further *theoretically* than we were before. Of course, as I have shown above, pitches are not place-values; they are ordinal, which is a very great difference, of great significance, not only for the theory of the senses, but as a ground for the permanent failure of the phenomenological identification of the essence of pitch and localisational values until—apart from the indications I have referred to throughout the preceding chapters,—the identity of the substratum of localisational values and pitches was discovered by my systematic search amongst the attributes of sound for the attributes prominent in most senses and my comparative study of the integrational forms apparent in the different senses (*v*. 133).

INDEX OF AUTHORS

INDEX OF SUBJECTS

CAMBRIDGE: PRINTED BY J. B. PEACE, M.A., AT THE UNIVERSITY PRESS.

THE
CAMBRIDGE
PSYCHOLOGICAL LIBRARY

GENERAL EDITOR:

CHARLES S. MYERS, M.D., Sc.D.,
University Lecturer in Experimental Psychology
and Director of the Psychological Laboratory.

Psychology has by now attained the position of an independent discipline, with methods of study and themes of research of its own. It is the intention of the Syndics of the Cambridge University Press to issue a series of books dealing with the various subjects which come within the field of Psychology. The extent of this field may be gauged from the titles of the volumes given below.

The Cambridge Psychological Library will appeal not only to students of pure Psychology but also to those who are interested in such subjects as Philosophy, Religion, Ethnology, Sociology, Art, Education, Medicine, Physiology and Zoology.

Now ready

An Introduction to the Study of Colour Vision. By J. H. PARSONS, D.Sc., F.R.C.S. With coloured frontispiece and 75 text-figures. Royal 8vo. 12s 6d net.

In preparation

Psychology. By Prof. JAMES WARD, Sc.D., F.B.A.

The Nervous System. By Prof. C. S. SHERRINGTON, M.D., F.R.S.

The Structure of the Nervous System and the Sense Organs. By Prof. G. ELLIOT SMITH, M.D., F.R.S.

Prolegomena to Psychology. By Prof. G. DAWES HICKS, Litt.D.

Psychology in Relation to Theory of Knowledge. By Prof. G. F. STOUT, F.B.A.

Mental Measurement. By W. BROWN, D.Sc.

The Psychology of Mental Differences. By C. BURT, M.A.

Collective Psychology. By W. McDOUGALL, M.B., F.R.S.

The Psychology of Personality and Suggestion. By T. W. MITCHELL, M.D.

The Psychology of Dreams. By T. H. PEAR.